GENERAL COLLEGE GEOLOGY

GENERAL
COLLEGE

HARPER'S GEOSCIENCE SERIES

Carey Croneis, Editor

GEOLOGY

A. J. EARDLEY

Professor of Geology and Dean,

College of Mines and Mineral Industries

University of Utah

HARPER & ROW, Publishers   New York, Evanston, and London

Contents

8. Streams Fashion the Landscape 119

9. Ground Water 148

10. Shore Processes and Forms 170

GENERAL COLLEGE GEOLOGY by A. J. Eardley is an introductory text especially designed to bring home to beginning students of the subject the extraordinary, and all too commonly neglected, cultural values to be derived from each a rudimentary knowledge of the facts and principles of the earth sciences. The writing of this text has been something of a "labor of love" on the part of the author who enjoys a deserved international reputation for an entirely different kind of volume—his monumental work entitled, *Structural Geology of North America,* now in its second edition. Of Eardley's *Structural Geology* reviewers have said, among many other complimentary comments, "A magnificent work, well-organized, effectively presented, and unusually well-illustrated," "In our opinion, the most valuable publication that has yet been issued along the line of structural geology," "One of the finest books in geology in the last three decades," and, finally, "It is a book that every advanced geology student should have at hand for ready reference."

In the present volume, however, Dr. Eardley has not been concerned with the "advanced" student. Instead, he has attempted to perform for the introductory student of the humanities, as well as of the sciences—not to mention the beginning student of geology—the same sort of service he has been able to render to graduate students and

Editor's Introduction

professional geologists. In short, the author has acted on the belief that everyone would lead a richer, and more enjoyable, life of understanding of the world around him, regardless of college major or later vocation, if he had a reasonable comprehension of the physical features and geological history of the planet on which he dwells.

Dr. Eardley brought to the preparation of *General College Geology* the same high level of scholarship and great breath of geological experience that contributed so richly to the development of his more advanced works in the subject. Before preparing the present volume, however, the author made a critical review of the current texts in physical and historical geology, and came to some conclusions which are shared by a growing group of his colleagues. In such texts, he found that a number of subjects are commonly duplicated. He believed, therefore, that a carefully integrated single text would not only eliminate such duplication, but improve the general level of presentation and thus develop greater interest on the part of the student. He also came to the conclusion that some authors more or less unconsciously attempt to impress their professional colleagues by including, in elementary texts, a great deal of material which, at such a level, is not only of limited scientific import, but also is of little or no cultural value to the average introductory student. Dr. Eardley's object, then, has been to eliminate all materials which can be regarded as "window dressing" in order to produce a medium size book which is at once succinct, scientifically accurate, and attractive to the average student.

In a sense, Dr. Eardley has modeled his text around the situation which would obtain if an able professor—which Dr. Eardley certainly is—were to take beginning students on an extended field trip. These beginners would then be taught directly and immediately the basic concepts of geology through observation in the outdoor laboratory. Thus, the standard, rather boring beginning chapters of most geological texts on "What is Geology?," or on the astronomical beginnings of the earth, or even the characteristic, academic discussions of minerals rocks, and the facilities for, and methods of, the study of geology are all avoided. Instead, the student encounters minerals, rocks, and so forth, just as he would discover them in studying one aspect of geology after another in the out of doors.

The author's first chapter is on the nature of earth materials. Discussion flows naturally into a discourse on the common sedimentary rocks and thence into a brief outline of their primary and secondary structures. The student now moves to an igneous province and discusses and studies the igneous rocks both intrusive and extrusive. Thus, by easy stages, the beginner is brought to the fascinating subject of volcanoes.

Everywhere in the field the student will have seen the alteration products of igneous and sedimentary rocks, and thus rock weathering and erosion are next discussed. Chapter 8 is entitled, "Streams Fashion the Landscape," and "Ground Water" is the material of Chapter 9. Shore processes and forms, or the work of waves, are then considered, and, in conventional fashion, the "Work of the Wind" and the "Work of Ice" follow, naturally, in Chapters 11 and 12. Chapter 13, in which the author discusses earthquakes, is the final portion of what might be regarded as the physical section of the volume.

The life of the past, which is brought into the discussion in Chapter 14, together with the preceding chapters, lays a satisfactory groundwork for Chapter 15 which deals with the methods of establishing the sequence of geological events. Chapter 16 presents the basic facts of what might be considered as the broad details of geological history. Most of the remaining chapters are concerned with the physical events and the history of life during the great divisions of geological time. The last three chapters, however, are devoted to the place of man in the geological framework, to the new field of astrogeology and to oceanographic geology and its intriguing research activities and possibilities.

Although *General College Geology* by Eardley has been specifically designed with a one semester course in mind, the book is so constituted that it also may be employed satisfactorily in a two semester sequence. Should it be used for the latter purpose, it would, of course, have to be supplemented by rather extensive laboratory work and field excursions so that—depending on the geological phenomena available within a relatively short distance of the campus— rocks, minerals, and fossils can be studied *in situ*, as well as in the laboratory. Topographic and geologic maps, bathymetric charts, seismograms, electric-logs, and simple geochemical and geophysical experiments could also contribute to the enrichment of such a course and increase the student's interest.

Although Armand John Eardley is particularly well-known to professional geologists, teachers and students may be interested to know that Dr. Eardley was born in Salt Lake City at the turn of the century, and that he was educated at the University of Utah, where he took his A.B. degree in 1927. His Doctorate was received at Princeton in 1930.

Dr. Eardley was a highly successful professor at the University of Michigan during the years 1930-1951, and he directed the geologic field camp of that University from 1943 to 1949. He has been a member of the faculty at the University of Utah since 1949, and was Chairman of the Division of Earth Sciences in the College of Mines and Mineral Industries until 1954, at which time he became the Dean of that College.

Dean Eardley has served recently as president of the National Association of Geology Teachers and is now president of the American Geological Institute and a member of the Steering Committee of the Earth Science Curriculum Project. It is perhaps fair to say, then, that he has a notable background—indeed, an impeccable one—for the development of the present text which attempts to integrate, in one volume, the important facts and concepts of both physical and historical geology commonly presented in two. It seems quite possible, therefore, that the members of the geological fraternity may come to consider themselves as indebted to him for the present volume as for his earlier and seemingly more monumental works.

CAREY CRONEIS

Rice University
August, 1964

THIS BOOK is intended for either a one- or two-term course. Its coverage of the subject matter in physical and historical geology is fairly complete, but to make this coverage possible in a one-volume edition of normal size, those subjects which are developed in laboratory sections are minimized, and the conventional introductory statements and chapters are largely omitted. An even greater saving of space is achieved by the elimination of the overlap that exists in physical and historical texts. Fully one-third of each is a duplication of the other.

General education requirements in many universities and colleges currently militate against the two-term sequence of physical and historical geology and permit only one course for the liberal-arts student. It is unfortunate to provide him with just the physical aspects of earth processes and change, but not the organic. Certain distinct advantages come from a logical integration of the two basic areas of geology in one text, and the preparation of this book has been an inviting and rewarding attempt to achieve such a composition. As any teacher knows, a one-term course combining both physical and historical geology must be a hurried affair, and certain subjects cannot be covered. In adapting this text to a one-term course, it may be necessary to skip parts of chapters or several whole chapters. If parts of the book must be omitted, I would suggest that

Preface

Chaps. 1, 6, 23, and 24 are the least essential. The rest seems basic to a cultural appreciation of geology.

If the book seems short for a two-semester or two-quarter course, laboratory work on minerals, rocks, maps, and fossils may be extended to compensate. Written reports involving outside reading are valuable assignments.

In the writing of any new textbook of geology the most pointed questions confronting the author concern the level of presentation and the selection of subject material. At what level of mathematics, physics, chemistry, mineralogy, and geography should it be written? Should it include astronomy, meteorology, physical geography, oceanography, and geophysics to the exclusion of a good part of the traditional aspects of geology? Should the term "earth science" supersede "general geology"?

As to the level of operation my experience at two large universities is that by now the majority of the students who take the introductory course in geology have had either a high school or a college course in chemistry. Most have an acquaintance with algebra and some odds and ends of knowledge about physics gained from a general science course in high school. Some know a little about the solar system, but most are shockingly weak in the geography of the earth. The college student is generally fascinated by our subject material, and can absorb and gain a great deal from the course, even though his background in science is limited. It is this student to whom I have addressed the book. He is a good student, and I have delighted in teaching him.

As to the choice of subject material I have proceeded largely with the conventional chapter headings, but to the best of my ability I have brought them strictly up to date as dictated by recent research in major lines of the geological sciences. Some of these "conventional" chapters are much different from other texts. I have emphasized those aspects which students like most and remember best, namely, earthquakes, volcanoes, and the evolution of the reptiles and mammals, including man. A chapter on astrogeology with special emphasis on the moon is included, and also one on the geology of the ocean basins. Considerable attention is given in several chapters to crustal and mantle constitution. The latest views on paleoclimates and polar wandering are emphasized. The life record is presented from a systematic point of view, with the major emphasis on the fossil evidence of evolution.

I am particularly grateful for the help of Dr. Richard A. Robison in the preparation of the chapters on fossils. He designed the illustrations in Chap. 14, and guided me in other chapters, that have to do with ancient life. Julian Maack drew these and other illustrations. Other colleagues, Professors Harry D. Goode, Matthew P. Nackowski, Ray E. Marsell, S. T. Algermissen, James A. Whelan, and Charles Dibble have read a number of chapters critically and have thus been of great help. I appreciate membership on the Steering Committee of the Earth Science Project of the American Geological Institute, because its deliberations point up the current needs and objectives in our written materials. Dean Chalmer J. Roy, chairman of the Education Committee of the AGI, has also been very kind in furnishing information and ideas about geological education at the elementary level.

This book is enhanced by many striking photographs, and for those of Canadian scenes and rocks I am particularly indebted to Edward Schiller, of the Geological Survey of Canada. I also appreciate very much the help of Drs. G. Arthur Cooper and Charles L. Gazin, of the U.S. National Museum of the Smithsonian Institution, in supplying photographs of their specimens and dioramas, and of Dr. Helen Foster, of the U.S. Geological Survey, in supplying photographs of Japanese volcanoes.

A. J. EARDLEY

GENERAL COLLEGE GEOLOGY

Chapter 1

INTRODUCTION

It is hoped that this book will introduce the liberal art student to the physical and organic aspects of the earth and open the door to a wonderful appreciation of nature. Regardless of his major interests he will generally find in an elementary understanding of the landscape around him a satisfaction that will endure through life.

The subject material may be grouped into three broad divisions:

First, the relation of earth to sun, especially in connection with the atmosphere and the oceans, the energy imparted by the sun to these systems, and the activity it engenders on the continents.

Second, the processes within the earth that cause volcanism, the building of mountains, and rock metamorphism.

Third, the history of the earth, both its physical development and the evolution of life on its surface.

The Nature of Earth Materials

Geology also deals with our mineral wealth, the topographic and environmental divisions of the earth's surface, and the soils in which our crops grow.

Geology is the science of the earth, and its materials are the atmosphere, the hydrosphere (oceans, lakes, rivers, and underground water), and the lithosphere (rocks and soils). This chapter will therefore deal with the basic properties of these three states of matter, gases, liquids, and solids, as a prelude, first, to the study of minerals and rocks and, second, to the physical and chemical processes which are active on the earth's surface and which shape its landforms.

If you have not had chemistry, don't panic! You can understand every concept presented on the following pages if you will read attentively. As for those who have had chemistry the following will be a good review.

STATES OF MATTER

Atomic Theory

The Concept. As minerals are the building blocks of rocks, so are atoms the building blocks of minerals, and thus it is necessary to take a brief look at the atom.

From information at his disposal, John Dalton proposed the idea in 1805 that all matter is composed of tiny individual particles that he called atoms. Many momentous discoveries in the past 150 years have added greatly to our understanding of the atom, and a simplified description of it today would be as follows:

✦ Atoms are porous and composed of bits of matter in a vacuum.

✦ The principal subatomic particles are electrons, protons, and neutrons.

✦ The particles of atoms are under the influence of strong forces.

✦ Most of the mass of an atom is concentrated in a minute nucleus, which has a positive charge.

✦ The nucleus is made up of tightly packed neutrons and protons.

✦ There is one electron for each positive charge on the nucleus, and an atom as a whole is neutral.

✦ The electrons travel around the nucleus at relatively great distances with almost the speed of light.

Table 1–1 THE STRUCTURE OF A FEW SIMPLE ATOMS

Atom*	Symbol	Atomic number	Nucleus	Electron configuration by shells		
				1	2	3
Hydrogen	H	1	1 proton	1		
Helium	He	2	2 protons 2 neutrons	2		
Lithium	Li	3	3 protons 4 neutrons	2	1	
Beryllium	Be	4	4 protons 5 neutrons	2	2	
Sodium	Na	11	11 protons 12 neutrons	2	8	1
Chlorine	Cl	17	18 neutrons 17 protons	2	8	7

* Only one isotope of each element is considered.

✦ The electrons are regarded as circulating within concentric "shells," and each shell has a definite capacity for electrons. For instance, the first shell has a capacity of 2; the second shell 8; the third shell 18; and the fourth shell 32.

The simplest atom is that of hydrogen, which consists of a nucleus of one proton about which one electron travels. It and the next simplest atoms, helium and lithium, are illustrated in Fig. 1-1.

The number of protons, neutrons, and electrons of a few simple atoms is given in Table 1-1.

If the mass of an electron is taken as 1 unit, then the mass of a proton is 1,836 units. Likewise the mass of a neutron is 1,836 units. The proton has one positive charge, but the neutron possesses no electrical charge. The number of protons in the nucleus is taken as the *atomic number* of the atom, or of the element represented by the atom. An *element* is defined as a substance composed of atoms all of which have the same atomic number. For instance, hydrogen atoms form the element hydrogen, oxygen atoms form the element oxy-

gen, and iron atoms form the element iron.

The infinitesimally small size of the atom is impossible to imagine. The number of atoms in the tip of your pencil is greater than the number of people on earth. In spite of this minuteness, the diameters have been measured by modern physicists and are expressed in angstrom units (one hundred-millionth of a centimeter, or generally written 10^{-8} cm). The comparative size of the three simplest atoms is shown in Fig. 1-1. Some are larger than those of lithium, such as sodium, potassium, magnesium, and calcium. The size of an atom changes somewhat when combined with other atoms, and the distances between centers of atoms are especially amenable to measurement when they are closely packed and in orderly arrangement, as in crystals.

The weights of atoms in absolute terms are now known, but it is more convenient to use relative weights. The oxygen atom is taken as standard and arbitrarily assigned a weight of 16.000 units. Its actual weight is only 2.66×10^{-23} g. Relative to oxygen, hydrogen has a weight of 1.008.

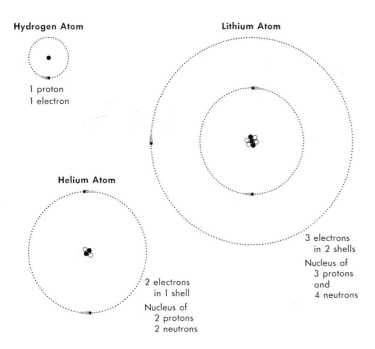

Hydrogen Atom

1 proton
1 electron

Helium Atom

2 electrons
in 1 shell
Nucleus of
2 protons
2 neutrons

Lithium Atom

3 electrons
in 2 shells
Nucleus of
3 protons
and
4 neutrons

FIG. 1-1 Structure and relative size of hydrogen, helium, and lithium atoms. The electrons of helium and lithium atoms may not orbit in one plane as shown, and the arrangement of the protons and neutrons in the nucleus is not known.

Isotopes. John Dalton postulated that all atoms of the same element have the same weight, but later studies have indicated that atoms of the same element can have different weights. The weight of an atom is dependent almost entirely on the weight of the protons and neutrons in its nucleus, since the weight of an electron is negligibly small. And if the number of neutrons varies but the number of protons and electrons remains the same, then the atomic number remains the same but the mass weight will vary. Atoms related in this way are called *isotopes*. The isotopes of an element have identical chemical properties and cannot be separated by chemical analysis, but are recognized and measured by mass spectrographic analysis.

Hydrogen, for example, has three isotopes with the following composition:

Name	Nucleus	Electrons	Notation
Hydrogen	1 proton	1	$_1H^1$
Deuterium	1 proton 1 neutron	1	$_1H^2$
Tritium	1 proton 2 neutrons	1	$_1H^3$

The subscript in front of the symbol is the atomic number (number of protons), and the superscript after the letter is the *mass number* (number of protons and neutrons).

The element oxygen also has three naturally occurring isotopes, which may be expressed as follows: $_8O^{16}$, $_8O^{17}$, and $_8O^{18}$, of which $_8O^{16}$ is the most abundant (Fig. 1-2). When hydrogen combines with oxygen to form water (two atoms of hydrogen and one of oxygen), there are thus 16 isotopic combinations, but $_1H^1_8O^{16}_1H^1$ is by far the most abundant. If both hydrogen atoms are the $_1H^2$ isotope, then a water results that weighs 1.1 g. per cu. cm. as compared with 1.0 g for ordinary water. This is called *heavy water,* but it looks and tastes like ordinary water.

Molecules. The union of two atoms of hydrogen and one of oxygen is the smallest unit that possesses the properties of water,

and this is called a *molecule* of water. A molecule may be defined as the smallest unit of a compound that displays the properties of the compound. Compounds are combinations of various atoms, and we will discuss them presently.

Gases

Matter exists in three states of aggregation, namely; gaseous, liquid, and solid. The principal properties of gases are as follows:

✦ They have neither definite shape nor definite volume. This means that when not confined in a container they expand indefinitely in all directions. If it were not for the earth's gravity, we would soon lose our atmosphere into space. When confined, as in a bottle, gases distribute themselves uniformly throughout the volume of the container.

✦ Gases have low density under ordinary conditions of temperature and pressure. Oxygen is a gas under ordinary conditions and 1 l of it weighs 1.43 g; 1 l of hydrogen weighs only 1.09 g, which is less than any other gas under similar conditions. Hydrogen and oxygen united form water for which, as a liquid, 1 l weighs 1,000 g.

✦ Gases can be compressed markedly. By increasing the pressure one thousand times, 1 l of oxygen is reduced in volume to 0.0017 l.

✦ Gases exert pressure.

✦ Gases diffuse spontaneously one through another, and also through certain liquids and solids. Agitation is not necessary.

✦ If gases are confined to a certain vol-

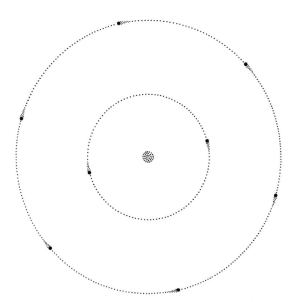

FIG. 1-2 Idealized structure of oxygen atom. The nucleus has eight protons and eight, nine, or ten neutrons. The orbits of the electrons are not in one plane, as represented, and are undoubtedly complex. The oxygen atom is about the size of the helium atom.

ume, and the temperature is increased, the pressure of the gas increases.

✦ Gases can be converted into liquids by subjecting them to increased pressure, or decreased temperature, or both.

These characteristics of gases will be better understood when it is known that they consist of molecules or individual atoms separated by a vacuum, that the distance between molecules is large compared with the almost negligible size of the molecules, and that the molecules are always in very rapid motion. They travel in straight lines until their direction is changed by collision with another molecule of the gas or with the walls of the container. As the temperature rises, the number of molecules with high velocity increases. The molecules are perfectly elastic, and collisions do not result in loss of energy. The collisions are like those of billiard balls. When a gas is compressed, its molecules are simply forced closer together.

The large distances between gas molecules and their continuous random movement result in rapid diffusion without stirring when two different gases are placed together.

Gas molecules have weak electrical forces of attraction that are normally negligible when the molecules are far apart. Their rapid motion carries them away from one another, but as the gas is compressed and the molecules brought closer together, their forces of attraction overcome the normal tendency to move about and apart, and suddenly the liquid state of aggregation occurs. A decrease in temperature slows down the motion of the particles and assists in bringing about the liquid state.

Liquids

The principal properties of liquids are as follows:

✦ They have a definite volume but not shape. If confined in a bottle they occupy the lower part of it, unlike gases, which would occupy all of it.

✦ They are fluids but display varying degrees of *viscosity*, which is defined as resistance to flow. Water and gasoline have low viscosity, but certain crude oils are rather stiff and have high viscosity.

✦ The *density* of liquids is generally much more than that of gases. For instance, water is about thirteen hundred times heavier than water vapor (its gaseous form).

✦ Liquids are very difficult to compress.

✦ Liquids may be converted into gases, and the process is known as *vaporization* or *evaporation*. The rate of evaporation depends on the nature of the substance. Ether, for example, evaporates more rapidly than water, and such liquids, when exposed to the open atmosphere, evaporate spontaneously.

✦ If a liquid is heated sufficiently, a temperature will be reached at which evaporation takes place within the liquid as well as on the surface, and the rate of conversion from the liquid to the gaseous state is greatly accelerated. This, of course, is *boiling*. The temperature of the boiling point depends on the nature of the liquid, and also on the pressure of the atmosphere above the liquid. Since boiling occurs when the *vapor pressure* of the liquid equals the pressure of the atmosphere above the liquid, water needs to be hotter at sea level to boil (100°C) than at high elevations (82°C at 18,400 ft above sea level).

✦ The surface of liquids appears like a tightly stretched skin, although very thin. Certain insects can walk on a water surface, and the tension draws drops of the liquid into spheres. This property is called *surface tension*.

✦ Liquids may turn to solids if they are cooled sufficiently. The process is called *freezing*, and the temperature at which the solidification occurs is called the *freezing point*.

All these properties may be understood by a modification of the *kinetic* theory of gases. Kinetic energy is that possessed by objects in motion. The basic particles of a liquid are in random motion but are packed close together. They are free to slip by one another, to collide, ricochet, and rebound, but they are held together by forces of attraction stronger than those of gas particles. This movement, or the effect of it, may be observed by placing a drop of a mixture of tiny pollen grains in water under a rather high-power microscope. The tiny pollen grains exhibit a spontaneous and haphazard motion, and this is due to the invisible water molecules striking the pollen grains, first on this side and then on the other. It is known as *Brownian motion*.

The relative high density of liquids is explained by the close packing of the molecules. The low compressibility is also explained by close packing. Spontaneous evaporation is explained by the escape of particles from the surface. Certain particles will have trajectories and speeds such that they overcome the mutual attractive forces

that bond the surface molecules together, and break out into the air above. The rate of escape or evaporation depends on the strength of the attractive forces of the particles of each liquid. If water and overlying air are in a closed container, some of the water molecules that have escaped from the liquid into the air (now in the gaseous state) will collide and rebound back into the liquid. When the number in the air reaches a certain amount, then as many will be returning to the water as are leaving it. We say at this stage that the rate of evaporation equals the rate of condensation and a state of *dynamic equilibrium* has been reached. See Fig. 1-3.

If the liquid is heated, the motion of the molecules increases, more escape each second, and the density increases in the air above until a higher rate of return has been established. In estimating the evaporation of water from oceans, lakes, and moist soils, one has to consider the temperature of the water. Wind conditions being equal, and with a fairly dry air, the amount of evaporation from a lake on a hot summer day will be five or six times as much as on a cold winter day.

Surface tension is due to the fact that the particles within a liquid are attracted in all directions by one another, whereas those at the surface lack upward pull and

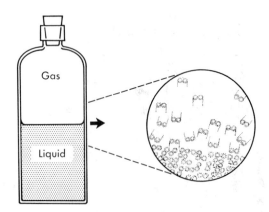

FIG. 1-3 Schematic representation of a liquid in equilibrium with its vapor in a closed container. The rate of evaporation is equal to the rate of condensation.

are hence drawn downward. This produces in effect a skin only one particle thick, but it has measurable strength.

The pressure exerted by the gaseous molecules of a substance is known as the *vapor pressure* of a liquid. The greater the vapor pressure, the greater the rate of evaporation. This depends on the composition of the liquid and its temperature.

At the boiling point the particle motion has increased sufficiently to overcome the attractive forces within the liquid. The motion must also be sufficient to overcome the pressure of the atmosphere above, and hence a lower boiling point for high altitudes than for low.

The freezing of liquids is also related to the motion of the particles. As the temperature of a liquid drops, the motion is finally reduced to a restricted vibration, because the attractive forces are able to hold the particles in relatively fixed positions. At this temperature the liquid turns solid or freezes, and the particles are no longer free to glide or pass by one another. We are thus introduced to the solid state and the world of minerals.

Combining Properties of Atoms

Atoms of one kind have long been known to combine with atoms of another kind, but the combining behavior may differ.

For instance, one atom of hydrogen combines with one atom of chlorine to form a molecule of hydrogen chloride, HCl. An atom of oxygen, however, combines with *two* atoms of hydrogen to form a molecule of water, H_2O. An atom of nitrogen combines with *three* atoms of hydrogen to form a molecule of ammonia, NH_3. But argon does not combine with hydrogen (or any other element) at all. What aspects of atomic structure explain this behavior?

The combining properties of atoms are related to the number of electrons in the *outer shell*, and these are called *valence* electrons. Valence simply signifies the capacity of an atom to combine with other atoms. Atoms that have the same number of valence electrons will have similar combining behavior. Chlorine (Cl), bromine (Br), and iodine (I), for example, have different atomic structures but they all have seven electrons in the outer shell, and each combines with one atom of hydrogen to form HCl, HBr, and HI, respectively.

It is customary to represent each atom by an electronic symbol, and in Table 1-2 the letters represent the nucleus and inner shells of electrons of the atoms, and the dots represent the number of valence electrons.

Atoms with atomic numbers 1 to 20 plus 10 additional common atoms are chosen for representation because their combining

Table 1-2   THE ELECTRONIC SYMBOLS FOR SOME COMMON ATOMS

H· (Hydrogen)							He: (Helium)
Li· (Lithium)	Be: (Beryllium)	B: (Boron)	C: (Carbon)	·N: (Nitrogen)	:O: (Oxygen)	:F: (Fluorine)	:Ne: (Neon)
Na· (Sodium)	Mg: (Magnesium)	Al: (Aluminum)	Si: (Silicon)	·P: (Phosphorus)	:S: (Sulphur)	:Cl: (Chlorine)	:A: (Argon)
K· (Potassium)	Ca: (Calcium)					:Br: (Bromine)	:Kr: (Krypton)
Rb· (Rubidium)	Sr: (Strontium)					:I: (Iodine)	:Xe: (Xenon)
Cs· (Cesium)	Ba: (Barium)						:Rn: (Radon)
	Ra: (Radium)						(Inert elements)

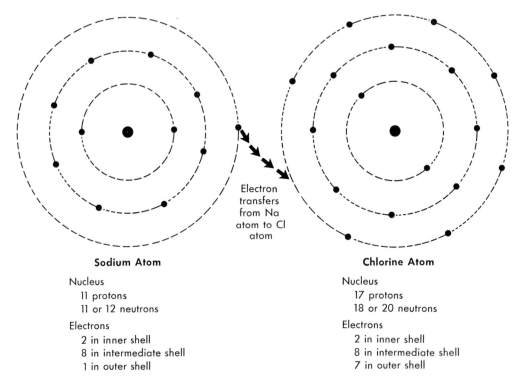

Sodium Atom	Chlorine Atom
Nucleus	Nucleus
11 protons	17 protons
11 or 12 neutrons	18 or 20 neutrons
Electrons	Electrons
2 in inner shell	2 in inner shell
8 in intermediate shell	8 in intermediate shell
1 in outer shell	7 in outer shell

Electron transfers from Na atom to Cl atom

FIG. 1-4 Structure of sodium and chlorine atoms showing the transfer of an electron from the sodium atom to the chlorine atom. Thus each atom becomes stable but of opposite charge.

properties are easily related. Hydrogen with one valence electron is shown as H·, calcium with two valence electrons as Ca:, and chlorine with seven as : Cl : .

Atoms will combine into pairs or groups if the resulting structure possesses a stability greater than the separate atom. An individual atom of hydrogen, H·, is unstable, but when two hydrogen atoms combine to form a molecule, H:H, they acquire an increased stability. The inert gases in Table 1-2 have eight valence electrons (helium has only two) and are exceedingly stable. It is recognized that eight is a stable number, and when atoms combine they generally acquire eight electrons in the outermost shell. Two electrons in the outer shell constitute a stable condition for the simplest atoms.

The bonding of atoms is accomplished in two ways, which are known as *ionic* and *covalent*. The ionic bond is represented by the union of atoms of sodium and chlorine. The two isolated atoms would be symbolized as Na· and :Cl· . See Fig. 1-4.

Sodium has one valence electron, but in the shell underneath are eight electrons. By losing the one outer electron it will acquire the stability represented by 8. At the same time if the chlorine atom could gain an electron in its outermost shell it would have increased its stability. Both the sodium and chlorine atoms are neutral, but if the sodium atom should lose an electron (and a negative charge) it will have a unit positive charge. Likewise, if the chlorine atom gains an electron, and a negative charge, the atom will then have a unit negative charge. They would then be written as Na⁺ and :Cl:⁻.

Particles that have either gained or lost electrons are called *ions*. Positive ions are called *cations* and negative ions *anions*. The transfer of an electron from a sodium atom to a chlorine atom renders the two atoms of opposite charge, and they attract each other and are bonded together.

Bonding may also be affected by *sharing* electrons. There are several variations, but only two will be described. In the first type we will consider two isolated hydrogen atoms. Each of the atoms has one valence electron, and each needs one more to acquire the stable number of two. If they share their electrons, then each has two, and the combination would be written H:H. This is a stable form, such as occurs in hydrogen gas. The hydrogen molecule thus produced is said to have a *covalent bond*.

Consider the water molecule. Two isolated hydrogen atoms and one oxygen atom would be expressed as follows: H·, H·, and :Ö: . In a water molecule they are joined by the sharing of electrons, and in covalent bond they would appear as H:Ö:H, whereby each hydrogen atom has the stable number of two electrons, and the oxygen atom has the stable number of eight electrons.

Water Solutions

Natural waters start with melting snow or rain and are fairly free of any dissolved content, but in the course of flowing over and through rocks they take up considerable solid material in solution. Limestone ($CaCO_3$), gypsum ($CaSO_4 \cdot 2H_2O$), and common salt ($NaCl$) are particularly susceptible to solution by water, and the process is analyzed as follows:

In the water molecule the oxygen atom has in effect gained two electrons and takes on a negative charge. The hydrogen atoms on the other hand have lost two electrons and become positive. This produces a molecule that acts like a rod with a positive charge on one end and a negative on the other. The ends are referred to as poles, and the molecule as a *dipole*. Now suppose some sodium chloride crystals are placed in the water. Remembering that the sodium chloride molecule is bonded of a sodium ion with a positive charge and a chlorine ion with a negative charge, we can see that the dipolar water molecules may be attracted to the salt crystals. In fact, they will attach themselves to, and break up, the salt crystals, separate the positive and negative ions, and disperse them uniformly through the water body. This *ionized solution* will then conduct an electrical current.

The word "compound" has been used previously, but we can now define it. *Compounds* are combinations of elements, formed mostly by the joining of ions. Sodium chloride is thus a compound.

Solids

These are the common properties of solids:

✦ They have a definite volume and a definite shape. Solids like rocks are mostly hard; others may be soft.

✦ The density of solids is of the same order of magnitude as that of liquids.

✦ Solids vary widely in compressibility, but in general they are less easily compressed than liquids. Rocks are difficult to compress.

✦ Many solids have a crystalline appearance, with definite patterns of faces and angles.

✦ Solids, like liquids, evaporate and have vapor pressure. Ice crystals in the form of snow flakes evaporate at temperatures below melting at a conspicuous rate, but most rocks resist evaporation. Naphthalene (moth balls) is a common substance that passes directly from the solid state to the gaseous. The evaporation of solids into the gaseous state and the subsequent condensation of the gas back to the solid is known as *sublimation*. Gas vents around volcanoes are sometimes the sites of sublimated sulphur.

✦ Most solids will become liquid when heated, and the process is called *melting*.

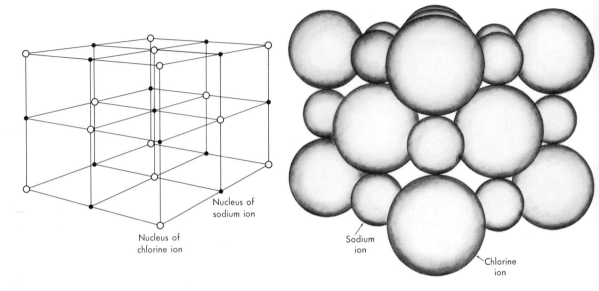

Nucleus of
sodium ion

Nucleus of
chlorine ion

Sodium
ion

Chlorine
ion

FIG. 1-5 Arrangement of sodium and chlorine ions in the mineral halite: left, the positions of the nuclei; right, the outer electron shells.

The temperature of melting varies widely with different substances. Iron melts at 1535°C, table salt (NaCl) at 800°C, ice at 0°C, and solid hydrogen at −259°C.

The particles of solids are closely packed but in a vacuum, like those of gases and liquids. The arrangement is in a regularly repeating, three-dimensional pattern in crystalline solids, but random in amorphous solids. Although the particles occupy relatively fixed positions they are in vibratory motion. The forces between particles in solids are stronger than those of corresponding liquids. As temperature rises, the vibratory motion increases, and eventually the stronger solid forces weaken to those of the liquid form, and melting ensues.

MINERALS

Definition

Each mineral has its own regular three-dimensional internal structure of basic particles and a definite or fairly definite composition. Similar-sized particles of other elements may substitute in certain amounts for the normal ones (such as Ca ions for Sr ions), and thus the chemical composition of some minerals varies within limits. Each mineral also has its singular physical properties, but in those minerals which have slight variable chemical composition there is also some slight variation in physical properties. True minerals, finally, must occur in nature. A number of compounds have been synthesized which are not known in nature but which have all the properties of minerals; yet arbitrarily, they are not recognized as minerals.

It should be appreciated that a certain mineral, whether found in Nevada, Nova Scotia, or New South Wales, has the same crystalline, chemical, and physical properties. Quartz from Brazil is the same as quartz from the Black Hills, except perhaps for the size of the crystals and their color. The angles between similar faces are the same, and the internal arrangement of the particles is the same.

The fundamental particle of almost all rock-forming minerals is the ion. The nature of the ionic structure of crystalline sodium chloride is shown in Fig. 1-5. Some chemists and physicists recognize two other fundamental particles in some crystals, namely, atoms and molecules, and suggest that the metals, when crystalline, such as copper in Fig. 1-6, are *atomic crystals,* and such substances as ice, sugar, iodine, and dry ice (solid carbon dioxide) have molecules as the fundamental particles. The sharing of electrons is a complicated consideration, and the subject will not be discussed further, but suffice it to say that the bonding of atoms is a subject still not completely understood.

Strictly speaking, crystals exhibit faces and crystal form, but many mineral grains have not had room to develop a normal outward crystalline form. These are better referred to as minerals than crystals, and it would be better as a result to speak of ionic minerals as the chief rock-forming materials rather than ionic crystals.

Crystals

Crystals grow by the addition of layers of particles, depending on the kind of mineral, and in nature the common carrier of the fundamental particles is water. The

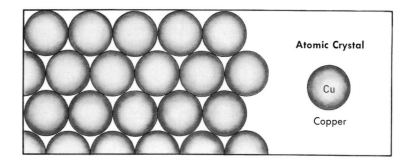

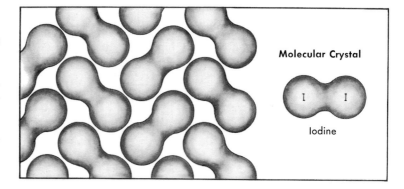

FIG. 1-6 Schematic representation of particle arrangement of atomic, molecular, and ionic crystals. The packing is actually three-dimensional. The ionic arrangement of the sodium chloride crystal is better shown in Fig. 1-5. (*After Compton, 1958.*)

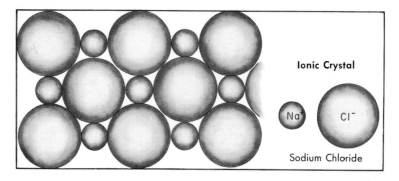

water becomes saturated with a particular compound, and the compound is precipitated out, first as microscopic crystals. These will be the sites of further precipitation, and the small crystals will thus grow in size. Imagine a salt-water lake in a desert climate. Evaporation will increase the concentration of sodium chloride until saturation is reached. Then, ions of Na^+ and Cl^- will start precipitating out as very small crystals of the mineral *halite* on the bottom. Further evaporation and precipitation results in the growth of the tiny crystals. Some will grow at the expense of others until perhaps large crystals result. The halite crystals in Fig. 1-7 grew in such an environment, and their growth had little interference except as neighboring crystals developed contact with one another. Minerals of many varieties grow in restricted places and hence cannot develop characteristic outward crystal form; yet the internal arrangement of the particles is constant.

Crystal Form

Every mineral has a characteristic form that is the expression of the internal molecular, atomic, or ionic structure. One of the earliest discoveries pertaining to minerals was by Nicolaus Steno (1631–1687), who showed that similar pairs of crystal faces of different specimens of quartz al-ways meet at the same angle regardless of the size or shape of the crystals. There is a constancy of interfacial angles of every mineral variety, and this fact was used not only for purposes of identification but to suggest to scientists before X-ray discoveries that minerals had a regular, geometric, internal arrangement of the fundamental particles.

All the minerals known today, over 2,000, have crystal symmetry that permits them to be neatly grouped into six crystal systems. We cannot go into detail here about the crystal systems, but perhaps some attention can be given to this subject in the laboratory. Figures 1-8 to 1-10 show a few common minerals in characteristic crystal form.

Optical Properties

Light rays passing through minerals are affected in several ways, and especially when thin sections of minerals are made for microscopic examination, most minerals are transparent and amenable to optical analysis. Certain minerals like copper and magnetite are opaque even in thin section, but light can be reflected from their surfaces and studied. It will have penetrated several layers of ions, and the reflected rays may have been altered. A particular ability of certain minerals is to restrict light to vibration in one plane when the light rays

FIG. 1-7 Natural growth of halite crystals from Great Salt Lake brine showing cubic symmetry. Photographed in transmitted light. (*Morton Salt Company.*)

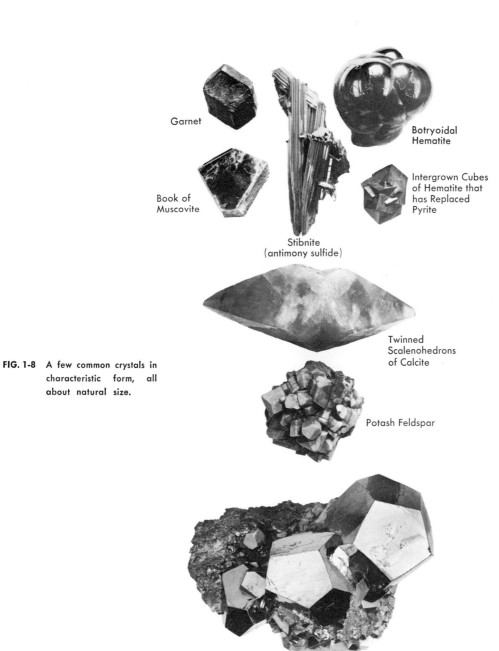

Garnet

Book of Muscovite

Stibnite (antimony sulfide)

Botryoidal Hematite

Intergrown Cubes of Hematite that has Replaced Pyrite

Twinned Scalenohedrons of Calcite

Potash Feldspar

Pyritohedrons of Pyrite

FIG. 1-8 A few common crystals in characteristic form, all about natural size.

are passed through them. Such *polarized* light is then passed through other minerals and singular effects noted. The microscope divised to study thin sections of minerals and rocks using polarized light is called the *petrographic microscope* and is a basic instrument of mineral identification and rock study by the geologist.

X Rays and Internal Structure

Electricity was a subject of much fascination to the early physicists, and a number of them had experimented with the passage of an electric current through gases. Michael Faraday (1791–1867) fitted a glass bulb with electrical terminals,

FIG. 1-9 Cluster of quartz crystals showing hexagonal prisms and pyramids.

FIG. 1-10 Cleavage fragments of halite showing cubic symmetry.

evacuated as much air from it as he could, and then turned on the current. The glass glowed with a flourescent light that could easily be seen in a dark room. A glass bulb was fitted up with a metal shield, as shown in Fig. 1-11, by the German physicist Johann Hittorf in 1869, and a shadow of the shield appeared on the glass at point A. It thereafter became apparent that this shadow was caused by rays which travel in straight lines from the negative electrode, and they were called cathode rays. Later William

Crookes of England found that cathode rays could be deflected by a magnet, and the direction of deflection indicated that the rays had a negative charge. In 1897 Joseph Thomson showed that the rays were composed of tiny negatively charged particles traveling at high velocity, and they were called electrons.

The German physicist Wilhelm Roentgen discovered in 1895 that other rays come from cathode tubes than those which cause a visible glow. He was not sure of the

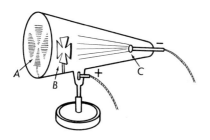

FIG. 1-11 An early type of cathode tube showing the shadow A from the metal cross B. The rays thus move in straight lines from their source C.

nature of the rays and called them X rays. They proved to be a form of energy similar to light rays but having remarkable powers of penetration. It was found that, when X rays were passed through a body and a photographic film exposed by them, the bones cast a shadow, whereas the flesh was nearly transparent.

Now, if a beam of X rays is passed through a mineral, its rays will be bent into a complex pattern that can be recorded on a photographic film. Figure 1-12 shows

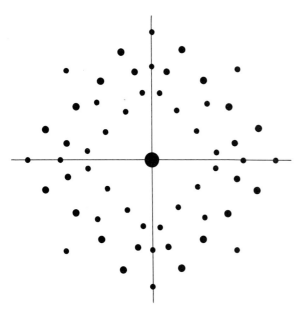

FIG. 1-12 Diagram of diffraction of X rays passing through halite.

the photographic pattern of X rays that have passed through a crystal of halite (NaCl), which, we have already learned, has a cubic crystal symmetry. A number of small dots are arranged around a central large dot in a pattern of quadrangle symmetry. It is believed that the small dots are produced by reflections of the rays from the regularly oriented planes of ions within the crystal. The large dot in the center represents the rays that passed through without being bent. The photograph is called an X-ray *diffraction* diagram.

Repetition of the experiment with other minerals gave conclusive proof of the regular packing of the submicroscopic particles of crystals. The X-ray instrument has since been developed into the most basic device for determining the internal structure of minerals and for their identification and analysis. Even microscopically small crystals can be analyzed.

Of course, the ultimate particles of minerals cannot be seen by microscopes, but the electron microscope comes close to photographing them. Magnifications of nearly one million are possible. Figure 1-13 shows a polished and acid-etched surface of magnetite taken by an electron microscope at about 2,500 times actual size and leaves little doubt of the persistent and trenchant arrangement of the basic particles in it.

MINERAL GROUPS AND ABUNDANCES

Mineral Groups

Minerals are classified commonly by chemical composition. There are the oxides, such as magnetite (Fe_3O_4), cassiterite (SnO_2), corundum (Al_2O_3), and ice (H_2O). There are the *sulfide* minerals, such as pyrite (FeS_2), chalcocite (Cu_2S), galena (PbS), and sphalerite (ZnS). Then there are the *sulphate* minerals, which bear the sulphate (SO_4^{--}) ion as a basic part of their constitution. An example is gypsum

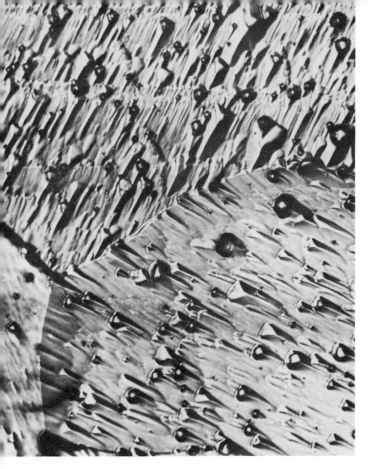

FIG. 1-13 Etch pits on a polished surface of magnetite. Three grains, each with different structural orientation, are present. This is an electron microscope photograph with a magnification of about 2,500. (*Courtesy of Professor John R. Lewis.*)

($CaSO_4 \cdot 2H_2O$). The *carbonate* minerals contain the ion CO_3^{--}, and its most common combining cation is Ca^{++} to form the mineral calcite ($CaCO_3$). The *chloride* minerals, such as sodium chloride (halite) and potassium chloride (sylvite) are also common. Finally the *silicates* must be mentioned because they are overwhelmingly the most abundant minerals of the earth's crust. They contain the silicate ion (SiO_4^{----}).

These groups are the most common, but others would have to be listed to comprise all minerals.

Relative Abundances

The silicate minerals compose more than 95 per cent by volume of the earth's crust, which has been considered as 10 miles thick in making the estimate. If a thicker shell is considered, the percentage of silicate minerals increases. There are many silicate mineral varieties, but a comparative few make up the great bulk of them. The feldspars, hornblende, augite, the micas, and quartz are about all that we need to mention or discuss here and in later chapters of the book. These minerals are composed of nine elements, and thus this small number of elements makes up most of the earth's crust. In fact, it is computed that they compose 99 per cent of it.

It should be noted that one of the most abundant minerals is quartz, whose chemical composition is SiO_2. It would thus seem to be an oxide, but its internal structure indicates that its basic structure is the silica tetrahedron (see below), and hence it is listed above with the silicates.

The Silica Tetrahedron and the Silicates

By X-ray analysis it is now known that all silicates have one basic unit **in** common. This is the so-called *silica tetrahedron* and is four oxygen ions and one silicon ion. The oxygen ions are at the four corners

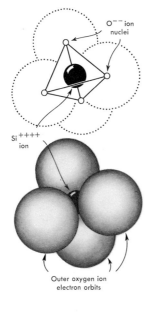

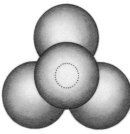

FIG. 1-14   The silica tetrahedron: above, the view empha-
sizes the structure (lattice diagram); below, the
drawing is of the tetrahedron used in Figs.
1-15 and 1-16.

than the silicon; from this it can be seen
that, in volume, oxygen must compose most
of the crust. In fact, Table 1-3 shows that
oxygen by weight is 46.6 per cent of the
crust but by volume is 91.97 per cent.

The combinations of the silica tetrahedra
with themselves and with the cations of
iron, aluminum, calcium, magnesium, sodium, and potassium are complex and

of the tetrahedron, and the silicon ion is in
the center. Study Fig. 1-14. It is estimated
that this basic mineral unit constitutes 90
per cent of all crustal matter. The silicon
atom has four electrons in its outer orbit.
Oxygen atoms have six electrons in their
outer orbit and thus need two for stability.
The four oxygen atoms bond firmly with
the one silicon atom, all thus becoming
ions, and produce a larger ion, the silica
tetrahedron, with four negative charges.
These must be satisfied when the silica
tetrahedons join together with one another
or with such cations as Ca^{++}, Mg^{++}, etc.

Note that the oxygen ions are much larger

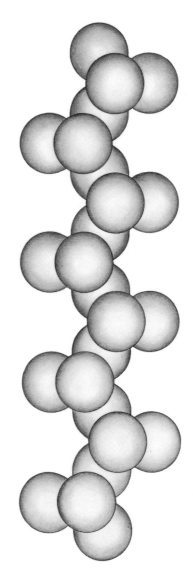

FIG. 1-15   Chain of silica tetrahedra. A silicon ion is in
the center of each tetrahedron, but not shown,
and each tetrahedron shares two oxygen ions
with adjacent tetrahedra.

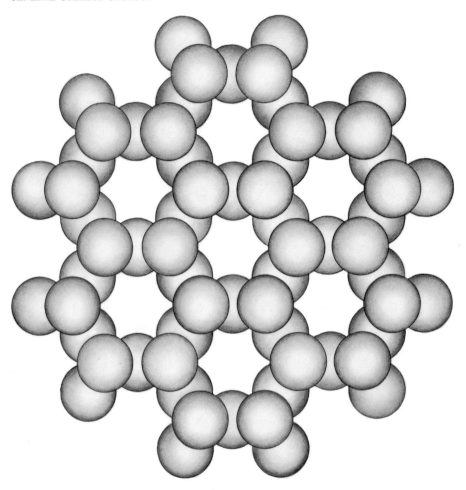

FIG. 1-16   Layer of silica tetrahedra. The silicon ions at the center of each tetrahedron of oxygen ions are concealed and not shown. Within the layer three of the oxygen ions of each tetrahedron are shared by adjacent tetrahedra; only one, the upper one in this drawing, is unshared. This unshared oxygen ion therefore has one unsatisfied valence, or needs to share another electron with some adjacent ion in order to be stable. Thus, a bond is provided with another similar layer of silica tetrahedra. The basic structure of mica is a double layer or plate.

varied, but the precision with which the structures are now documented is a testiment to the great strides that have been made in the understanding of the structure of solids.

The tetrahedons arrange themselves in chains and sheets (Figs. 1-15 and 1-16), which in turn are bonded together by the positive metallic ions. The chains of tetrahedrons impart cleavage directions to the silicate minerals, such as those of feldspar, hornblende, and augite. The sheets of tetrahedrons are weakly bonded together, permitting the easy splitting or peeling of flakes or sheets from mica crystals. Note these characteristics on your laboratory specimens.

Chapter 4 concerns rocks that have formed by cooling and crystallizing from a molten state. Such rocks are abundant at the earth's surface and even more abundant at depth. As the change from a liquid to a solid state occurred, the silica tetrahedons took form—the liquids were preponderantly composed of silicon and oxygen—and then combined with one another and also with the positive ions of the metallic elements to form the silicate minerals. Granite is such a rock and is composed commonly of quartz (SiO_2), orthoclase feldspar ($KAlS_3O_8$), hornblende ($Ca_2(Mg,Fe)_4$-$Al(OH)_2AlSi_3O_{10}$), and biotite mica (K-$(Mg,Fe)_3(OH,F)_2AlSi_3O_{10}$). The process of crystallization from silicate melts is com-

a consequence that someone would seek to find out what kinds of rays are given off by phosphorescent substances. Many minerals will glow in the dark after exposure to light. In 1896, while working on this problem, the French physicist Antoine Becquerel found out much more. He discovered that a substance containing atoms of uranium continually gives off rays even without exposure to light. Later, other

Table 1-3   ABUNDANT ELEMENTS IN THE EARTH'S CRUST

Atomic number	Element	Ion	Ionic radius, angstroms	Abundance in earth's crust Weight, per cent	Abundance in earth's crust Volume, per cent
8	Oxygen (O)	O^{2-}	1.40	46.60	91.97
14	Silicon (Si)	Si^{4+}	0.42	27.72	0.80
13	Aluminum (Al)	Al^{3+}	0.51	8.13	0.77
26	Iron (Fe)	Fe^{2+}	0.74	5.00	0.68
		Fe^{3+}	0.64		
20	Calcium (Ca)	Ca^{2+}	0.99	3.63	1.48
11	Sodium (Na)	Na^+	0.97	2.83	1.60
19	Potassium (K)	K^+	1.35	2.59	2.14
12	Magnesium (Mg)	Mg^{2+}	0.66	2.09	0.56
22	Titanium (Ti)	Ti^{3+}	0.76	0.44	0.03
		Ti^{4+}	0.68		

SOURCE: Complied from Brian Mason, *Principles of Geochemistry*, John Wiley & Sons, Inc., New York, 1952, and Jack Green, Geochemical Table of the Elements for 1953, *Bulletin of the Geological Society of America*, vol. 64, 1953, pp. 1001-1002.

plicated and will be mentioned again in Chap. 4. The complex formula need not be memorized, but reflect the complex structures of the silicate minerals.

RADIOACTIVITY

Emitted Rays

With the discovery of cathode rays that cause fluorescence in vacuum tubes, and the invisible penetrating X rays, it seemed

workers found that the spontaneous rays were of three different kinds.

+ Alpha rays—small particles of fairly high velocity with a positive charge

+ Beta rays—small, penetrating particles of high velocity with a negative charge

+ Gamma rays—a form of highly penetrating invisible light rays with no electrical charge

These properties were determined by penciling the rays through a magnetic field. The beta rays undergo the greatest deflection, the alpha rays are deflected in the opposite direction and to a smaller extent, and the gamma rays are unaffected.

Additional work by Becquerel, the Curies, Rutherford, and others established that alpha rays were helium nuclei and beta rays were electrons. Alpha rays can penetrate up to 0.002 cm of aluminum, beta rays up to 0.2 cm of aluminum, and gamma rays up to 100 cm of aluminum.

Decomposition of Nucleus

Rutherford and Soddy, British scientists, proposed in 1902 that the radioactivity of uranium involved a decomposition of the atomic nuclei and that the alpha, beta, and gamma rays were emitted from the nucleus in the course of the transformation. The first step in the spontaneous decomposition of uranium involves the conversion of uranium to thorium, with an emission of an alpha particle, and may be represented as follows:

$$_{92}U^{238} \rightarrow {}_{90}Th^{234} + {}_2He^4$$

The lower left subscripts are the atomic numbers (number of protons in the nucleus), and the upper right superscripts are mass numbers (sum of protons and neutrons). It should be noted that the sum of the atomic numbers for Th and He equals

Table 1–4   URANIUM-RADIUM SERIES OF RADIOACTIVE DISINTEGRATIONS (SIMPLIFIED)

Atom	Symbol	Particle emitted	Half-life
Uranium	$_{92}U^{238}$		4.5×10^9 years
	↓	α	
Thorium	$_{90}Th^{234}$		24.5 days
	↓	β	
Protactinium	$_{91}Pa^{234}$		1.14 min
	↓	β	
Uranium	$_{92}U^{234}$		2.7×10^5 years
	↓	α	
Thorium	$_{90}Th^{230}$		8.3×10^4 years
	↓	α	
Radium	$_{88}Ra^{226}$		1,590 years
	↓	α	
Radon	$_{86}Rn^{222}$		3.82 years
	↓	α	
Polonium	$_{84}Po^{218}$		3.05 min
	↓	α	
Lead	$_{82}Pb^{214}$		26.8 min
	↓	β	
Bismuth	$_{83}Bi^{214}$		19.7 min
	↓	β	
Polonium	$_{84}Po^{214}$		1.4×10^{-4} sec
	↓	α	
Lead	$_{82}Pb^{210}$		22 years
	↓	β	
Bismuth	$_{83}Bi^{210}$		5.0 days
	↓	β	
Polonium	$_{84}Po^{210}$		140 days
	↓	α	
Lead	$_{82}Pb^{206}$		Stable

SOURCE: From Charles Compton, *An Introduction to Chemistry*, D. Van Nostrand Co., Inc., New York, 1958

the atomic number of U and also that the sum of the mass numbers of Th and He equals the mass number of U. This kind of a change is called a *nuclear chemical change* or *transmutation,* because the nuclei of the atoms are altered and the identity of the atoms is changed. In ordinary chemical reactions only the outer electrons are affected, and the identity of the atom is preserved.

The second step in the decomposition of uranium involves the decomposition of the thorium isotope into a protactinium isotope, with the emission of a beta particle. In the complete process there are fourteen successive steps involving intermediate isotopes that are unstable, finally resulting in the stable lead isotope 206. Table 1-4 shows the fourteen steps and also the *half-life* of the unstable isotopes of the different elements that result.

Rates of Decay

It should be observed that radioactive decomposition takes place at a constant rate that is independent of the temperature, independent of the pressure, and independent of the state of chemical combination. The rate is dependent only on the number of radioactive atoms present. Recognizing the constant rate of decomposition, it is convenient to express the rate in terms of the half-life. By this is meant that after a certain time one-half of the original isotope will have decomposed; for

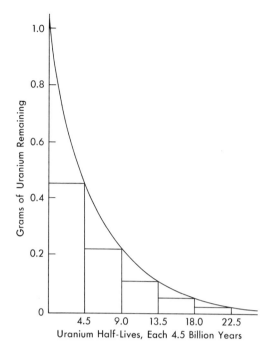

FIG. 1-17 Graph of radioactive decay of 1 g of uranium.

uranium 238 this will take 4.5 billion years. Then half of the unchanged half will decompose in the next 4.5 billion years, and so on. This is represented in Fig. 1-17.

The rates of decay have proved to be a device for the determination of the age of certain rocks and events in the geologic past and have proved immensely valuable in deciphering the history of the earth. The subject will be pursued in later chapters.

Suggested Aids

Readings
Compton, Charles: *An Introduction to Chemistry,* D. Van Nostrand Company, Inc., Princeton, N. J., 1958.

Or any new college text in general chemistry.

Chapter 2

KINDS OF SEDIMENTARY ROCKS

Sedimentary rocks are the hardened products of past accumulations of sediments. The original sediments may be thought of, for example, as clays on lake bottoms, sands along the shores of oceans, lime muds on shallow tropical banks, salt precipitates from saline lakes, or river flood deposits of gravel, sand, and mud. They are classified in three main groups: clastic, chemical, and organic. The clastic sedimentary rocks are composed of discrete mineral grains or broken-down particles of previously existing rock. The chemical sedimentary rocks are composed of various precipitates from solution, such as common salt ($NaCl$), gypsum ($CaSO_4 \cdot 2H_2O$), limestone ($CaCO_3$), and chert (SiO_2). The organic sediments are such deposits as coal and calcareous reefs.

We have learned much about old sedimentary rocks from the study of modern sediments in the process of accumulation, and such research has taken geologists to

Common Sedimentary Rocks

FIG. 2-1 Thick conglomerate exposed on Weber River, north-central Utah.

the seas, lakes, and rivers of all parts of the earth.

Layers of sedimentary rock blanket three-fourths of the surface of the continents and hence are of great importance to an understanding of the earth on which we live. A multitude of land forms has been sculptured from them by erosional processes, the soils that support our agricultural economy developed on them, and they contain many valuable mineral deposits, including coal and practically all oil and gas.

CLASTIC SEDIMENTARY ROCKS

Classes Depending on Size of Particles

Clastic sediments are divided into groups, depending on the size of the particles, as listed in Table 2-1.

Accumulations of boulders, cobbles, and pebbles are characterized as coarse, and when cemented together to form a rock, are called conglomerate. Sand grains become cemented to form sandstone, whereas silt

FIG. 2-2 Close view of conglomerate exposed on Hoback River, western Wyoming.

leaving a residue of cobbles and pebbles on the floor of a desert. Such accumulations of coarse particles are often buried by other layers of sediments, become cemented together, and form conglomerates (Figs. 2-1 to 2-3).

The coarse rock fragments have come from preexisting rock of one kind or another that has been broken up by weathering processes (Chap. 7) and made available in angular fragments to the streams or waves. As the rivers transport the angular rock particles downstream or the waves pound them back and forth on the beaches, the fragments become rounded to various

and clay particles compact into a close arrangement to form siltstone and shale respectively.

Origin of Coarse Clastics

The coarse clastics are commonly formed during torrential floods where swollen, fast-flowing rivers spread the large particles on a gently sloping surface at the foot of a precipitous terrain. Sometimes waves leave a layer or lens of boulders, cobbles, and pebbles along a beach during a storm. Wind may carry the finer particles away,

FIG. 2-3 Close view of conglomerate in southwestern Montana. (*Photograph by E. L. Dillon.*)

Table 2–1

Name of particle	Size in millimeters	Name of sedimentary rock
Boulder	Larger than 256 mm.	Boulder conglomerate
Cobble	64–256 mm	Cobble conglomerate
Pebble	4–64 mm	Pebble conglomerate
Granule	2–4 mm	Granule sandstone
Sand	1/16–2 mm	Sandstone
Silt	1/256–1/16 mm	Siltstone
Clay	Less than 1/256 mm	Shale

degrees. The boulders, cobbles, and pebbles that we see in conglomerates are commonly fairly well rounded.

Sandstone

Size of Particles. Sand grains as specified in Table 2-1 range in size from $\frac{1}{16}$ to 2 mm. They are large enough to be distinguishable by the unaided eye, but under a low-powered hand lens, say with 10-power magnification, they are clearly seen, and their characteristics determinable. They settle through water readily and are rolled along by moderate winds but picked up only by strong winds.

Minerals. Most sand grains are rounded or subrounded particles of the mineral quartz. Quartz is generally colorless and clear, and the crystals grow when possible in hexagonal prisms and pyramids. Quartz is rather hard and will scratch glass. It is resistant to solution in most natural waters, and to mechanical abrasion, and hence outlasts other common and abundant minerals in weathering and transportational proc-

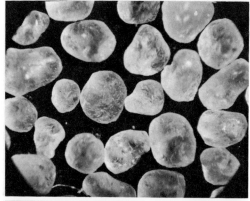

FIG. 2-5 Rounded and angular sand grains. Enlarged about 75 times.

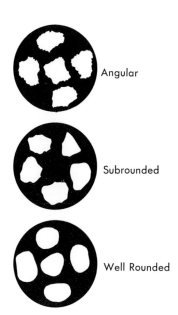

Angular

Subrounded

Well Rounded

FIG. 2-4 Angular to rounded sand grains.

esses. For this reason immense volumes of quartz grains accumulate to the exclusion of almost all others, and many sandstone formations are composed almost entirely of quartz grains. Sandstones of multiple mineral and rock-particle assemblage will be described in Chap. 6.

Degree of Roundness. Quartz grains seldom start out as nicely formed hexagonal crystals but rather as irregular angular, sharp-edged little grains. They have their origin in a rock like granite (Chap. 4), which is composed of an interlocking mixture of crystal grains of several minerals. Quartz commonly fills irregular spaces between the other minerals. In the weathering of granite the other minerals hydrate, oxidize, and dissolve, freeing the resistant quartz grains to the rivers, waves, and wind.

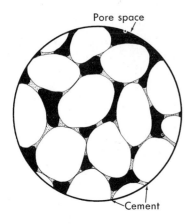

FIG. 2-6 Sand grains cemented together.

Transportation of quartz grains by these agents causes wear and rounding of the grains, and they are thus found in nature in various stages of rounding. See Figs. 2-4 and 2-5.

Cement and Color. Some sandstones are purple-red, some brick red, some rusty, some tan, some gray, and some nearly white on freshly broken surfaces. Colors are mostly imparted by the cement. The spaces between grains render sand porous, and water is able to move into the pores and through the rock. Ground water carries certain compounds in solution, such as calcium carbonate, iron oxide, and silica, and if the chemical conditions are changed as the water passes through the sand, then one or more of these materials may be precipitated as films on the sand grains and as cement between grains. See Fig. 2-6. This bonds the grains together and gives a color to the rock.

FIG. 2-7 Beds of various thickness, here severely bent. Near Biarritz, France.

FIG. 2-8 Massive sandstone beds of the Colorado Plateau, near Glen Canyon Dam. This vertical cliff is about 1,000 ft high.

If the cement is pure calcium carbonate, which precipitates out as the mineral calcite, then the color of the sand grains will not be changed, and the rock may be light gray. A drop of weak hydrochloric acid on the rock will cause effervescence, which denotes the calcium carbonate cement.

If iron oxide is the coating and cementing material, then various shades from tan to rust to deep red will result. The vivid red colors of the Colorado Plateau are due in part to the red hematite cement of the several sandstone formations that crop out in the walls of the deep gorges and that form mesa and bench surfaces.

The cement of sandstone may be silica, which is held in alkaline or basic solutions, and then precipitated out when the basic condition is neutralized by mixing with weak acid solutions. Sandstones whose cement is silica are very hard generally and break with glasslike surfaces. Such a sandstone is called a quartzite (orthoquartzite in specific geologic terminology).

Some sandstones whose cement is calcium carbonate or iron oxide are only weakly cemented, and one may rub off some of the sand grains with the thumb. Such a sandstone is said to be *friable*. A fri-able sandstone is not good for constructional purposes.

Occurrence. Sandstone occurs in layers, which are also called *beds* or *strata*. The layers may be a fraction of an inch, a few inches, a few feet, or many feet thick. See Figs. 2-1 and 2-7. The layers in places extend for many miles as sheets of fairly uniform thickness, in other places they are lens-shaped, and in still others they represent the sand fill of old river channels and hence are stubby lenses in cross section but winding, narrow bodies in ground plan.

When sand is deposited by rivers, waves along beaches, or wind, it commonly develops a layering effect called *cross* or *false bedding*. By this is meant that a sheet of sand is composed of small layers or *laminations* obliquely across the main bed or sheet. See Fig. 2-8. Cross bedding forms where a shallow current capable of transporting sand and silt particles enters deeper water, as shown in Fig. 2-9. Its velocity is suddenly checked, and the grains are dropped down the slope. The continued growth of this slope by further accretion produces a layer with cross-bedded structure.

The surfaces that separate beds are called *bedding planes*, and these surfaces are commonly marked by ripples (Fig. 2-10), tracks of various shelled invertebrates and crustaceans that inhabited the sea or lake floor, and less commonly by tracks of birds, reptiles, and mammals.

How Sand Layers Were Deposited. As already indicated, sand grains are concentrated and cleaned of silt and clay particles principally by running water, by waves and currents playing along shore lines, and by wind. Rivers, especially in flood time, build bars of various kinds in their channels, levees along their banks, and sheets across their flood plains. Some transport the sand to their mouths to build large deposits called *deltas*.

In thinking of wave activity along shore lines, we must consider the situation of a sea advancing over the land or a sea withdrawing from the land. These are slow processes but are happening today and have occurred many times in many places in the past. In the case of an advancing sea, either the land is subsiding or the water level is rising; in the case of a retreating sea, either the land is rising or the water level is falling. Now, if the water level and land are relatively stationary, a belt of sand will form along a fairly stabilized shore, but if the sea advances, the belt of sand is extended as a sheet across all the land invaded by the sea, and if the sea retreats, the shore line retreats also, and a sheet of sand may be spread across the exposed bottom. Sheets of sand of the most uniform thickness and widest distribution were formed under the conditions of advancing or retreating seas. If the position of the shore line holds constant for a while, then various kinds of cross-bedded bars, spits, and cuspate beaches will form, and the sand accumulations will be far less regular. The various types of beach deposits will be discussed in Chap. 10.

Sand dunes built by the wind are made up of large, wedge-shaped units, each with its own cross bedding. See Fig. 2-11. These are usually so distinctive that the deposit can be identified as of wind origin, but the cross bedding of river and shore-line accumulations is usually not distinctive enough to identify the medium of deposition without other characteristics or clues.

Siltstone

The size of silt particles may be thought of as dust particles. They are gritty to the touch or between the teeth and are barely visible as individual grains. They show up well under the microscope, however, and may be studied by this means easily. They

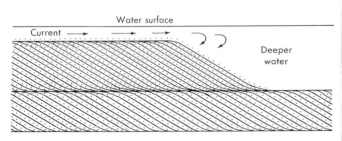

FIG. 2-9   Origin of cross bedding and example of cross bedded sandstone, Grand Canyon of the Colorado River.

FIG. 2-10 Various ripple marks and possible rain-drop impressions on bedding surfaces of a sandstone from the Moenkopi formation, Colorado Plateau. This is a masonry wall.

settle slowly through water and are picked up by the wind and carried hundreds of miles before falling to the surface again. A good rain cleans the air of silt particles.

Unlike sand grains, which are commonly quartz, silt grains are made up of several minerals, each in good proportion. These are quartz, mica, feldspar, calcite, hornblende, and augite. A number of other minerals occurs in minor amounts.

A sedimentary-rock layer is seldom composed wholly of silt-sized particles. They are usually mixed with sand on the one

hand or clay on the other, and geologists working in the field are prone to call a rock that is mostly made up of silt-sized particles a shale.

Silt layers accumulate seaward of the sandy beach zone and in places are deposited by heavy mud-laden bottom currents that flow many miles down-slope into deep water. As these turbid bottom currents spread out and slow down, the largest particles that they carry settle out first, the next smaller later, and the smallest last. This produces a layer composed at the bottom perhaps of fine sand grading upward into a layer of silt, which grades upward into clay. See Fig. 2-12. This is called *graded bedding*.

Shale

Size of Particles. An accumulation of clay-sized particles hardens into a rock called shale. Clay-sized grains are so small that they feel smooth between the fingers and, when mixed with water, remain suspended for hours before reaching the bottom in the process of settling. The smooth

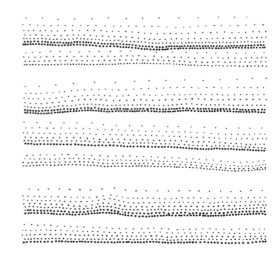

FIG. 2-12 Graded bedding. Each layer is made up of coarsest particles at the bottom and finest particles at the top.

FIG. 2-11 Navajo sandstone of southern Utah showing cross bedding of sand-dune origin. The vertical marks are cracks, called joints.

pastelike layer that forms on the bottom contains much water, and it is principally a matter of losing the water that turns the soft plastic clay into a shale.

Beds of clay or shale are rarely formed entirely of the very small clay-sized particles; silt particles are present in various proportions mixed with those of clay size. Also, more or less calcium carbonate may be present. At any rate, when the fine sediment has dehydrated enough to have hardened somewhat, it generally has the fissility to part in thin layers. This parting is generally considered characteristic of shale. If the sediment becomes very hard and does not split readily in thin plates parallel to the bedding surface, then it is called *argillite*.

Minerals. Clay particles are so small that their mineral constitution is difficult to determine. Analyses are mostly made with X rays, and we recognize chiefly quartz, sericite, chlorite, hydroxides of iron, and the clay minerals. By clay minerals is meant a group of complex hydrous aluminum silicates. *Kaolinite* is one, for instance, from which the white porcelains are made. The clay deposits composed mostly of kaolinite are valuable for the making of many ceramic products, and clay deposits of this kind are much sought after.

Occurrence. Clays are deposited in the central areas of certain lakes at sufficient distance away from shore so as not to be contaminated with coarser particles. They form in arms or embayments of the sea and in waters adjacent to low-lying land. In the central part of fresh-water lakes and in protected basins of the sea black or gray clay often accumulates. This contains up to 20 per cent organic matter and, when dehydrated, forms the so-called oil shales. The organic matter in oil shale is really a solid hydrocarbon, but when heated several hundred degrees it turns into a black, pitchy liquid. The black shales are also the source rocks of much of our natural oil and gas.

Shales commonly occur in thin alternating light and dark layers called *laminations*. These laminations are caused by alternations of layers of coarse and fine particles, by variations in the amount of organic material, or by alternations of calcium carbonate with clay and silt particles. Almost all laminae are produced by seasonal climatic changes during the course of deposition. The temperature and salinity of the water may be affected by the cyclical climatic changes, the silt and clay content brought to the basins of deposition may change with the seasons, and the amount of life and consequent productivity of organic material will also alternate.

Color. Shales are of many colors, and in the desert climates the colors may be vivid. The Chinle and Morrison shale formations, both widely displayed in the Colorado Plateau, are particularly noted for their intense greens, yellows, purples, reds, chocolates, and grays. The tones become most intense when moist after a rain. Some shale formations are made up of beds each with its own color, and such formations are said to be variegated. The colors are due mostly to iron in various degrees of hydration and oxidation.

Vividly colored shales usually contain appreciable volcanic tuff (volcanic dust)

that has altered to the clay we call *bentonite*. Bentonite is highly absorbent of water and swells conspicuously when wetted. The exposed surface becomes slippery and sticky, and ranch roads over these clays when wet are generally impassable by car. Upon drying, the clay surface is left puffy and powdery. The bentonite clay slopes are usually rather barren, even of desert vegetation.

CHEMICAL SEDIMENTARY ROCKS

Limestone and Dolomite

Composition. Limestone and dolomite are the carbonate sedimentary rocks. Pure limestone is made up of crystals of calcite ($CaCO_3$) and pure dolomite of the mineral dolomite $CaMg(CO_3)_2$. If the crystals are microscopic in size, the rock appears dense, but if they are visible to the eye, then the rock is said to be crystalline. Commonly limestones contain some dolomite and dolomites some calcite. There are all gradations between the two. Also limestones and

FIG. 2-13 Oölites from Great Salt Lake magnified about 50 times.

dolomites commonly grade into shales on one hand and sandstones on the other, and we speak of shaley limestones and sandy limestones.

Origin. Most calcium and magnesium carbonate is probably extracted from ocean and lake waters by organisms. The shells of clams and snails and the skeletons of corals are composed of it. Extensive carbonate reefs are forming today, such as the Great Barrier Reef off eastern Australia, and similar reefs were built in many seas and at many times in the past.

With bacteria as the cause of precipitation, a lime mud or ooze collects on the bottom. Evaporation may concentrate and cause the precipitation of the carbonates, which is also in the form of lime ooze.

Some limestone beds are composed of small spherical calcareous concretions the size of sand grains, called oolites. See Fig. 2-13. In thin section under the microscope they appear as shown in Fig. 2-14. Here we can see the small amount of cement necessary to hold the oolites together. The oolites form under beach conditions where the waves play strongly and where calcium carbonate is being precipitated copiously (Fig. 2-15).

Occurrence. We find limestone and dolo-

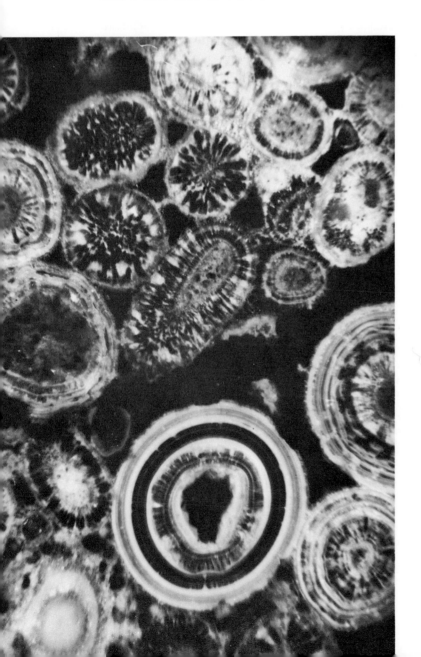

FIG. 2-14 Thin section of oölites from Great Salt Lake.

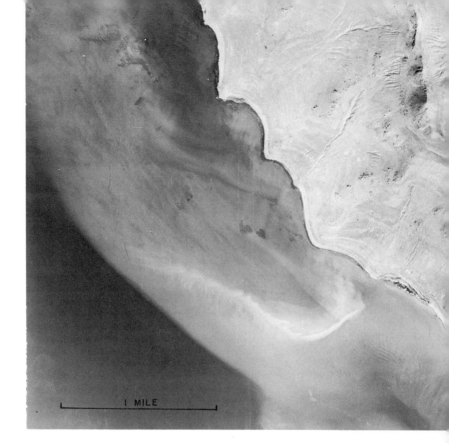

FIG. 2-15 Vertical aerial photograph of a sandy shore on the west side of Antelope Island, Great Salt Lake. Sand is made up of oölites.

mite beds or groups of beds inches to hundreds of feet thick widely distributed across North America. They are numerous and widespread in the Appalachian Mountains, in the Ohio, Mississippi, and Missouri Valley regions, and in the great western Cordillera. They have formed in all past geologic ages. With their abundant marine fossils, they indicate that shallow seas spread here and there widely across the continent at numerous times in the past. In the Appalachian Mountains and in many ranges of the western mountain systems, the beds have been much deformed, elevated, and dissected by erosion. We thus inspect the broken and weathered edges and bedding surfaces of the strata up mountain slopes to high elevations and find the marine fossils there.

Salt and Gypsum

Interstratified in shale and limestone beds are layers of salt (NaCl) and gypsum ($CaSO_4 \cdot 2H_2O$). Geologists have determined that, where these deposits occur,

arms of the invading seas over the continents have been cut off, or nearly so, and these isolated bodies of salty ocean water have evaporated until the sodium chloride and calcium sulphate precipitated out (Fig. 2-16) to collect as layers on the bottom. In the process of evaporation to dryness of a body of sea water the carbonates precipitate out first, then the calcium sulphate, then sodium chloride, and finally the potassium and magnesium salts. An evaporation cycle would be represented by a layer of limestone on the bottom, over this a layer of gypsum, then of salt, and finally on top a thin layer of potassium and magnesium salt. This sequence may be repeated several times, or an evaporation cycle may become interrupted and only proceed part way.

Interior basins and arms of the sea conducive to salt precipitation have occurred in several places in the United States in the past. Salt beds hundreds of feet thick occur beneath the surface in western New York and Michigan. The same is true under a wide region in Kansas, Oklahoma, Texas,

FIG. 2-16 Salt precipitating out of saturated water in Great Salt Lake, 1934.

and southeastern New Mexico. Salt is several thousand feet thick under parts of the Colorado Plateau of Utah, Arizona, Colorado, and New Mexico. Figure 2-17 shows the bed of salt that has been left by

FIG. 2-17 Bonneville salt crust, Great Salt Lake Desert, western Utah. Note the high shore lines on the distant mountains, made by a former fresh-water lake.

the evaporation of a salty lake in western Utah.

Chert

Chert is composed of very finely crystalline, or in part amorphous or hydrous, silica. The term "flint" with which we are all familiar is a synonym or variety. Chert occurs in all colors, the red and yellow varieties, which contain iron oxide, being called jasper. Extensive beds of chert form parts of the sedimentary sequences in places. In other places we note that nodules of chert one to several inches across are abundant in limestone and dolomite.

The origin is complex, but a good deal of it was formed as a chemical precipitate. Possibly the original precipitate was in the form of a silica gel that later lost its water to form the very hard chert.

SEDIMENTARY ROCKS OF ORGANIC ORIGIN

Limestone Reefs

The Great Barrier Reef off the east coast of Australia is an example of an extensive deposit of calcium carbonate that has been extracted from sea water chiefly by the organisms that live on the reef. Algae and bacteria, among the plants, are abundant, and among the animals are corals, bryozoa, sponges, clams, snails, foraminifera, and ostracods. These organisms are discussed in considerable detail in later chapters.

The algae, through the process of photosynthesis, extract CO_2 from the water and cause the precipitation of crusts of $CaCO_3$ (Fig. 2-18). The skeletal forms of the corals and bryozoa contribute to the $CaCO_3$ of the reef, and the shells of other forms add still more $CaCO_3$. The waves break up some of these deposits and build them into clastic accumulations, but it is probably only a short time before more precipitating

FIG. 2-18 Algal heads of Great Salt Lake. The lake level has recently fallen, exposing the deposits.

FIG. 2-19 Reefs in limestone strata exposed in deep canyons of Canadian Rockies, Flathead Range, Alberta. *(Courtesy of Geological Survey of Canada, through Ed Schiller.)*

FIG. 2-20 Bituminous coal bed, about 25 ft thick, near Kemmerer, Wyoming. Shale and sandstone beds overlie the coal bed.

$CaCO_3$ cements the fragments together into a firm rock.

Needless to say, a reef is generally a very porous mass and long afterward, when buried by other sediments, is a good container of oil. Much oil and gas has been found in old buried reefs. See Fig. 2-19.

Oil Shale

Shale in certain places contains so much organic matter that it will burn hesitatingly with a yellow, smoky flame. In an airtight retort, it may be heated, and oil and gas driven off. The so-called Green River shale formation of Wyoming, Colorado, and Utah contains beds from which over 40 gal of oil per ton of rock can be distilled off. This deposit formed in a large inland lake of ancient time (Eocene epoch) where algae contributed a great deal to the organic content of the shale.

Coal

Of all sedimentary rocks, coal is obviously of organic origin. Only the ash content can be said to be of physical origin. The ash is the clay and sand washed into the peat swamp during the accumulation of

peat from the plants growing there. Upon burial the peat changes to lignite and then to bituminous coal. The change is brought about chiefly by the loss of water. See Fig. 2-20.

Oil and Gas

Oil and gas occur below the surface in the pores of rocks and are believed to come from organic matter that accumulated along with the bottom clays and lime oozes. The process of transformation of the organic matter to oil and gas may be caused by the action of bacteria living in the bottom clays and muds. The oil and gas are forced out of the fine-grained sediments into the pores of adjacent porous and generally coarser-grained rocks. The cause of further movement and collection into major accumulations, and the search for such, is the subject of petroleum geology, which must be left for another course.

INTERLAYING OF VARIOUS SEDIMENTARY ROCKS

Sedimentary rocks generally occur in alternating layers, building sequences many thousands of feet thick in places. Figure

FIG. 2-21 Limestone and shale beds exposed on the steep walls of the San Juan River, Utah.

FIG. 2-22 Smooth slopes are shale beds, and thin cliff-making beds are sandstone. San Rafael Swell, Utah.

2-21 shows a series of alternating limestone and shale layers through which the San Juan River has cut a gorge. The limestone layers form the vertical cliffs and the shale layers the slopes and notches. Figure 2-22 shows a butte with the slope eroded from horizontal shale beds (also one or two thin sandstones forming vertical cliffs) and what is left of a thick sandstone layer forming the cap. Figure 2-23 shows a series of sandstone beds above and shale below tipped up on end and eroded away. The valley is eroded in a soft shale formation.

Some sedimentary sequences are composed dominantly of limestone and shale beds, some of sandstone and shale, and some of limestone and sandstone. Sediments have accumulated in some basins to

FIG. 2-23 Upturned beds on the east flank of the San Rafael Swell, central Utah.

thicknesses of thousands of feet, and since the sediments have signs of shallow-water origin, we can only postulate that the floor of the sea sank as the sediments accumulated, thus maintaining shallow-water conditions for a long time.

Suggested Aids

Readings

Heller, Robert L. (ed.): *Geology and Earth Sciences Sourcebook*, Holt, Rinehart and Winston, Inc., New York, 1962.

Pearl, R. M.: *How to Know the Minerals and Rocks*, McGraw-Hill Book Company, Inc., New York, 1955.

Pettijohn, F. J.: *Sedimentary Rocks*, 2d ed., Harper & Row, Publishers, Incorporated, New York, 1957.

Pough, F. H.: *Field Guide to Rocks and Minerals*, Houghton Mifflin Company, Boston, 1953.

Schrock, R. R.: *Sequence in Layered Rocks*, McGraw-Hill Book Company, Inc., New York, 1948.

Movie

The Bahamas: Where Limestone Grows Today, Humble Oil Refining Co., Houston, Tex., 40 min.

PRIMARY AND SECONDARY STRUCTURES

We speak of primary and secondary structures in
sedimentary rocks. The primary structures are those
previously described, such as ripple marks, mud cracks,
cross bedding, and fossil imprints. Secondary structures are
the result of deformation of the beds. We presumed
that sedimentary beds were deposited in a near-horizontal
position and that, if tilted appreciably, folded, or faulted,
secondary structures have been formed.

COMMON PRIMARY STRUCTURES

Cross Bedding

There are several kinds of cross bedding,
which are generally classified according to the agent
that formed them. Waves and currents along a shore drift
sand and build bars, spits, and other beach

Structures
of Sedimentary Rocks

FIG. 3-1 Cross bedding formed by a river. This is a vertical section parallel with the current, which flowed from right to left. (Shell Oil.)

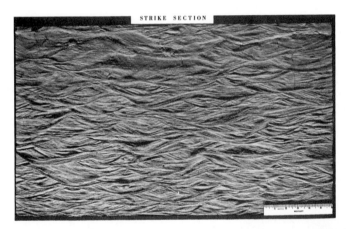

FIG. 3-2 Cross bedding formed by a river. This is a vertical section at right angles to the current (Shell Oil.)

FIG. 3-3 Cross bedding of dune variety, in Jurassic sandstone near Kanab, southern Utah.

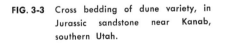

FIG. 3-4 Ripple marks on a bed of siltstone, Parleys Canyon, Utah. (Photograph by M. K. McCarter.)

FIG. 3-6   Contorted bedding due to flowage soon after deposition. Soft glacial clays near Gunnar Mine, Beaverlodge area, Saskatchewan. (Courtesy of C. K. Bell and Geological Survey of Canada.)

FIG. 3-5   Large ripples on a limestone bed exposed in a quarry in Stansbury Range, Utah.

FIG. 3-7   Primary deformation of plastic sediments, now hard rock in Canadian Rockies. (Courtesy of Canadian Geological Survey and E. Mountjoy.)

deposits, all of which are made up of cross-bedded layers or lenses. Figure 2-8 is a cross-bedded shore-line deposit of an ancient sea. Rivers fill their channels and flood over their banks to build flood-plain deposits. They also build deltas at their mouths, which are commonly composed of cross-bedded masses of sand and silt. Figures 3-1 and 3-2 are examples of river deposits; one is a vertical section through the deposit parallel with the direction of the current, and the other is at right angles to the current. Still other types of cross bedding are formed by the wind (Fig. 3-3).

Ripple Marks

Newly deposited sediment becomes rippled in many environments. We see ripples in the sand in stream beds, along lake and ocean shores, and on desert dunes. Underwater cameras reveal ripple marks in sediments down to great oceanic depths. The forms are generally due to currents and, when thus formed, are asymmetrical. Note such ripples shown in Fig. 3-4. However, there are symmetrical ripples, and these are formed by water particles rocking back and forth without appreciable forward movement. These are called oscillatory ripples, as opposed to current ripples. An example of large ripple marks that appear to be asymmetrical or of current origin is shown in Fig. 3-5. This is a bedding surface of an ancient limestone sediment, since hardened, turned up on end in a mountain-making disturbance, and then exposed in a quarry operation.

There are many other kinds of markings on bedding surfaces, and perhaps you will see some on field trips. Watch for mud cracks, various rill marks and flutings caused by breaker swash, and tracks, trails or borings of the numerous invertebrates that lived in and on the bottom sediments.

Deformation of Soft Sediments

When sediments, especially silt and clay layers, are deposited on sloping bottoms, the force of gravity is often sufficient to cause the weak or almost soupy sediment layer to slump or flow. Its laminations then become folded in complicated patterns. See Fig. 3-6. Then more sediments are deposited on top of the deformed mass. These may be sufficiently strong to resist slumping or sliding down the slope, but the next layer may yield again. This is the story revealed in Fig. 3-6. Of course, long after the total accumulation has lithified or become cemented, we may wonder how the hard, brittle rocks could have been so intricately folded, but we realize that the folding occurred before lithification. This is called a primary structure.

Figure 3-7 is another case of primary deformation in which we can see that the layers yielded more like stiff clay than soup, and some of them broke in blocks or cakes.

JOINTS

Any exposure of hard rock will exhibit cracks. These are called joints. They may be as much as 20 ft apart but generally are about 1 to 5 ft apart. See Fig. 3-8. In quarrying building and monumental stone, joints always have to be contended with, and it is impossible in some quarries to obtain blocks more than 2 or 3 ft on a side because of the numerous joints. Large monumental blocks are found only in certain places.

Some joints develop soon after the sediments are deposited. Drying and compaction of the fine-grained sediments are partly responsible, but warping and tilting of the unconsolidated sediments may also play a role. Long after the sands have been cemented to sandstones, the lime muds have hardened to limestones, and the clays compacted to shale, the beds may be deformed and new sets of joints superposed on the old. Thus we may see parallel or semiparallel sets of joints in two or three directions. Examine Fig. 3-9.

FIG. 3-8 Weathering along joints in granite. Wasatch Mountains, Utah.

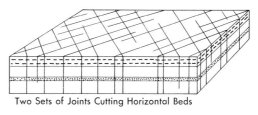

Two Sets of Joints Cutting Horizontal Beds

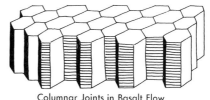

Columnar Joints in Basalt Flow

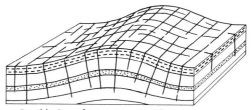

Possible Sets of Joints in an Anticline

FIG. 3-9 Various relations and settings for intersecting sets of joints.

Joints provide the weathering agents access to the rocks, and commonly decay and disintegration along the points result in fissures and the intricate dissection of the rock surface. See Fig. 3-8 again, and Fig. 3-10.

The massive sandstone formations of the Colorado Plateau are jointed to form impressive columns, such as seen in Fig. 3-11. When a person is 2 miles above the surface and looking straight down, the pattern formed by erosion along joints is sometimes striking. See if you can discern two directions or sets of joints in the vertical air photograph of Fig. 3-12.

Joints of other kinds, especially in volcanic rocks, will be described in Chap. 4. See Fig. 3-13.

FIG. 3-10 Vertical aerial photograph of a granitic terrane showing preferential erosion along faults and joints. Laramie Range, Wyoming. *(Courtesy of W. W. Doeringsfeld.)*

ANTICLINES AND SYNCLINES

Sedimentary strata are commonly folded. Most mountain systems exhibit numerous folds; in fact, the mountains are there because once flat-lying sedimentary rocks have been folded and faulted, with concurrent uplift.

Up-arched strata are called anticlines,

FIG. 3-11 Joints in massive sandstone, near Glen Canyon Dam, in northern Arizona.

FIG. 3-12 Vertical aerial photograph showing particularly sets of joints in massive sandstone, Colorado Plateau.

and down-bent strata are called synclines. Examine Figs. 3-14 to 3-16. Anticlines and synclines occur in all sizes from almost microscopic to great folds scores of miles across. When beds are hard and brittle and the folding pronounced, the deformation is accomplished by breaking of the massive beds. The shale beds in between generally deform plastically. See Figs. 3-16 and 3-17. Gypsum, salt, and coal beds deform readily as if by flowing (Figs. 3-18 and 3-19).

Folds may be gentle and symmetrical, or sharp and asymmetrical. Depending on the intensity of the deforming forces the folds may be gentle, sharp, overturned, or overthrust. See Figs. 3-20 to 3-22. Figure 3-20 shows the folds to be due to horizontal pressure causing a set of upper beds to glide and fold over a stable foundation rock. The Jura Mountains of Germany are erosional remnants of this kind of structure. See Fig. 3-23.

Anticlines as described so far are long structures, but others may be circular or domal. Here the deforming force is vertical and has acted upward. The oval or circular uplifts are generally referred to as *domes*.

As the strata are folded, the erosional processes begin to cut or dissect the uplifted parts. Soon, just the stumps of the upturned beds appear at the surface, and various outcrop patterns betray various kinds of folds. For instance, circular outcrops indicate a dome, oval outcrops indicate a dome longer than wide, and parallel outcrops a long anticline. See Figs. 3-24 to 3-26. If crests of anticlines and troughs of adjacent synclines are not level, but plunge, then a zig-zag outcrop pattern results. See Figs. 3-27 and 3-28.

THRUST FAULTS

Faults are fractures in the rocks along which the blocks on either side have moved relative to each other.

The southern Appalachian Mountains

FIG. 3-13 Jointing of vitric volcanic ash fall in Japan.

and the Rocky Mountains of Alberta, British Columbia, Montana, Wyoming, Colorado, and Utah exhibit impressive examples of sheets of rocks that have been thrust along fractures or shear surfaces. The evidence is usually clear that older rocks have been thrust up and over younger ones, in the manner of the lower diagram in Fig. 3-20. The thrust sheets become deeply dissected by the erosional processes, and often remnants, called *klippe*, are left generally as caps of mountains. Examine Figs. 3-29 to 3-31.

NORMAL FAULTS

Normal faults are those in which the relative movement or displacement of the blocks is up and down, and the downdropped block is on the side toward which the fault plane dips. See Figs. 3-32 to 3-34. In large scale we have to deal with the rift valleys of Africa and the ranges and basins of the Great Basin of Utah and Nevada. In these places the earth's crust seems to have been stretched with the development of the normal faults. See Figs. 3-35 and 3-36. Part of the Rhine Valley through the Black

FIG. 3-14 Anticline and synclines in foreground. Folded limestones and dolomites near Jasper National Park, Alberta. *(Courtesy of Geological Survey of Canada.)*

FIG. 3-15 Half of a gentle anticline that has been trenched by the Colorado River. Anticlines are likely structures for oil accumulation.

FIG. 3-16 Sharp folding of shales and limestones near Biarritz, France.

FIG. 3-17 Sharp folding of alternating brittle and flexible layers. Foothill belt of Alberta. (Courtesy of Geological Survey of Canada.)

Forest is a rift valley, but more generally called a *graben*, meaning trench. A valley formed by faults is called a graben.

FAULTS WITH HORIZONTAL DISPLACEMENT

By horizontal displacement is meant that the blocks on either side of a fault shifted horizontally in respect to each other, as shown in Fig. 3-37. A number of great faults are known to be of this kind. The San Andreas fault of California is an outstanding example. It starts in the Gulf of California and extends up the Coast Ranges to Cape Mendocino north of San Francisco, a distance of 800 miles or more. Some

geologists postulate that the block or slice of crust on the ocean side has moved 350 miles to the northwest. An air photograph of a small part of the long San Andreas fault is shown in Fig. 3-38. Such faults are straight over long distances and the fault plane is nearly vertical.

The cause of faulting will be taken up in Chap. 13.

FAULT SCARPS

When displacement along a fracture breaks through to the surface, a fault scarp is produced. See Fig. 3-39. Movements are generally sudden and range from 1 in. to 50 ft. The jolting and destructive earthquake

FIG. 3-18 Folded gypsum beds, Port Hood, Nova Scotia. Gypsum deforms plastically under low pressure, and often is deformed as shown, whereas beds above and below of other rock will have been folded only gently. *(Courtesy of Geological Survey of Canada and D. G. Kelley.)*

FIG. 3-19 Highly deformed coal in the core of an anticline. Canadian Rockies of British Columbia. Coal is like gypsum, it deforms easily. *(Courtesy of Geological Survey of Canada.)*

at Hebgen Lake near the west entrance of Yellowstone National Park was the result of vertical movement of 10 to 25 ft on the known Hebgen Lake fault. The scarp, which formed instantly, is 16 ft high on the Madison River (Fig. 3-40). These movements will be treated more fully in Chap. 13. Many of the imposing ranges of Nevada, eastern California, and western Utah owe much of their height to displacement along

Gentle, Symmetrical

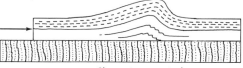

Sharp, Asymmetrical

FIG. 3-20 Progressive development of folds. The deforming force is probably a component of gravity. ▶

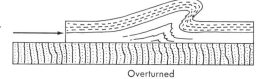

Overturned

FIG. 3-21 Overturned fold in the Rockies of the Yukon. (Courtesy of Geological Survey of Canada and L. H. Green.) ▼

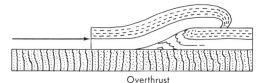

Overthrust

FIG. 3-22 Recumbent fold in Canadian Rockies near Jasper National Park, Alberta. *(Courtesy of Geological Survey of Canada and E. Mountjoy.)*

normal faults, but it is certain that the total displacement of several thousand feet, which we can measure, is a summation of many small displacements. Like the Hebgen Lake faulting, each movement was only a few feet. The individual small movements occur at intervals of hundreds and even thousands of years, so the growth in height of a range is a slow process.

It must be evident that, if two great

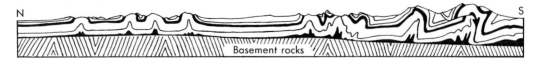

FIG. 3-23 Cross section showing folds of the Jura Mountains, Germany.

masses of rock rub along each other, much crushing, shattering, grinding, and even polishing may occur. The badly broken rock is called *fault breccia,* and the striated and polished surfaces are called *slickensides.* See Fig. 3-41.

UNCONFORMITIES

When a sequence of stratified rocks is folded or faulted, and much erosion occurs,

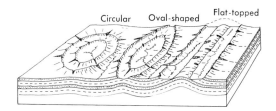

FIG. 3-24 Outcrop patterns of various kinds of anticlines.

FIG. 3-25 Erosional pattern of nearly circular dome. Here the strata have been domed up by a cylindrical plug of gypsum that rose from below. The gypsum plug actually penetrated through the beds as it domed them up and extruded at the surface. The central rough area is gypsum, and the circular belts are upturned and eroded sedimentary rocks. Ellef Ringnes Island, Canadian Arctic. *(Courtesy of Geological Survey of Canada and W. W. Heywood.)*

FIG. 3-26 Outcrop pattern around an elliptical uplift. Canyon Range, Yukon Territory. *(Courtesy of Geological Survey of Canada and Ed Schiller.)*

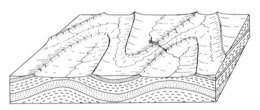

FIG. 3-27 Outcrop pattern made by plunging anticlines and synclines.

FIG. 3-28 Anticline plunging to north. Southwestern Montana.

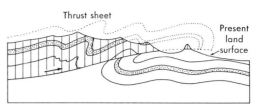

Thrust sheet

Present
land
surface

FIG. 3-29 Thrust sheet after
considerable erosion.

FIG. 3-30 Old strata of Devonian and Mississippian ages are thrust over young strata of Late
Cretaceous age. See Chaps. 18 and 19. *(Courtesy of Geological Survey of Canada.)*

FIG. 3-31 Klippe in west-central Colorado. Precambrian
rock thrust over Cretaceous strata.

▶

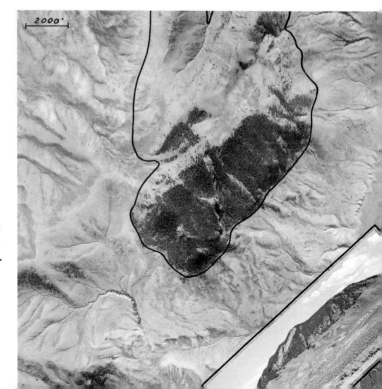

2000'

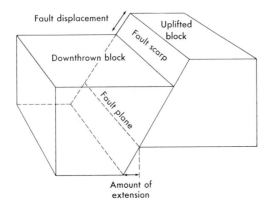

FIG. 3-32 Parts of a normal fault.

FIG. 3-33 Faulting of shale and limestone beds near Soldier Summit, Utah.

FIG. 3-34 Faulting of volcanic ash beds in Japan.

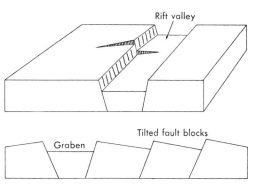

FIG. 3-35 Normal faults resulting in rift valleys (graben) and tilted fault blocks.

FIG. 3-36 West front of Wasatch Mountains near Nephi, Utah. This is in large measure a dissected fault scarp. See Chap. 8. *(Photograph by H. J. Bissell.)*

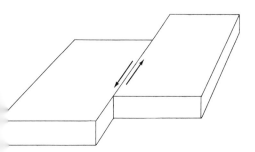

FIG. 3-37 Fault with horizontal displacement.

FIG. 3-38 San Andreas fault, southern California. *(Vertical aerial photograph, Fairchild Aerial Surveys, Inc.)*

FIG. 3-39 A 10-foot-high scarp formed here incident to sudden movement on the Hebgen Lake fault. This caused the Hebgen Lake earthquake of 1959.

FIG. 3-40 A 16-foot-high fault scarp on Madison River, southwestern Montana.

FIG. 3-41 Slickenside surface of uplifted block of Wasatch fault. The surface had been protected by sand and gravel deposits, which, when quarried, left the striated and polished scarp in good shape. The weathering agents are now eating into it.

FIG. 3-42 Unconformity seen in canyon wall, Yaka-
taga District, Alaska. *(Photograph by D. J.
Miller, U.S. Geological Survey.)*

FIG. 3-43 Unconformity between Dakota sandstone and Morrison shales north of Boulder, Colorado. Immediately beneath the sandstone is a reddish-brown soil about 2 ft thick
that formed on the shale before burial by the sand. *(Courtesy of Walter Sadlick.)*

the beds are commonly trimmed off so that we see the beveled edges of inclined layers in outcrop. Now if more sedimentary layers are deposited across these eroded stumps of beds, then a structure is produced, called an unconformity. There are many kinds of unconformities, but all are included under a simple definition. It is a buried erosion surface. Any kind of rock may be undergoing erosion, and if the rock is buried by new sediments, or even volcanic rocks, an unconformity is created.

An unconformity is illustrated in Fig. 3-42, where the beds below the old erosion surface are inclined and the beds above are nearly horizontal. Another unconformity is seen in Fig. 3-43, where the beds above and below are both horizontal, yet with an old erosion surface and soil separating them.

Suggested Aids

Readings

Badgley, Peter C.: *Structural Methods for the Exploration Geologist,* Harper & Row, Publishers, Incorporated, New York, 1959.

Billings, Marland P.: *Structural Geology,* 2d ed., Prentice-Hall, Inc., Englewood Cliffs, N. J., 1954.

Movie

Mountain Building, Encyclopaedia Britannica, 16 mm, 11 min.

Filmstrip

The Story of Mountains, Encyclopaedia Britannica, FSC-483.

Chapter 4

DEFINITION

An igneous rock is one that was once molten but, as a result of cooling, has solidified. The molten rock material is referred to as *magma* if it is below the surface in some kind of chamber or reservoir but as *lava* if it pours out on the surface. After solidification the lava is referred to as lava rock.

REASONS FOR MANY VARIETIES

There are many kinds of igneous rocks. This is due to variable mineral composition on the one hand and to variable textures on the other.

Texture Variable

By texture is meant the size, shape, and arrangement of the mineral particles that make up the rock. Texture also refers to the condition of a rock when it is filled with cavities or is fragmented or badly crushed.

Igneous Rocks

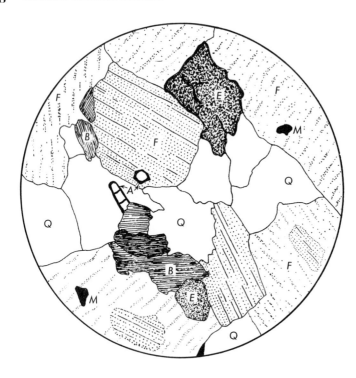

FIG. 4-1 Interlocking mineral grains of Feldspar (F), Quartz (Q), Biotite (B), Epidote (E), Magnetite (M), and Apatite (A), such as would form a typical granite. Magnified about 20 times.

The rock may not even be made up of grains but may be glassy. Except for the glassy varieties all igneous rocks are crystalline, and texture applies mostly to the fineness or coarseness of the mineral grains. If the particles range in size from grains of wheat to kernels of corn, the rock is said to be *coarsely crystalline* (granitoid, granular, or coarse-grained). Granite is a typical example of a coarsely crystalline rock, Fig. 4-1). If the crystals are so small that only tiny light flashes from the mineral cleavage faces betray the crystalline nature, or that the rock must be studied under the microscope to discern the crystals, then it is said to be *finely crystalline* (felsitic).

Some igneous rocks are composed of large crystals surrounded by a groundmass of small crystals. Such a texture is said to be porphyritic, and the rock is called a *porphyry* (Fig. 4-2).

The size of the crystals is determined by the rate of cooling. If the magma cools very slowly, then the ions have opportunity to migrate to small centers of crystallization (seed crystals) and cause them to grow large, as in a granite. If the magma contains considerable water in parts, there the crystal growth is even better facilitated, and crystals 1 in. or larger develop. Under very favorable conditions of cooling and in the presence of much water single crystals of certain minerals, like feldspar and mica, grow to a length of several feet. The unusually coarse textures develop within the body of the magma and also in dikes fed by the aqueous magma. They form a rock called *pegmatite* (Figs. 4-3 and 4-4).

Mineral Composition Variable

In the course of cooling the magma grows mineral grains of several kinds, because it is chemically complex. Study Table 4-1. In this table the common minerals of both the sedimentary and igneous rocks are listed. Rock specimens will be shown in class, and you should get acquainted with their appearance and characteristics.

The silicates make up the bulk of crystalline igneous rocks, and two main groups should be noted, the feldspars and the iron-magnesian minerals. In a freshly broken surface of granite, for instance, the glassy-like mineral grains are quartz, the fairly opaque milky white or pink grains are feldspar, and the dark minerals are the iron-magnesian minerals (also called ferromagnesian minerals). Mica grains may also be recognized, the colorless ones being musco-vite and the black ones biotite. We should know also that feldspar has two main varieties: the potassium-bearing orthoclase and the sodium- and calcium-bearing plagioclase.

CLASSIFICATION

With the previous information in mind regarding variable textures and variable

FIG. 4-2 Representative igneous rocks.

GRANITE

RHYOLITE

DIORITE

PORPHYRY

GABBRO

BASALT

OBSIDIAN WITH SPHERULITES

OBSIDIAN

FIG. 4-3 Pegmatite dike and veins in older layered crystalline rock. Note the very coarse texture of the pegmatite.

FIG. 4-4 Contact of intrusive pegmatite and gneiss. The heat and fluids of the pegmatite softened a zone of the gneiss about 1½ ft thick and caused it to flow and become crenulated near the contact. Near Renbugten, East Greenland. *(Courtesy of John Haller, Switzerland.)*

Table 4–1 COMMON ROCK-FORMING MINERALS

Chemical group	Mineral	Chemical composition
Oxides	Magnetite	Fe_3O_4
	Hematite	Fe_2O_3
	Limonite	$FeO(OH) \cdot nH_2O$
Sulphides	Pyrite	FeS_2
Sulphates	Gypsum	$CaSO_4 \cdot 2H_2O$
	Anhydrite	$CaSO_4$
Carbonates	Calcite	$CaCO_3$
	Dolomite	$CaMg(CO_3)_2$
Haloids	Halite	$NaCl$
Silicates	Feldspar:	
	Orthoclase	$K(AlSi_3O_8)$
	Plagioclase	$Na(AlSi_3O_8$ and
		$Ca(Al_2Si_2O_8)$
	Iron-magnesian minerals:	
	Olivine	$(Mg, Fe)_2SiO_4$
	Augite	$Ca(Mg, Fe, Al) (Al, Si)_2O_6$
	Hornblende	$Ca_2(Mg, Fe)_4Al(OH)_2AlSi_2O_7$
	Biotite mica	$K(Mg, Fe)_3(OHF)_2AlSi_3O_{10}$
	Muscovite mica	$KAl_2(OH, F)_2AlSi_3O_{10}$
	Quartz	SiO_2

mineral composition, a simple classification of igneous rocks may now be presented. See Table 4-2. The specific rock names are printed in italic type. We see that granite, for instance, is coarsely crystalline, light-colored, and is composed predominantly of quartz and orthoclase. Dark iron-magnesian minerals are generally scattered through it. Gabbro is dark gray and consists of plagioclase and iron-magnesian minerals (Fig.

─ely crystalline equivalent of a ⌐alled rhyolite (felsite) and may gray to dark gray to reddish. Basalt ely crystalline black rock.

gma of granitic composition, if ⌐ry rapidly and turned to glass, say margin of a lava flow, would be ⌐bsidian (Fig. 4-2). A glass of basal-

tic composition would be referred to as a basalt glass. Obsidian is somewhat transparent on thin edges, but basaltic glass is fairly opaque.

At the bottom of the table we can see the principal variations in chemical composition. The granite-rhyolite group is rich in silica, contains appreciable potassium, and is low in iron and magnesium. The gabbro-basalt group is low in silica, has appreciable sodium and calcium, and is rich in iron and magnesium. All have considerable aluminum.

The specific gravity of the granite-rhyolite group is about 2.7; that of the gabbro-basalt group is 3.0. A rock not listed but which should be mentioned, *peridotite*, is made up almost entirely of the iron-magnesian minerals, olivine and augite, and has a

Table 4–2 CLASSIFICATION OF IGNEOUS ROCKS

Occurrence	Texture	Color and mineral composition		
		Light-colored	Intermediate	Dark-colored
		Quartz and ortho-clase	Approximately equal amounts of each	Plagioclase and iron-magnesian silicate minerals
Batholiths, stocks,* laccoliths*	Coarsely crystalline	*Granite*†	*Diorite*	*Gabbro* *Diabase*
Dikes, sills, surface flows	Finely crystalline	*Felsite*		*Basalt*
		Rhyolite	*Andesite*	
Surface flows, crusts of flows	Glassy, vesicular	*Obsidian* *pumice*	*Andesitic* *glass* *pumice*	*Basaltic* *glass* *scoria*
Beds and layers	Fragmental	*Fragmental* *pumice*	**Tuff** (fine) **Breccia** (coarse)	*Fragmental* *scoria*
Chemical composition ⟶		High silica and potassium; low iron and magnesium	Low silica, sodium, and calcium; High iron and magnesium	

* Commonly porphyritic, with finely crystalline groundmass.
† The words in italic type are the rock names.

density of 3.3. In major perspective the earth has three outer layers, corresponding to the above densities. The top is a layer of sedimentary and granite-like rocks with a density of 2.3 to 2.7; under this is the gabbro-basalt layer with a density of 3.0; and under this is the peridotite layer with a density in its upper part of 3.3. The peridotite layer is very thick and is called the mantle. The layers above the mantle constitute the crust. More will be said about these layers in the chapter on earthquakes.

Some magmas contain much water. Under high pressures, such as exist several miles below the surface, the water is as much part of the magma as silica, alumina, or iron oxide. When this water-rich magma rises in a conduit that feeds a volcano, the confining pressures decrease, and finally the water begins to be released as gas. It fills the magma with bubbles, and finally as the magma reaches the surface it may expand to a froth. If the magma cools and solidifies in this form, and if of felsitic composition, it will result in *pumice*. If of basaltic composition *scoria* will form (Fig. 4-5). The thin partitions between the myriad of bubble holes are mostly volcanic glass.

Any lava rock containing bubble holes is said to be *vesicular*. Pumice is an extremely vesicular lava rock, and scoria is generally moderately vesicular.

FIG. 4-5 Scoria. This is a moderately vesicular basalt.

In some eruptions there is so much highly heated water that the froth is blown into tiny particles high in the air amidst a tremendous emission of steam (Fig. 4-6). The particles are generally not larger than dust and settle on the countryside in blankets several inches to several feet thick to form a deposit called *tuff* (Fig. 4-7). The volcanic dust particles consist largely of glass shards and small pieces of pumice. Fragments of several different minerals are also identified in some tuffs.

Fragments of pumice or scoria the size of buckshot to marbles are called *lapilli* or *cinders* (Fig. 4-8). Some cones are built up almost entirely of such fragments, and are called cinder cones (Fig. 4-9). The explosions are generally mild but frequent, with each small eruption producing considerable lapilli and perhaps large fragments and building a symmetrical, but generally small cone.

Volcanic bombs are common around cinder cones, and some are shown in Fig. 4-10. Blobs of molten magma are hurled from the crater into the air, and as they rotate they become spindle-shaped, very vesicular in the center, and with crust or skin commonly checked like bread crust.

Volcanic Breccia is a rock mass composed of large and small particles without sorting or layering. See Figs. 4-11 and 4-12. Mudflows or slides down the volcanic cone, or possibly an explosion of variable-sized particles, may result in a volcanic breccia. The particles may be so hot that they weld together.

KINDS OF IGNEOUS ROCK BODIES

We have been concerned with the kinds of igneous rocks in preceding paragraphs. Now, the modes of occurrence, the shapes and sizes of the rock masses, and the relation of these bodies to adjacent rocks must be considered. There are two main categories of igneous rock bodies. The intrusive rocks are those that cooled and solidified below the surface, the magma having made its way upward from some deep-seated source into the upper part of the crust. Extrusive rocks are those whose magmas have issued out on the surface.

Intrusive Bodies

A *batholith* is a very large mass of coarsely crystalline intrusive rock, generally granitic in composition. The bulk of the Sierra Nevada of California, a range of 70 miles across and 400 miles long, is granite or a near relative and is an example of a batholith. The depth to which the granite extends is a question, but probably a number of miles, so that thousands of cubic miles of rock are involved. Batholiths constitute the largest rock units of the crust. They are generally not formed of a single intrusion of magma but are compound in being made up of several separate and successive intrusions. They occur in the belts of major crustal deformation or mountain building, generally along the continental margins.

Figure 4-13 is a diagrammatic illustration of a batholith. It cuts through or across the sedimentary strata in one place, and there is said to be *discordant,* but at other places has pushed aside or wedged between the strata and does not cut across them. Such a contact is said to be *concordant.* The sedimentary rocks have generally been deformed by folding and thrusting before the great intrusions made their way up into and through them.

The magma emplaces itself into the rock above by thrusting it aside, by melting or assimilating it, or by a process of blocks dropping off the roof and sinking into the magma. It is difficult to see how some batholiths have made the great room that they occupy.

A *stock* is a discordant intrusive but much smaller than a batholith. Most stocks are 1 to 10 miles across as exposed at the surface (Fig. 4-14). Most of the silver, gold, lead, zinc, and copper ore deposits of the West are clustered about stocks, and the

FIG. 4-7   Layer of ash 20 ft thick recently ejected on the island of Iwo Jima, Japan. The cliff is part of a new explosion crater. *(Courtesy of Helen Foster.)*

▲ FIG. 4-6   A new volcano bursts from the Atlantic like the mushroom cloud of an atomic blast. Dwarfing the 115-ft Capelinhos lighthouse and Capelinhos rocks in the foreground, the black sulphurous smoke spurts to height of 1 mile. This picture, taken in October, 1957, shows the crater shortly before it disappeared. It was then reborn a few days later.

FIG. 4-8   Pumice fragments of nut size. Japan. *(Courtesy of Helen Foster.)*

▼

FIG. 4-9   Cinder cone of Parícutin Volcano, Mexico. The fall of volcanic fragments has stripped trees of foliage. *(Photograph by F. O. Jones, U.S. Geological Survey.)*

FIG. 4-10 Volcanic bombs lying on cinders of cinder cone. Craters of the Moon, Idaho.

FIG. 4-11 Hill of volcanic breccia near Marysvale, Utah.

FIG. 4-12 Close-up view of volcanic breccia, Japan. ▶

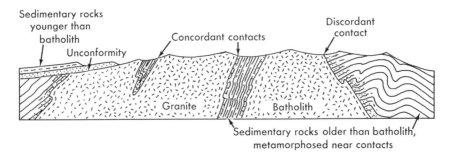

Sedimentary rocks younger than batholith

Unconformity

Concordant contacts

Discordant contact

Granite

Batholith

Sedimentary rocks older than batholith, metamorphosed near contacts

FIG. 4-13   Various relations of sedimentary rocks to intrusive rock.

stocks are regarded as having nurtured the ore deposits by feeding *mineralizing solutions* upward into the adjacent or *country rock.*

Stocks are commonly formed of granite-like rocks, and many are porphyritic, with a finely crystalline groundmass.

A *dike* is a sheetlike mass of intrusive rock, generally in the near vertical position and cutting through other rocks. It forms when the crustal rocks fracture and pull apart to form an open *fissure*, with the fissure penetrating downward into a magma chamber. The magma under pressure then surges up the fissure, cools rapidly, and crystallizes into a fine-grained rock. Diagrammatically, dikes are shown in Fig. 4-15. Basalt dikes are shown in a road cut in Fig. 4-16 and as a large one might appear on a rolling landscape in Fig. 4-17.

FIG. 4-14   Granite (light-colored) intrusive into quartzite series (dark, stratified). The contact is covered by talus. At head of Bredefjord, East Greenland. *(Courtesy of John Haller.)*

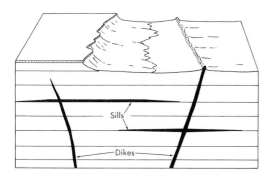

FIG. 4-15 Relation of dikes and sills to sedimentary rocks.

FIG. 4-16 Basalt dikes cutting metamorphic rocks 10
miles west of Revelstoke, British Columbia.
(Courtesy of Geological Survey of Canada
and Ed Schiller.) ▼

FIG. 4-17 A dike at the surface after
much erosion. The adjacent
rock has eroded away
faster than the dike rock,
leaving the dike standing
as a wall.

FIG. 4-18 A dark (basaltic?) sill in stratified Precambrian rocks. Banks Islands, Arctic Archipelago. *(Courtesy of R. L. Christie and Geological Survey of Canada.)*

FIG. 4-19 Laccoliths, one fed laterally from a stock and one by a conduit from below. Erosion has stripped the sedimentary rocks from the top of the laccolith on the left.

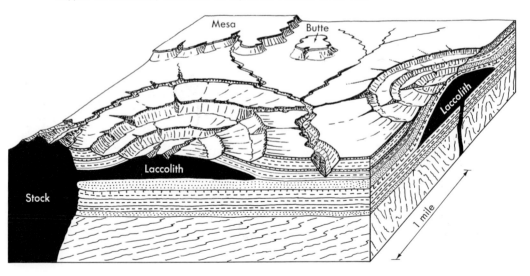

The magmas that surge up the fissures often wedge between the beds in thin sheets to form *sills*. Refer to Fig. 4-15 again, and also Fig. 4-18. When lava flows out on accumulating sediments and is later buried by more sediments, it may appear like a sill. The sill will have "baked" or bleached the sediments both above and below, whereas the lava flow will only have affected the sediments below. The lava flow may also have a frothy or vesicular upper layer, owing to the escaping gas, but not the sill.

The sill, since it penetrates between the beds and is parallel with them, is said to be a *concordant* intrusion. Intrusions in certain near-horizontal sedimentary sequences are thickened domed-shaped sills, such as illustrated in Fig. 4-19. These are called *laccoliths* and are about 1 mile or so across.

They are usually made up of felsite porphyry. The laccoliths were originally thought to have been fed by stubby dikes or circular conduits from below, and perhaps some are, but a new study in the classic locality of the laccolith, the Henry Mountains of Utah, shows that a central pipelike stock through the beds has fed thickened sills out between the sedimentary layers and that each lateral intrusion, therefore, is not a mushroom-shaped body but a partial dome. In either type of intrusion the beds above are domed upward. After a long episode of erosion the domed beds are removed, and the igneous rock of the laccolith is exposed.

Since laccoliths are generally porphyritic, it might be well to explain here the meaning of this texture. The two distinct sizes

FIG. 4-20 Hexagonally jointed basalt of Giants Causeway, North Ireland. The slope in the rear is a layer of ancient lateritic soil, 40 ft thick, that rests on the jointed basalt flow, and on top of the soil, forming the upland cap, is another jointed basalt flow. *(Courtesy of Dr. A. M. Gooding.)*

FIG. 4-21 Close-up view of the hexagonal columns of the Giants Causeway. (Courtesy of Dr. A. M. Gooding.)

FIG. 4-22 Segmented character of certain polygonal columns of basalt. These are the so-called Organ Pipes of the Giants Causeway in North Ireland. (Courtesy of Dr. A. M. Gooding.)

FIG. 4-23 Columnar jointing of basalt flow cut by Yukon River at Whitehorse, Yukon.

FIG. 4-24 Vesicular pillow lava, Newfoundland. This is one of the rare occurences of igneous rock of Cambrian age. See Chap. 18 (Courtesy of W. D. McCartney and Ed Schiller.)

FIG. 4-25 The Purcell lava of Waterton Lakes National Park, Alberta, showing cross sections of pillows. (Courtesy of R. A. Price and Geological Survey of Canada.)

▼

of mineral grains mean two episodes of cooling, and it is thus believed that in a deep-seated magma chamber the large crystals grew while the magma slowly cooled. Then this mixture of crystals and melt was suddenly injected as a sill or laccolith between relatively cold sedimentary layers. The melt froze quickly, allowing only very small crystal growth, and thus a matrix of fine crystals surrounds scattered large crystals. Stocks, sills, dikes, and flows all may have porphyritic texture, and in any case there was an early stage of cooling and partial crystallization and then a later stage of quick cooling and complete solidification.

Extrusive Bodies

Magma is known to issue at the surface either as *fissure* eruptions or as *vent* eruptions. Cracks or fissures open up in the crust and provide passage of magma from some deep reservoir to the surface. In the case of basaltic magma it wells up the fissure and then pours out as broad thin sheets on the land surface on one side or both. The Columbia River Plateau is North America's most notable example of fissure eruptions of basalt. There, many flows are piled on top of one another to build a layered accumulation 2,000 to 3,000 ft thick in places. The basalt flows spread over a large part of the states of Oregon and Washington, and it has been estimated that about 40,000 cu miles of lava has been erupted.

Magmas of felsitic composition have issued through fissures in tremendous amounts in Nevada and western Utah. This is the Great Basin province. Sufficient water was present to expand and distend the magma into dust-sized particles (glass shards, principally) as it issued from the fissures. The emissions were not explosive, as sometimes they are when much hot water vapor is present, but instead, the water vapor was released slowly and was just enough to hold the particles apart, so that the combined water vapor and volcanic dust moved as a heavy incandescent cloud and poured or flowed outward over the land surface from the fissure. The postulated phenomena occurred when Mount Pelée on the Caribbean island of Martinique erupted in 1903, and a searing-hot dust cloud rolled down the mountain side, consuming all vegetation and animal life in its wake. It overran the village of St. Pierre, and all but one person perished—he, a miserable prisoner in an underground dungeon.

The fissure eruptions in the Great Basin were almost unbelievably large. One emission would leave a blanket of tuff over 100 ft thick in places across a plane 50 miles wide or more. Such an avalanche probably happened in the course of a few minutes. The front of the cloud may have advanced at the rate of 60 miles per hr or more. The water vapor separated out and was lost by the tuff particles, which often consolidated into a light gray, banded glassy rock called a *vitric*, or *welded, tuff.*

Structures of Flows. Basalt flows commonly develop columnar structure, such as shown in Figs. 4-20 to 4-22. The perfection of the hexagonal columns is amazing in this famous locality, the Giants Causeway in North Ireland. Many basalt flows develop polygonal columns, such as seen in Fig. 4-23, but not so regularly nor so perfectly in six-sided forms as at the Giants Causeway. After the lava has crystallized and solidified, it cools to ground temperature and, in so doing, shrinks. The resulting joints define the four-, five-, or six-sided columns. Why not seven- or eight-sided columns? Talk it over with your instructor.

Basalt flows erupt beneath marine waters on ocean floors at times, and there are many examples of ancient flows of such origin. When they do, however, large vesicular rolls or pillows develop, such as shown in Fig. 4-24. In cross section the pillows look like those of Fig. 4-25.

ORIGIN OF MAGMAS

The origin of magmas leads into considerable speculation. It should first be pointed out that there are three kinds of igneous rock that exist in great volume: the basalts, the felsites, and the granites. There are many other kinds of igneous rock that occur in relatively small volume, and these are interesting but are more or less oddities. To make a long and complicated story short, it may be said that the voluminous black basalts come from the basal crustal layer or from the underlying mantle. Possible radioactive elements in the mantle raise the temperature in "hot spots" to the point of melting.

The vast granitic magmas of the batholiths probably originate by melting of the lower part of the crustal layer that overlies the basaltic layer. The granitic layer consists of metamorphic rocks having a chemical composition similar to granite. One theory proposes that the granitic layer is locally thickened and bulges downward into the basaltic layer, thereby bringing it into higher temperatures, at which it melts. Another theory suggests the rise of basalt magma from the mantle to the base of the granitic layer, thereby supplying enough heat to melt the lower part of the granitic layer.

Some of the extensive felsitic magmas, like those of the vitric tuffs of the Great Basin, may also result from the melting of the lower part of the granitic layer. Some felsitic magmas, however, may come from basaltic magmas through a process called differentiation. By this is meant that the basaltic magma may yield a succession of mineral assemblages in the process of cooling and crystallization, resulting in the end in one that is felsitic in composition and another one that is high in iron and magnesium.

GRANITIZATION

It has become clear in the last twenty-five years that not all granites are crystallized magmas. Some have undoubtedly resulted from the recrystallization of other rocks at a temperature considerably below melting. This is a solid-state transformation that occurs *in situ;* there has been no movement of magma or intrusive activity. The absence of chilled border zones of some of the granite masses and the presence of faint stratification and undisturbed relics of former beds are evidence of this process of recrystallization. It is called *granitization.*

To what extent the great batholiths of the continental margins are magmatic on the one hand or granitized masses on the other is a controversial subject. It may be observed, however, that the batholithic masses since early geologic times are restricted to the zones of intense crustal deformation and mountain building and are exposed today only after extensive erosion. They are therefore phenomena of deep or fairly deep crustal origin and are viewed by many as the melt or recrystallization product of roots of mountain ranges. Origin in such a setting could be either by melting or by metamorphism.

Suggested Aids

Readings
Heller, Robert L. (ed.): *Geology and Earth Sciences Sourcebook,* Holt, Rinehart and Winston, Inc., New York, 1962.

Pearl, R. M.: *How to Know the Minerals and Rocks,* McGraw-Hill Book Company, Inc., New York, 1955.

Pough, F. H.: *Field Guide to Rocks and Minerals,* Houghton Mifflin Company, Boston, 1953.

Movie
Crystals, Educational Services, Inc., 25 min.

Collections
Ward's Natural Science Establishment, P.O. Box 1712, Rochester 3, N.Y.

HISTORIC INTEREST

Volcanic eruptions have captivated, dismayed, and terrified mankind from primitive times to the present. The fiery cataclysms, when seen from a safe distance, are nature's most spectacular extravaganzas; yet lava flows overrun fertile farm lands, and ash falls bury villages and cities and often extract a fearful toll of lives. Through the centuries man has stood helpless to prevent the eruptions, and as an only recourse has supplicated the deity for help or mercy. Volcanic mountains in many places have come to have a supernatural significance. For instance the common name for the highest and most exquisite volcanic cone in Japan is Fujiyama, but in a religious sense it is referred to as Fujisan (Figs. 5-1 and 5-2). To propitiate the angry spirit of the Peruvian volcano, El Misti, the Incas built a temple as close to the elemental forces as possible, right in the crater, and often offered up human sacrifices.

Volcanoes

FIG. 5-1 Fujisan, the sacred mountain.

In Italy and Japan especially, the eruptions of certain volcanoes have been chronicled for over 2,000 years, and some of the records are very interesting indeed. Vesuvius has had 18 major eruptions since A.D. 79, the last in 1944. Seventy-one eruptions have been recorded at Aso-San since A.D. 864. Historical times in other volcanic regions such as the Aleutians take us back only 200 years, but in most places, the geologic record is replete with the evidence of many and varied eruptions of over 300 volcanoes around the world.

Volcanoes are commonly classed as ac-tive, dormant, or dead. According to the Japanese, active volcanoes are arbitrarily defined as having erupted in the past fifty years, whereas dormant volcanoes are those which have erupted in historical time but not in the last fifty years. Dead volcanoes, presumably, are those which have been inactive historically and display badly gullied and dissected cones, with the form commonly so much modified that a crater no longer exists. The geological evidence would point to the conclusion that activity has ceased for good.

TYPES OF VOLCANIC MOUNTAINS

Eruptions of the vent type are those in which the magma rises through a more or less circular conduit and issues from a localized vent at the surface. A pile of extrusive rock, which we call the volcanic cone, is soon built up around the vent. The apex of the cone is usually marked by a depression. This is called the *crater*. Most craters where explosive eruptions have occurred are less than 2,000 ft across. Those which have emitted chiefly basalt flows may have larger craters, however.

There are three types of volcanic mountains, namely, the *shield* type, the *composite* type, and *lava domes*.

Shield-shaped Domes

When the eruption is chiefly basaltic lava and the lava issues quietly from the central crater to pour down the slope in thin interlacing streams, the sides of the cone have low declevity, and the cone takes the shape of a broad, flattish dome. Numerous small fissure eruptions generally mark the gentle slopes and contribute to the building of a shield-shaped accumulation. The Island of Hawaii is a complex of several shield volcanoes, with Mauna Loa the central and highest one. It rises nearly 14,000 ft above sea level and has a crater 2 miles wide and 1,000 ft deep. A pit of molten lava in the floor of the crater occasionally wells up and overflows the crater rim, spilling a thin flow down the mountain side. Kilauea is a cone 20 miles away and with a crater 9,000 ft lower than Mauna Loa. It, too, has an active, and at times, seething lava pit in the floor of the large crater. Refer to Fig. 5-3.

Geologists are now certain that the Island of Hawaii is entirely a massive and broad pile of volcanic rock built up from the

FIG. 5-2   Aerial view of the crater of Fujisan. *(Courtesy of Helen Foster.)*

ocean floor, which is 15,000 ft deep round about. The complex of shield volcanoes, therefore, represents a bulky, sprawling pile 28,000 ft high and several hundred miles across the base. In fact, the several islands of the Hawaiian group are all volcanic and build an immense volcanic "rise"

referred to as strato-volcanoes. Composite cones are usually built of rocks of felsitic composition, because this lava is stiff (viscous), whereas basalt lava is rather liquid and runs rapidly in thin streams. If water vapor is present it is released easily from basalt lava.

FIG. 5-3 Shield volcano. The upper sketch is from a painting in *Volcanoes Declare War,* by Jaggar, 1945, and is the crater of Mauna Loa, Hawaii. The lower profile is the complex of shield volcanoes of the Island of Hawaii shown in relation to the ocean floor, after Stearns and MacDonald, Hawaii Division of Hydrography, 1946.

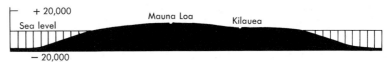

from the central Pacific floor (cross section of Fig. 5-3).

Composite Cones

Many volcanoes have exhibited intermittent explosive action and passive emission of flows. The cones are thus built of layers of fragmental debris and flows and are called *composite*. If none of the eruptions has been destructively violent, then fairly symmetrical, steep-sided cones are built. Such are the beautiful snow-capped Fujiyama in Japan (Fig. 5-1), Mount Hood in Oregon, Cotopaxi in Ecuador, Kilimanjaro in Tanganyika, and Mount Shishaldin in Alaska (Fig. 5-4). Such structures are also

Lava Domes

The term "lava dome" is used to denote a mountain that has been built by a very stiff magma. Either the stiff magma domes up surficial layers of rock, or the very viscous magma breaks through and piles up in an irregular dome much like shaving cream would do if ejected from below through a tube to the surface.

Mount Showa-Shinzan, in Japan, is a lava dome that rose in stages from a peaceful cornfield during the period 1943 to 1945 (Fig. 5-5). The area before eruption is shown in Fig. 5-6, as well as the dome as it now stands. Lava, or rock at a temperature over 800°C, reached the surface at

FIG. 5-4 Mount Shishaldin, Unimak Island in the Aleutians, Alaska, a composite cone.

one or two small points. The rock at these places still records 400°C. Much steam or water vapor was released, as well as volcanic dust at times. Around the steam-releasing cracks or vents some native sulphur collects. Volcanologists are much interested in a number of other elements in small amounts that the water vapor contains. Large river-rounded boulders that made up the rock layers immediately under the cornfield may be seen on the slopes of the dome and even on the very top.

Cinder Cones

The habit or conduct of volcanism in some areas is to build numerous small cinder cones. See Fig. 5-7. A column of lava seems to bore through to the surface and then it proceeds to cough up cinders such that after a few days or weeks a small, but delicately fashioned cone is built. This is followed generally by a basalt lava flow, and then the activity is over, the volcano dead, and a new outlet breaks through in another place, perhaps nearby. The Snake River lava plains of southern Idaho contain about five hundred such cones. It must be pointed out that some cones here are shieldlike and are composed mostly of lava.

Cinder cones are common and numerous as small satellitic structures on the flanks of large strato-volcanoes. Sunset Crater is a well-known cinder cone in the San Francisco Peaks volcanic field of northern Arizona. It is considerably higher, how-

FIG. 5-5 Mount Showa-Shinzan, Hokkaido, Japan. Lava dome formed in 1943–1945. *(Reproduced from* Volcanoes of Japanese Archipelago, *Geological Survey of Japan, 1960.)*

ever, than the small cinder cones of the Snake River field.

Spatter Cones

Instead of spitting out cinders, some small vents in volcanic fields throw out blobs of lava and hard chunks of rock. These build rough and irregular piles usually called spatter cones (Fig. 5-8). Look at the queer tumulus (mound) in Fig. 5-9. There are all manner of variations in the play of the vents, both large and small.

TYPES OF VENT ERUPTIONS

Besides a classification of types of cones, the manner of eruption of different volcanoes has led to another classification.

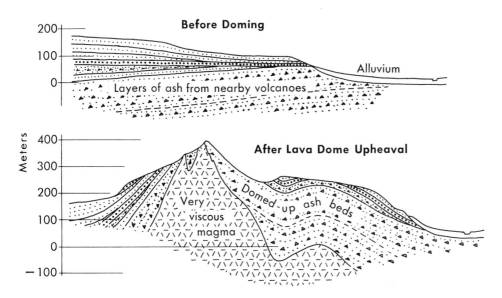

FIG. 5-6 Lava dome of Mount Showa-Shinzan, Hokkaido, Japan. *(From* Volcanoes of Japanese Archipelago, *Geological Survey of Japan, 1960.)*

FIG. 5-7 Two views of a cinder cone in the Snake River volcanic plains.

Hawaiian Type

Abundant outpouring of basaltic lava in a passive manner is the rule. Gases are liberated more or less quietly, although lava fountains sometimes erupt in the craters to heights of 1,000 ft. The passive eruptions of basaltic lava builds cones of the shield type.

Strombolian Type

The volcano Stromboli, in the Aeolian Islands near Sicily, erupts in mildly explosive form every half hour or so. Incandescent lava is hurled in the air with each explosion, and a white vapor cloud hangs almost continuously over the crater. The cloud glows, particularly at night, in reflected light from the incandescent lava, and may be seen for many miles around from ships at sea. The volcano has been called the Lighthouse of the Mediterranean.

Vulcanian Type

The Island of Vulcano, also in the Aeolian group, is representative of volcanoes that erupt violently. Often the cone is split from top to bottom and lava pours out along the entire fissure; parts of the cone may be blown away. The circumstances necessary to produce such violent explosions are, first, a viscous felsitic magma, and second, the freezing or solidification of a thick crust across the crater floor. Thereupon, the escaping water vapor is trapped below the crust. The orifice is thought to become plugged, and eventually a violent explosion occurs that cleans out the obstruction, and commonly at the same time part of the cone is blasted away.

Mount Vesuvius near Naples had been inactive so long that it was not known to be a volcano when in A.D. 79 an eruption of extreme violence blew at least half of the cone away. Since then a new cone has been built. See Figs. 5-22 and 5-23.

Another example of a violent, cone-rending eruption in historical time (1912) is that of Mount Katmai in Alaska. There had been no sign of activity in historic time, and the volcano was considered possibly dead or, at best, dormant. Its cone was deeply gullied by erosion and it looked old. After the tremendous explosion the cone stood shattered, irregular, and containing a large basin. Pumice fragments and glass shards fell on Kodiak Island 60 miles away to a depth of 10 ft or more. The plant cover was buried for miles around, and broad sterile slopes and plains resulted. It was not many years, however, before the plants reestablished themselves, and the previously indigenous animals moved in again.

FIG. 5-8 Spatter cone in Craters of the Moon National Monument, Idaho.

FIG. 5-9 "Entrail" pahoehoe lava, on small tumulus near summit of Mauna Loa, Hawaii. (Courtesy of Helen Foster.)

Peléan Type

The Peléan type is like the Vulcanian, but with the additional characteristic that glowing clouds called *nueé ardentes* are emitted. Such eruptions have already been described in connection with Mount Pelée on the Island of Martinique in the Caribbees.

The Strombolian, Vulcanian, and Peléan types of eruption all build cones of the composite variety.

CAUSE OF ERUPTIONS

Molten rock is lighter than crystalline rock, and hence when solid rock melts, there is a buoyant force that drives the magma upward if it can find passage ways to make the ascent. In the quiet or passive eruptions, perhaps this is all that is necessary to explain the phenomenon, but even so in such eruptions there is always a release of much gas in the form of water vapor. The fountains in the Kilauea lava

ing out of a lava flow on the side or near the base. The drawing of the Three Sisters (Fig. 5-10) illustrates such a flow. Even the near-perfect symmetry of Mount Fuji (Fig. 5-1) and Mount Spurr (Fig. 5-4) is marred by the outbursts of lava from the flanks. The general conduct of Japanese volcanoes in a single eruptive cycle is an explosion of ash, or pumice fragments, and then a lava flow. The crater may have been blown out on one side by the explosion, and the flow may have issued from the gap, but more

Lava flow

FIG. 5-10 The Three Sisters, in the High Cascades of Oregon. A fairly recent outburst of lava partly down the closest cone is evident; also, a new cone with crater. The middle and distant cones are badly eroded and presumably dead.

pit and the scoriaceous lavas that pour over the rim attest to the presence of much gas as part of the rising magmas.

The explosive eruptions are entirely due to the release of water vapor. The violence of the eruption is due to several factors, namely, the amount of gas, the degree of plugging of the orifice, and the viscosity of the magma containing the gas. Many variations in the nature of the eruptions and the fragmental ejecta result from an interplay of these factors.

LAVA FLOWS FROM FLANKS OF CONES

In both shield and composite volcanic cones a common occurrence is the break-

commonly the flow breaks out somewhere down the slope.

SOME CHARACTERISTICS OF LAVA FLOWS

On the Island of Hawaii the flow surfaces are classed as *pahoehoe* or ropy, and *aa* or blocky. There are many variations of each. Figure 5-11 will give some idea of the interesting types of pahoehoe, and Fig. 5-12 shows an aa or blocky flow.

Blisterlike swellings develop in the crust of basalt flows in places. Figure 5-13 shows one in which the crust has cracked apart over the blister. Note the peculiar glazed-like surface of the flow. On the right side is a small blister with a squeeze-up of lava emerging in the central crack. Figure 5-14 shows a very conspicuous squeeze-up. In fact, it looks as if the crust of the blister were about to submerge and be engulfed in lava.

The sides and top of a basalt flow may freeze solid while the central part still flows. In fact the interior may run on out and leave a tube or tunnel that can be walked through for thousands of feet. A remarkable cross section of one of these is shown in Fig. 5-15.

ASH FALLS

Mapping an Ash Fall

When a volcano ejects fragmental material high into the air, the small and medium-sized particles, especially if they are lightweight pumice particles, may be carried a considerable distance and deposited over the countryside. Note the dust and steam cloud of Mount Asama, Fig. 5-16. After an eruption the limits of the ash fall can be charted on maps, and also its thickness from place to place can be shown by thickness contours. The direction of the wind at the time of eruption determines the position of the ash fall in relation to the vent. Not only may ash falls, which have been witnessed, be mapped, but older ash falls, perhaps laid down before the region was inhabited, may be distinguished and charted, and much learned about the history of the volcano. Figure 5-17 is a remarkable map of several ash falls in the Sapporo-Tomakomai lowland of Hokkaido, Japan, and Fig. 5-18 is a highway cut showing the several ash falls as well as other layers. The amount of material ejected differed from time to time, and also, the wind direction was not always the same. Figure 5-19 shows a 3-ft layer of pumice 10 miles from the site of eruption. This is the last ash fall, namely *Ta* of Figs. 5-17

FIG. 5-11 Two varieties of pahoehoe lava in Craters of the Moon, Idaho. (Courtesy of Walter Sadlick.)

FIG. 5-12 Blocky flow, Craters of the Moon, Idaho.

FIG. 5-13   Blisters in Craters of the Moon.

and 5-18. The pumice particles range in size from ½ to 4 in. in diameter; yet they were carried 10 miles. Some fragmental pumice layers apparently poured down the volcanic cone and spread out on the skirting areas as flows.

Productive Soils

Soils that form on volcanic rocks generally support a lush vegetation. This is because of the mineral nutrients, particularly potassium, in the igneous rocks. When the volcanic rocks are loose ashes, soils are quick to form and easily tillable.

FIG. 5-14   Squeeze-up on the floor of Kilauea Caldera.
(Courtesy of Gordon MacDonald and Helen Foster.)

FIG. 5-15 Cross section of lava tube or tunnel. Hawaii island. *(Courtesy of Gordon MacDonald and Helen Foster.)*

FIG. 5-16 Mount Asama in eruption, 1954. The ash fall of 1783 eruption ruined the harvest of all Kwanto Plain, covering 24,000 sq km. *(Photograph courtesy of Dr. M. Minakami, Earthquake Research Institute, University of Tokyo.)*

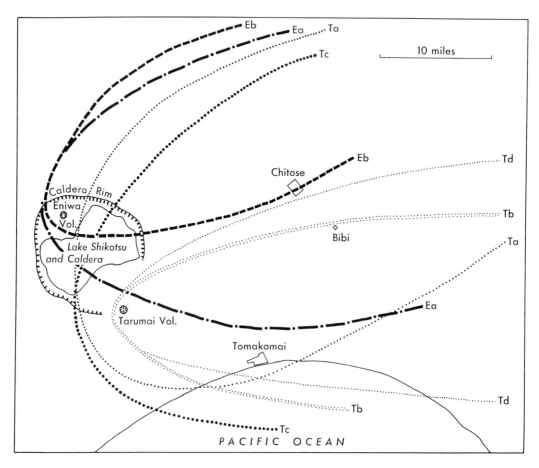

FIG. 5-17 Pumice falls from Tarumai Volcano and Eniwa Volcano near Chitose, Hokkaido, Japan. Compare with the highway cut through the ash falls at Bibi, Fig. 5-18, which gives the ages of the pumice falls. The Shikotsu pumice which underlies all the other beds is not shown. *(From Uragami, Doi, and Katsui, Supplement to Guidebook, 1962, International Symposium on Volcanology, Japan.)*

Therefore the hills and plains that have been covered by old ash falls are particularly good agricultural areas. Even though a soil only 6 in. thick has formed in the last 230 years on the ash fall of Fig. 5-19, it produces good crops. Note the three ash falls in Fig. 5-20, with a soil on top of each.

Soils are further discussed in Chap. 7.

NECKS AND RADIATE DIKES

Long after the eruptive activity has ceased and the erosional processes have carried much of the cone away, the solid resistant *neck* and radiate dikes stand etched out in relief. Shiprock of northwestern New Mexico is a notable example. In south Africa some old cones have been removed by erosion entirely, but the solidified conduit rock is mined below the surface for its diamonds. These circular, downward-extending structures are called *pipes*.

CAULDRON SUBSIDENCE

After majestic composite cones are built, their fate frequently is partial destruction by collapse. Crater Lake, Oregon, is an

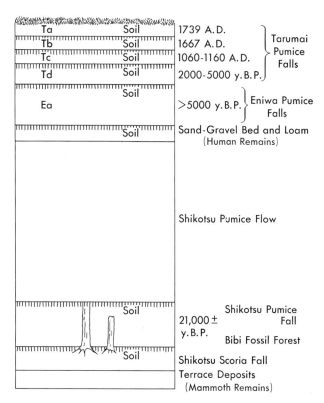

Ta	Soil	1739 A.D.
Tb	Soil	1667 A.D.
Tc	Soil	1060-1160 A.D.
Td	Soil	2000-5000 y.B.P.

Tarumai Pumice Falls

	Soil
Ea	>5000 y.B.P.

Eniwa Pumice Falls

Soil — Sand-Gravel Bed and Loam (Human Remains)

Shikotsu Pumice Flow

Soil — Shikotsu Pumice Fall

21,000 ± y.B.P.

Bibi Fossil Forest

Soil — Shikotsu Scoria Fall

Terrace Deposits (Mammoth Remains)

FIG. 5-18 Ash beds of three volcanoes and nine eruptions at Bibi, Hokkaido, Japan. B.P. means years before the present and is a C^{14} age determination. Refer to Fig. 5-17 for distribution of falls. *(Simplified from Y. Katsui, Supplement to Guidebook, 1962.)*

FIG. 5-19 Last pumice fall of Tarumai volcano (Fig. 4.18).

FIG. 5-20 Three ash falls with soil on each. Near Tokyo, Japan. *(Courtesy of Helen Foster.)*

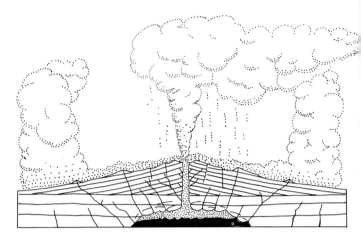

FIG. 5-21 Climactic eruptions, above, and cauldron subsidence, below, representing the manner of formation of Crater Lake, Oregon. (After Howell Williams.)

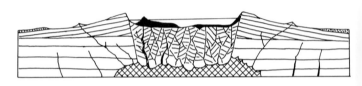

example of a volcanic cone that had been built to a great height, like Mount Rainier or Mount Hood, when finally it erupted violently with the emission of incredible amounts of water vapor, ash, and lava and then collapsed. By collapse is meant that the top part of the cone simply subsided into the depths of the crust to form a pit several miles across and perhaps 3,000 ft deep. See Fig. 5-21. The great pit is called a *caldera*.

The loss of water vapor, ash, and lava from the magma reservoir below is thought to have removed support of the overlying cone, with resultant collapse. In the case of Crater Lake, the caldera was partially filled with lava and pyroclastics in lingering eruptive activity afterward. A small cinder cone was built inside the caldera, which became Wizard Island when the lake waters collected.

Mount Vesuvius is a notable example of a remnant of a once great volcano and the growth of a new one. The history is de-

picted in Figs. 5-22 and 5-23. Mount Somma is the highest peak on the remaining rim of the old volcano, but it is the remains of a cone blasted away by a terrific eruption rather than the rim of a collapse caldera. Now, however, as collapse calderas all over the world are recognized, the surviving rim of the early cone is called the *somma*, meaning skin.

Aso-san, in Japan, is the largest collapse caldera yet found and is a circular area between the somma walls about 35 miles in diameter. Various small cones have been built in the great caldera, where 71 eruptions have been recorded since A.D. 864.

ERUPTIONS OF SUBMARINE VOLCANOES

Man has seen the spectacle a very few times of an eruption from a submarine volcano. Some are in every respect the equivalent of an H bomb. Figures 5-24 to 5-27 are photographs taken by the Tokyo

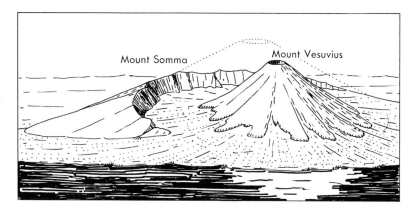

FIG. 5-22 Mount Somma, the remnant of the old cone, and Mount Vesuvius, the new cone.

College of Fisheries of the eruption of Myojin-sho on September 22 and 23, 1952. Figure 5-24 shows the rise of muddy water and some steam and yellow sulphur on September 22. Even rocks of the top of the volcanic cone appeared. They had appeared before, and are known as a reef, and part of the Bayonnase Rocks south of Tokyo at the southern end of the Izu Islands. On the next day the great explosions

FIG. 5-23 Inner cone of Mount Vesuvius, Italy. *(Photograph by Cecil B. Jacobson, U.S. Bureau of Reclamation.)*

FIG. 5-24 Beginning of eruption of Myojin-sho on September 22, 1952. The yellow cloud in the water is pronounced. (Courtesy Tokyo University of Fisheries and Helen Foster.)

began, and at a distance of 5 nautical miles Fig. 5-25 was taken. Figures 5-26 and 5-27 show the development of maximum eruption. A ship of Japanese scientists, dispatched to study the phenomenon, evidently approached too close and vanished.

For accounts of other great submarine eruptions see suggested readings at end of this chapter.

PREDICTION OF VOLCANIC ERUPTIONS

The lower flanks and surrounding plains of volcanic cones are generally areas of considerable population because of the fertility of the soil. In the volcanic archipelagos an entire island is commonly that part of a volcanic pile built up from the ocean floor that projects above sea level. Its inhabitants are crowded into limited shoreline areas with little chance to escape in the event of a major eruption. Needless to

say such people are most anxious to know, if possible, when the volcano around which they live is going to erupt.

Fortunately, geologists have been able to do a good job of predicting eruptions. Their predictions may only be a few days or weeks in advance, but this gives sufficient time for evacuation. Long-range (several years) predictions, however, are still impossible or insecure in their reliability.

As magma charged with steam rises in the vent that feeds the volcano and as the confining pressures become less, rumblings from the pent-up gas occur and become more frequent as the eruption stage approaches. Major rumblings may be felt as earthquakes, but these generally come too late, because the eruptive activity follows soon or immediately in the wake of strong earthquakes. But by establishing a network of seismological listening stations around a volcanic cone and by watching the buildup of seismic activity, the attendant geologist or seismologist can learn to predict

FIG. 5-25 Early stage of eruption of Myojin-sho, September 23, 1952. Submarine volcano south of Tokyo. (Courtesy of the Tokyo College of Fisheries and Helen Foster.)

eruptions. He gets to know the habits or conduct of the monster he has been assigned to observe. The listening stations are equipped with geophones, and the earth vibrations that they detect are wired to a central observatory where small seismographs record the information day and night. The progress of rise of the restless magma in the depths of the volcanic cone can actually be followed in some instances.

Preceding an eruption the surface of the cone is sometimes bulged and deformed, but in a manner too slight and gentle to be detected by the unaided eye. For the purpose of detecting deformation of the volcanic cone, instruments known as tiltmeters have been perfected, and they have brought to light the fact that tilting is much more frequent and significant than previously thought.

On the basis of data collected by seismographs and tiltmeters around Kilauea the internal structure of the volcano and its manner of eruption can be constructed.[1] Recurrent swarms of earthquakes originating about 60 k (40 miles) beneath the crater are taken to mark the forming of magma at this place and to indicate also that the magma is moving upward through perennial conduits to collect in a shallow magma reservoir only 2 or 3 miles below the summit. The growth or inflation of this shallow reservoir causes the summit area to swell, creating sporadic sequences of small earthquakes in the rocks surrounding the reservoir. Swarms of tiny shallow earthquakes mark the progress of penetration of magma into fissures around the expanding reservoir. When a magma-filled fissure finally splits to the surface, a parasitic eruption occurs.

A major fracture or rift zone exists across

---

[1] Paper by J. P. Eaton, U.S. Geological Survey, at International Symposium on Volcanology in Japan, 1962.

FIG. 5-26 Another explosion of Myojin-sho. (Courtesy Tokyo University of Fisheries and Helen Foster.)

FIG. 5-27   Still another explosion of Myojin-sho during the day of September 23, 1952. *(Courtesy Tokyo University of Fisheries and Helen Foster.)*

the shield volcano of Kilauea, and sometimes the magma leaks through fissures in this rift zone to erupt at the surface. Rapid escape through the rift zone of magma from the expanded reservoir leads to the sudden subsidence of the summit of the volcano, with attendant earthquake activity (thousands of small to moderate local earthquakes) and deepening of the lava level in the great crater.

Suggested Aids

Readings

Bullard, Fred M.: *Volcanoes in History, in Theory, and in Eruption,* University of Texas Press, Austin, Tex., 1962.

Rittman, A.: *Volcanoes and Their Activity,* John Wiley & Sons, Inc., New York, 1962.

Williams, Howell: *The Ancient Volcanoes of Oregon,* Oregon State System of Higher Education, Eugene, Ore., 1948.

————: "Volcanoes," *Scientific American,* November, 1951. Reprints may be purchased from W. H. Freeman and Company, San Francisco.

Movies

Eruption of Kilauea: 1959 and 60, U.S. Department of Agriculture, color, 33 min., $8.50.

Volcanoes in Action, Encyclopaedia Britannica, black and white 11 min., $2.25.

6

PYROCLASTIC AND FELDSPATHIC SEDIMENTS

Sedimentary Rocks Interlayered with Volcanic Rocks

Some of the thickest known sequences of stratified rocks are those which contain numerous lava flows and beds of pyroclastic material. The sandstones in these sequences are contaminated with volcanic fragments and the shales with tuff, and it becomes necessary to understand a few essentials about them before proceeding further.

The very thick-volcanic-sedimentary successions of strata have accumulated in zones along the Atlantic and and Pacific margins of the continent in times past. A zone possibly 200 miles wide along the Atlantic from Alabama to Newfoundland consists of such rocks, now deformed and more or less metamorphosed. A zone over 300 miles wide in California and western Nevada contains vast thicknesses of interlayered volcanic and sedimentary rocks. See Fig. 6-1. They are large and distinct geologic provinces.

Pyroclastic
and Metamorphic Rocks

Sediments Derived from Volcanic Rocks

Volcanic Breccia. A heterogeneous mixture of large and small angular fragments of volcanic rock is called a volcanic breccia (see Chap. 3) and under certain conditions may accumulate voluminously and become interbedded in other kinds of rock.

Volcanic Agglomerate. If streams transport the volcanic fragments very far, the fragments become rounded and, when deposited, look like a conglomerate. The activity of the stream in sorting large and

a shallow body of water or on a river flood plain it forms a layer on the sediments accumulating at the time, probably of an entirely different nature. As soon as the ash fall is over, the usual sediments start to accumulate again. Thus, tuff beds generally stand out conspicuously in sedimentary sequences.

Since the glass shards in different tuffs are distinctive in shape, size, optical properties, and chemistry and since the ash falls sometimes spread over many miles of country, it is sometimes possible to relate the

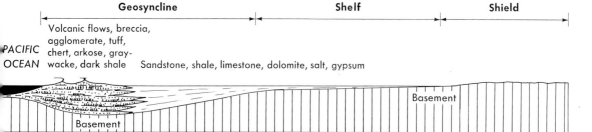

FIG. 6-1 Idealized cross section of the western half of the continent of North America in ancient times (Paleozoic era), showing the place and nature of the thick accumulation of interlayered volcanic and sedimentary rocks. See maps in Chap. 17. The basement is ancient foundation rock of igneous and metamorphic nature.

small particles into separate beds is generally apparent. Thus, if beds of boulders, cobbles, and pebbles are interlayered with sand and all particles are volcanic rock, the resultant deposit is called a volcanic agglomerate. See Fig. 6-2.

The Great Basin of the western United States is a region where the intermountain valleys are partially filled with such sediments. Thousands of cubic miles of volcanic debris has been erupted in this region, and much of it has been picked up by running water, transported, rounded, sorted, in places mixed with other types of sediments, and finally deposited as agglomerate and various volcanic sediments.

Tuff. Tuff is an accumulation of fine volcanic ash or dust and has previously been described. When volcanic ash falls in

sediment accumulations in widely separated regions by means of the tuff beds.

Volcanic glass containing mica crystals lends itself to age determination by the potassium-argon method, and we have recently witnessed the dating of some new, momentous, early human fossils from Kenya, Africa, by this method, because they were found between two tuff beds. The fossils represent the very primitive man, *Zinjanthropus* of Olduvai Gorge, found by Dr. Louis Leakey in 1960.

Bentonite and Bentonitic Shale. Bentonite is an altered volcanic tuff in which certain highly water-absorbent clay minerals dominate. The tuff beds seem to alter to bentonite when they accumulate in shallow inland arms of sea water. When pure, bentonite has industrial uses and is

FIG. 6-2 Agglomerate and tuff beds, central Utah.

extensively mined. More commonly than not, however, bentonite is mixed with shale, and the shale is said to be bentonitic. It makes ranch roads very slippery when wet, and in the Morrison and Chinle formations of the Colorado Plateau is quite colorful, with shades of red, purple, yellow, and chocolate.

Feldspathic Sandstones

Arkose. The sandstones with which we generally deal are made up of grains of quartz or quartz and chert, but when an appreciable amount of the grains is the mineral feldspar, then the rock is called an arkose. Such a sediment accumulates in a basin adjacent to an upland consisting of granitic and gneissic rocks and where erosion is rapid.

Graywacke. Some sandstones contain, in addition to quartz and feldspar grains, considerable amounts of mica, chert, chlorite, volcanic rock fragments, slate fragments, and the iron-magnesian minerals. Such a sandstone is called graywacke. The grains other than quartz and feldspar give some sandstones a dark color and others a "salt and pepper" appearance.

Association with Volcanic Rocks. Arkoses and graywackes are the common types of sandstones in the volcanic sequences. The margins of the continents were the sites of extensive eruptions of lava, particularly basaltic, and the accumulations were thick. The volcanic islands were intensely eroded, and streams carried much agglomerate, arkose, and graywacke to the sea, to become interlayered beds in the volcanics. Great thicknesses of dark clay also accumulated in the troughs.

These coastal zones were regions of crustal deformation as well as volcanism, and the stratified sequences later became folded and somewhat metamorphosed. Even later, the great batholiths invaded the folded, metamorphosed volcanic and sedimentary sequences and produced the complex of rock found today, for instance, in the White Mountains of New Hampshire and in the Sierra Nevada of California.

METAMORPHIC ROCKS

Definition

Metamorphic rocks are changed or altered sedimentary or igneous rocks. Since there are numerous kinds of sedimentary and igneous rocks and also since the degree of metamorphism may be variable, there are many kinds of metamorphic rocks. The rock may be so intensely altered that its original identity is obscure. In fact, several kinds of sedimentary rocks and igneous rocks, after intense alteration, may end up as approximately the same metamorphic rock.

In the process of metamorphism, the overall chemical composition of some rocks has remained the same—no elements or compounds have been added or removed—but, on the other hand, considerable chemical change has been effected in others.

so that we presume that a limestone has been affected in some way to cause the microscopically small calcite grains to consolidate into larger crystals. The process is called recrystallization. We have little doubt that this is the origin of some marbles when we find them associated with other

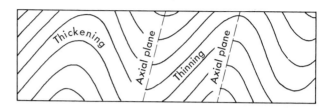

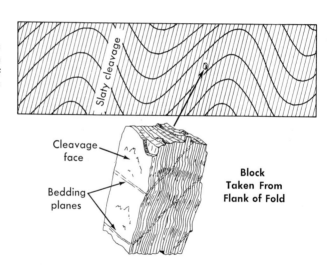

FIG. 6-3 Relation of slaty cleavage to folds: top, plastic flow of shale beds upon sharp folding; middle, position of slaty cleavage; bottom, relation of cleavage to bedding.

Evidence of Change

Probably the most immediate evidence of change is the fact that we recognize many rocks that are not obviously the common sedimentary or igneous rocks, and we imagine them therefore to be metamorphic rocks. Direct evidence of change may be seen in a marble, for instance, which is made up of visible mineral grains of calcite, all tightly interlocked. We have never seen a lime sediment being deposited in this manner or a limestone develop from lime ooze in this coarsely crystalline nature,

metamorphic rocks, or can trace a bed of limestone into marble.

Again, if we examine a series of sharply folded sedimentary strata, we see that some beds particularly have thickened in the crests of anticlines and the troughs of synclines and have thinned on the flanks. See Fig. 6-3. This indicates plastic flow of the beds. Plastic deformation is prominent in limestones and is helpful in inducing recrystallization to marble. It is also common in shale and creates cleavage at an angle to the bedding. Refer to the middle and lower drawing of Fig. 6-3. The beds become somewhat welded together and fail to split apart, but on the other hand, a new cleavage direction is set up in the rock that is in planes approximately parallel to the axial plane of the fold. This is called slaty cleavage, and the rock thus formed from the shale is called slate (Fig. 6-4). Actually there has been a transformation on a microscopic scale of some of the clay minerals that make up the shale to a certain mica mineral called sericite, with the tiny sericite plates all oriented in the direction of flow. This establishes cleavage, or the property that permits the slate to be split into thin sheets. The overall chemical composition has not been altered, however.

Another clear evidence of alteration of a previously existing rock can be seen in some metamorphic conglomerates. In these, pebbles have been drawn out into spindle-shaped forms, all having their long axes parallel. This attests to plastic deformation of the rock.

In the study of certain sandstones under the microscope it can be seen that the sand grains have been lengthened into spindle form and often thoroughly broken in the process. The rock then becomes a *quartzite*.

Common Kinds of Metamorphic Rocks

Table 6-1 lists a few common metamorphic rocks, with their texture, chief minerals, and the rocks from which they are derived.

Examples of these rocks will have to be handled and observed in class or laboratory in order to gain a proper appreciation of them. Comments on a few varieties follow.

Quartzite. As described above, when the sand grains are somewhat crushed, drawn out, and rehealed, the rock exhibits a glassy or vitreous surface and is a true metamorphic rock. However, certain sandstones are composed of quartz grains cemented by silica. Although not metamorphosed in any way, a freshly broken surface is glassy because the sand grains break across instead of separating where cemented and the

FIG. 6-4 Slaty cleavage across fine-grained beds. At Moe River, Quebec. *(Courtesy of Geological Survey of Canada and C. K. Bell.)*

Table 6-1 KINDS AND CHARACTERISTICS OF COMMON METAMORPHIC ROCKS

Name	Texture	Chief minerals	Derived from
Marble	Granoblastic*	Calcite	Limestone
Quartzite	Granoblastic	Quartz	Sandstone
Slate	Slaty	Sericite, quartz	Shale
Metafelsite	Slaty, phyllitic	Sericite, quartz, feldspar	Felsite
Metabasalt	Slaty to schistose	Sericite, feldspar, amphibole	Basalt
Metagraywacke	Granoblastic to phyllitic	Feldspar, amphibole	Graywacke
Phyllite	Slaty, phyllitic	Sericite, quartz	Shale, tuff
Schist	Schistose	Muscovite, quartz, biotite, plagioclase	Shale, tuff, felsite
Gneiss	Gneissose	Feldspar, quartz, mica, amphibole, garnet	Granite, felsite, shale

* Granoblastic means granular texture caused by recrystallization.

rock may not be distinguishable megascopically from a true quartzite. Technically, such a sandstone is called an orthoquartzite. Its constitution can easily be discerned under the microscope.

Slate. Slate develops from shale that has been deformed and caused to "flow." As previously noted, shale beds, when deformed under considerable pressure, thicken in the crests of anticlines and in the troughs of synclines, and the deformed rock develops the property of cleavage across the old bedding surfaces. Some slates have cleavage so well developed that slabs ¼ in. thick and 3 ft across can be split off. These make excellent shingles. Slate comes in gray, green, and various shades of brown and red, and the colored varieties are generally desired. A slate roof is expensive but lasts a lifetime or more.

The cleavage is due to the development of microscopic sericite grains (a form of mica) all oriented in one plane—the cleavage plane.

Phyllite. Phyllites were once shales that developed so much sericite that a micaceous sheen was imparted to the cleavage surfaces by the abundant tiny mica flakes. Cleavage may take a direction across the bedding or parallel with it.

Schist. A schist is an intensely metamorphosed fine-grained sedimentary or igneous rock. Mica is dominant and in flakes large enough to be clearly visible. The flakes are packed together in parallel but possibly wavy arrangement, wrapping around other minerals that may be present, such as quartz, feldspar, amphibole, and garnet. In *mica schists*, muscovite mica is dominant, but in other schists biotite mica and chlorite are prominent. Chlorite imparts a green color to the rock.

Gneiss. A gneiss is a coarsely crystalline rock that looks like granite except that the light and dark minerals are segregated into thin layers or lenses. See Figs. 6-5 to 6-7. The layers are commonly folded or crenulated. The minerals are much the same as in granite, with the feldspars especially abundant. Quartz, amphibole, mica, and garnet make up a good part of the rock. Gneisses are commonly the most voluminous types in metamorphic rock terranes and may have been derived from many different rocks, such as granite, shale, slate, and schist. Their texture is said to be *gneissose*.

FIG. 6-5 Close-up view of gneiss that has been abraded and striated by a glacier (Chap. 12). *(Courtesy of Geological Survey of Canada and J. D. Aitken.)*

FIG. 6-6 Another close-up view of a gneiss from northern Saskatchewan. *(Courtesy of Geological Survey of Canada and C. K. Bell.)*

FIG. 6-7 Granite masses (light) intruding gneiss (dark and stratified). Rushmore Memorial, Black Hills, South Dakota.

Causes of Metamorphism

Pressure and heat are the common causes of rock transformation. Pressure in one direction, if great enough, will either shear the rock or cause it to flow plastically. Besides directional pressure rocks come under the influence of confining (all-sided or hydrostatic) pressure when buried below the surface. At a depth of several miles the confining pressure is great, and when subjected to directional pressure in addition, most rocks yield plastically. If the temperature is elevated, the plastic deformation is great. These are the conditions that effect recrystallization, say of limestone to marble, or the transformation of shale to slate or phyllite. Temperature increases approximately at the rate of 1°C for every 100 ft of depth and confining pressure at the rate of about 120 lb per sq in. for every 100 ft of depth, so that we can compute the temperature and pressure conditions that prevail approximately at any depth. It is easy to see that at depths of 20,000 to 100,000 ft below the surface the rocks are subjected to conditions that might easily cause their alteration.

In addition to elevated temperatures and pressures water, if present, is influential in furthering recrystallization and mineral reconstitution. Water may also carry various compounds in solution and bring new materials to the rock that is suffering change, thus resulting in minerals that would not form otherwise.

The geochemist today has constructed presses in which carefully sized pieces of rock are placed and subjected to confining pressures up to those that prevail 50 miles below the surface. Also, the temperatures may be elevated several hundred degrees. In other presses the influence of water can be determined. And thus it is found that certain minerals form and exist (are stable) at certain temperatures and pressures, other minerals at other temperatures and pressures. The *stability ranges* are said to be determined. Now, when a metamorphic rock is found to be made up of a certain group or association of minerals, it may be known at what pressure (depth) and at what temperature the minerals were formed. At least, this is the experimental goal, and much progress has been made.

We observe zones of metamorphism next to the contact of intrusive igneous rocks. Dikes and sills bake red shales gray and turn soft coals to anthracite or coke near the contact. Magmas react with limestones below the surface, and sometimes the more unusual associations of minerals are formed, such as those of the iron and copper ore deposits.

Meaning of Metamorphic Rock at the Surface

Extensive terranes of gneiss and schist now occur at the surface, and we are sure that the metamorphism that caused these rock types occurred several miles below the surface. It may only be concluded, therefore, that several miles of rock has been eroded away from such areas. Where the granites of batholiths are exposed at the surface, there also a great deal erosion has occurred. In constructing the geologic history of a region, this is an important item. It is also meaningful to those who explore for various kinds of ore deposits.

Further, these metamorphic rocks have given us a better appreciation of conditions deep in the earth's crust, and with this understanding, we shall see in later chapters how the crust is deformed, mountains are built, and magmas are formed.

Suggested Aids

Readings

Eardley, A. J.: *Structural Geology of North America*, 2d ed., Harper & Row, Publishers, Incorporated, New York, 1962, chaps. 6 and 7.

Judson, S., and M. S. Woyski: *Manual for Physical Geology*, William C. Brown, Dubuque, Iowa, 1950.

White, A. T.: *All about Our Changing Rocks,* Random House, Inc., New York, 1955.

Chapter 7

DEFINITION

The paint on an automobile, when subjected to the hot sun and seasonal rains, gradually deteriorates. You may note pits on the fenders and forward parts of the hood due to sand grains and pebbles that have hit the car. We call these processes *weathering*. Rocks are also subject to weathering, and, in fact, the modern automobile finishes are probably more durable and resistant to weathering than some rocks. Other rocks, of course are fairly resistant, but none escapes serious deterioration over a long time.

The loosening and removal of weathered particles by surface processes is called *erosion*. The wind, streams, and glaciers remove and transport rock material from the places where weathering produces them to other places or sites of deposition. The weathering processes are static, or take place *in situ,* whereas the erosional processes are dynamic in that they represent motion or transport.

Rock Weathering and Erosion

FIG. 7–1 Talus of granite due to frost pry, in Big Cotton-wood Canyon, Wasatch Mountains, Utah.

WEATHERING PROCESSES

When analyzed, the weathering processes are found to be of chemical and mechanical nature. We use the word *decomposition* to refer to chemical weathering of rock and *disintegration* to refer to mechanical weathering. In decomposition we deal with solution or chemical reaction, whereas in disintegration we deal with mechanical breakdown, such as cracking, wedging apart, and separation of mineral grains from one another.

Mechanical Weathering

Frost Action. All consolidated rocks are jointed, as we have seen in Chap. 2. Some rocks are so badly broken that pieces larger than a foot across are hard to find. This condition makes such rock masses particularly susceptible to frost pry. Water seeps into and fills the cracks, and then if the weather turns cold, the water may freeze. As you realize, there is an increase in

volume when water turns to ice, and the expansive force is great. Automobile radiators and even engine blocks crack open, and so also the rock fragments are pried apart as the cracks are widened by the ice.

If one deep freeze sets in in the fall and last until spring, then only a little disintegration is accomplished, but if the climate is one in which alternate freezing and thawing take place fifty times a year, then the rock is severely disrupted. We find that the angular blocks between joints have been wedged apart, heaved, and thrown into a rubble of jagged fragments, such as seen in Fig. 7-1.

The places where alternate freezing and thawing occur the most times in a year are those near the timber line in high mountain ranges. Nearly every night in the fall and spring it freezes in these places, and in the day it melts. The result is a prolific generation of loose rock fragments called *talus* (Fig. 7-2). Steep mountain slopes are conducive to downhill sliding and tumbling of these loose fragments. They converge at the base of the cliffs into fan-shaped accumulations called *talus* fans or *talus cones* (Figs. 7-3 and 7-4). In some places the talus becomes so bulky that it actually flows like a glacier (Figs. 7-5).

In the arid Colorado Plateau we note an absence of or very little talus at the base of many of the high imposing cliffs. This may be due to a paucity of rainfall and only a few alternations of freezing and thawing each year, but it is generally due to the fact that the cliffs are formed of friable or poorly cemented sandstone and that the sandstone grains break apart easily, thus producing fragments so small that the wind and occasional thunder showers remove them about as fast as they accumulate. We commonly see large scattered blocks of sandstone broken loose from a sandstone formation above in various stages of sliding down a shale slope below. The farther down the slope, the smaller the blocks become, owing to disintegration into sand grains and the removal of the sand

FIG. 7-2 Middle and lower slopes almost completely blanketed with talus of volcanic rocks. This is Sewell at the site of the famous copper mine called Braden, in the high Andes of Chile. Freezing and thawing occur many times a year. *(Kennecott Copper Corporation.)*

grains by the wind. Examine Figs. 7-6 and 7-7. Frost pry probably helps dislodge the large blocks of sandstone from above, but also the shale underneath the sandstone weathers so rapidly that it undermines the sandstone and leaves an overhanging ledge, likely to cave off.

Plants. The roots of plants extend into cracks and openings in the rocks, and as the roots grow larger, they exert considerable pressure on the walls and often wedge open the crack or split the rock. Plants of many kinds are effective, even the lichens and mosses. They help in the soil-forming processes and will be mentioned again later.

Other Agents of Disintegration. Wetting and drying of shales contribute to their weathering; the process, however, may be in part a chemical one. Heating by the sun on a hot summer day and cooling at night may contribute to the decay of certain rocks, such as friable sandstone (Fig. 7-8), but laboratory experiments in which granitic rocks have been repeatedly heated and cooled tend to show that temperature changes are not of much importance in causing the rock to be disrupted into fragments, scales, or particles. As we shall see, the swelling of decomposing minerals, a chemical process, is more significant than expansion and contraction due to heating and cooling.

Chemical Weathering

The chief chemical reactions that take place in nature in the decomposition of rock are solution and hydration.

Solution. Limestone and its metamorphic equivalent, marble, are fairly susceptible to erosion. In humid climates the rate of erosion is conspicuously greater than that of shale, sandstone, the igneous rocks, or the common metamorphic rocks other than marble (Fig. 7-9). Dolomite is dissolved away in major proportions but not generally as rapidly as limestone.

Pure limestone is made up of mineral particles of calcium carbonate that are not in themselves very soluble in pure water. But if carbon dioxide is present in the water, then the limestone is particularly soluble. We deal with the formation of an acid as follows:

$$H_2O \quad + \quad CO_2 \quad \rightarrow \quad H_2CO_3$$
$$\text{water} \qquad \text{carbon} \qquad \text{carbonic}$$
$$\text{dioxide} \qquad \text{acid}$$

Now the acid reacts with the calcite to form calcium bicarbonate, which is held in solution and is carried away by the moving ground waters:

$$H_2CO_3 \quad + \quad CaCO_3 \quad \rightarrow \quad Ca(HCO_3)_2$$
$$\text{carbonic} \qquad \text{calcite} \qquad \text{calcium}$$
$$\text{acid} \qquad \text{or} \qquad \text{bicarbonate}$$
$$\text{calcium}$$
$$\text{carbonate}$$

In most limestone terranes, particularly in semihumid and humid climates, the limestone layers are so extensively channeled and tunneled by circulating groundwaters that elaborate networks of caves result (Chap. 9). The carbon dioxide, so essential to solution, is derived in part from the atmosphere while the waters are at the surface, but more abundantly from decaying vegetation in the soil as the surface waters filter through to become ground water.

In desert regions limestone and dolomite formations are resistant to weathering and form conspicuous ridges and cliffs, whereas in humid climates they dissolve away rapidly and usually result in valleys. This is due on the one hand to the sparcity of rainfall and soils in the desert but on the other hand to the abundance of rain and the production of much carbon dioxide in the thick soils of the humid regions.

Hydration. All rocks containing feldspar minerals are easy prey to the chemical process called hydration. Such rocks as the granites, felsites, arkoses, and graywackes contain much feldspar and thus decay badly, particularly in humid climates. The reactions are complex, with various clay minerals forming from the feldspars together with the loss of potassium, sodium,

FIG. 7-3 Veritable streams of talus due to frost pry in the Canadian Rockies near Banff.

FIG. 7-4 Talus cone in Glacier National Park. *(Photograph by H. E. Malde, and courtesy U.S. Geological Survey.)*

FIG. 7-5 Rock glacier at Hart Lake, Yukon Territory. So much talus has accumulated here that it is flowing like a glacier. The upper part of the cliff is mainly limestone and the lower part, conglomerate. The front of the rock glacier is about 1,000 ft across. *(Courtesy of Geological Survey of Canada and P. Vernon.)*

FIG. 7-6 Sandstone talus disintegrating and sand being blown away by the wind. Note the general absence of talus except for the cone of broken rock. This is probably a landslide from the cliff above, but the rock fragments are rapidly breaking down into sand grains and being removed.

calcium, and magnesium ions that pass off in solution. An example of the alteration of plagioclase feldspar is as follows:

$$CaAl_2Si_2O_8 \cdot 2NaAlSi_3O_8 + 4H_2CO_3$$

calcium   sodium   carbonic
feldspar   feldspar   acid

$$+ 2(nH_2O) \rightarrow Ca(HCO_3)_2 + 2NaHCO_3$$

water   calcium   sodium
           bicarbonate   bicarbonate

$$+ 2Al_2(OH)_2Si_4O_{10} \cdot nH_2O$$

clay mineral

It can be seen that the clay mineral that forms is a hydrated aluminum silicate but that carbon dioxide in the water is necessary to remove the calcium and sodium ions.

Now, in the above conversion of feldspar to a clay mineral, considerable expansion occurs, and this is the chief cause of decay. In the case of a granite composed of feldspar, quartz, and ferromagnesian minerals, the feldspar particles alter to clay with expansion, the bonds between the particles are loosened, and the rock crumbles (Fig. 7-10). The clay is washed away, and a residue of quartz grains remains. This marks the beginning of quartz sand. But what happens to the ferromagnesian minerals?

An iron-magnesian mineral like biotite alters to a hydrated clay mineral plus a hydrated iron oxide called limonite. As in feldspar alteration, the potassium and magnesium ions are carried away in a bicarbonate solution, and also a little silica is lost in solution. The limonite stains the crumbling granite rusty and makes the resultant clay yellowish or rusty too.

Even in arid climates granites decay somewhat, but in humid climates the alteration proceeds from the surface down for 10 to 100 ft or more. Bulldozers and power shovels can generally cut and move the decayed rock without the use of explosives. A hand pick sinks an inch or two into the "rotten" rock. The chief visible result is crumbling. Large boulders of granite display a crumbling surface, and the base of steep slopes are marked by the granular debris of the decaying rock.

Some rocks shed scales or shell-like peels in the process of weathering. The layers range from ¼ in. (Fig. 7-11) to several feet in thickness (Fig. 7-12). They occur in granite most commonly, but in places in sandstone. Scaling of granite is due to feldspar alteration, but in sandstones containing little feldspar another cause must be sought. It may be due to heating and cooling, but we are not sure. The process of scaling or shedding of peels is called *exfoliation*.

FIG. 7-7   Friable sandstone talus breaking down before it reaches the shale beds in the foreground. The imposing cliff is the Navajo sandstone in southern Utah.

Rates of Weathering

Stones used for building or monument purposes often decay rapidly, and since dates of construction are known and the amount of decay can be measured, the rates of decay can then be told. Limestones and marbles weather rapidly in humid climates, and inscriptions on grave stones and markers soon become illegible. Heads of statues lose their features to become round knobs. Slate under similar conditions stands up for centuries with little change.

Granite lasts well in desert climates but in moist and freezing climates sometimes crumbles disconcertingly. A notable example is Cleopatra's Needle in Central Park, New York City. It is a tall column of granite, referred to as an obelisk, and was inscribed profusely from top to bottom with deep-cut hieroglyphics. It stood for 3,500 years in the dry desert of Egypt with little sign of deterioration, but then was brought to New York and set up in Central Park, an entirely different environment. Frequent rains, frost action, and the atmospheric acids of a big city caused a disastrous crumbling and scaling, completely erasing the hieroglyphics in places. Attempts to permeate the crumbling rock with organic preservatives have not had much effect in halting the weathering processes.

Frost action must be the chief agent of destruction of the New York obelisk. We conclude this because in the humid but frost-free climate of London a similar obelisk has resisted serious weathering, although some decay is apparent.

FIG. 7-8 Upper surface of friable sandstone in the middle of the picture is weathering into various domes and gullies. The relative effectiveness of heating and cooling, frost pry, and sandblasting in dislodging the sand grains is not known, but probably all three contribute. East escarpment of Kaiparowitz Plateau, Utah.

These examples show that the kind of rock as one variable and the climate as another produce highly variable rates of weathering. The geologist would like to know how fast cliffs are receding in the Colorado Plateau or how rapidly the high mountain peaks of the Sierra Nevada are being reduced. This is a difficult research project, but we are certain of two things:

first, that the rate is real and appreciable, and second, that our calculations will carry into thousands and perhaps millions of years.

SOIL FORMATION BY WEATHERING

Definition of Soil

To the soils scientist any unconsolidated material that will support plant growth is a soil, but to the soils engineer plants are immaterial; he is interested in the ability of the unconsolidated material to support structures of one kind or another, and it is unfortunate that he refers to the unconsolidated material as soil. A true soil to the geologist is a result of weathering in which products of mechanical and chemical alteration are present and mixed with more or less organic matter near the surface.

To be more specific, any rock (granite, sandstone, shale) or unconsolidated material (flood-plain silt, alluvial-fan debris, dune sand, or lake-bed clay), if exposed to the atmosphere for a few centuries, will

FIG. 7-9 Solution pitting of a boulder of white marble. Note the boulders of gneiss that have been rounded by abrasion but not pitted by solution.

develop a profile of weathering, and the upper part of this profile will come to contain organic material because of the activity of plants and animals growing and living in it. If a granite weathers, and the weathering products accumulate, as they will on a flat or gently inclined surface, we note that the solid granite is broken into fragments or blocks, the blocks decay into clay, quartz grains, and limonite, and considerable organic material becomes added to these products. We see this transition in road cuts, trenches, and pits and call it the *soil profile*. The first results of weathering, the blocky fragments, are referred to as the *rock mantle*. Study the soil profiles of Fig. 7-13.

Factors that Determine Type of Soil

Soils are complex and of many kinds. They have been extensively studied and elaborately classified, and they truly deserve all this attention, because they are the most basic and essential material that we have to deal with. Crops may be grown year after year when the soil is maintained,

FIG. 7-10 Weathered granite surface. Joints are spaced about 15 in. apart. Wasatch Mountains, Utah.

whereas a mineral deposit, once mined, is gone forever. Soil, if not protected and safeguarded, can also disappear, and man has lost a most valuable source of food, cotton, lumber, and energy. Soils can be remade, but it may take centuries to do so. They may disappear by erosion in a few years by careless farming.

The climate is the chief factor in determining the type of soil that will form. The kind of parent rock and the time that

FIG. 7-11 Exfoliation of thin crust in granite of Yosemite National Park, California. Granite had previously been abraded and striated by glaciers. (Courtesy of U.S. Geological Survey and G. K. Gilbert.)

FIG. 7-12 Exfoliation of a layer 1 to 6 in. thick in sandstone. Near Hole in the Rock on the Colorado River in Utah.

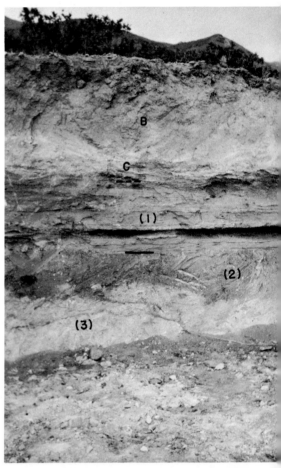

FIG. 7-13 Soil in an excavation in the piedmont of the Wasatch Mountains, Utah. The soil at the top is marked by three "horizons": A, B, and C. This is the soil profile and is about 4 ft thick. It has formed in about the last 15,000 years on lake-shore beds since the lake disappeared. (1) represents the lake beds below the upper soil profile, and (2) represents an ancient soil developed on a sandstone labeled (3).

the weathering processes have been active are also important. In the early stages of soil formation the kind of parent rock is strongly expressed in the soil type, but given time under a certain climate, all rocks gradually are transferred to a common soil. The kinds of plants that grow on the soil are also said to help determine the properties of the soil, but then plants are dependent upon the climate. Also topography is listed as a factor, and by this is meant whether the land surface is flat and swampy, hilly and well drained, or one of steep slopes (Fig. 7-14). These conditions are, of course, significant.

Soil Processes

Basically the same processes that were discussed under weathering are operative in the formation of soil. Frost action, hydration, solution or leaching, and oxidation are the most important. Earthworms, insects, and burrowing rodents mix and turn over the soil and afford percolating water better transit through it. Soils, called *podzols*,

FIG. 7-14 Soil on river gravels, near Darwin City, Yukon Territory. *(Courtesy of Geological Survey of Canada and C. F. Gleeson.)*

develop in forested terranes, *chernozems* develop under grasslands, and desert soils in sagebrush country.

In a warm humid climate like Cuba, with the parent rock being serpentine, which is high in iron, the silica and alumina are mostly leached out for tens of feet below the surface, and a soil rich enough in iron oxide to be mined as iron ore, is left. Such a soil is called a *laterite.* In certain other tropical regions the silica and iron are largely leached out, leaving a soil rich in alumina (the material is called *bauxite*), and this is mined as aluminum ore.

Soils as Indicators of Past Climates

Besides the incalculable value of soils in agriculture they help the geologist interpret the climates and history of the past. Commonly soils are buried by accumulating sediments and thus preserved for future study. For instance, in Fig. 7-13 we see two soils; the lower one seems to be a semi-tropical lateritic soil developed on a red sandstone. It was buried by lake deposits of gravel, sand, and silt, and then the present modern soil, which reflects a temperate, semiarid climate, developed on the lake deposits.

FIG. 7-15 Collapse of the front of a buttress or salient to form a pile of debris at the foot, due to the pull of gravity. East side of Kaiparowitz Plateau, southern Utah.

EROSIONAL PROCESSES

The erosional processes remove and transport the rock particles that have been prepared by the weathering processes, and in addition water can transport material taken into solution. The wind, waves, rivers, and glaciers are all powerful transporting agents, and each is considered at length in following chapters. The force of gravity should be mentioned here, lest in other places it should not be properly emphasized.

In Fig. 7-15 the front or point of the high buttress has caved off, owing to the pull of gravity, and a pile of rubble lies at the foot. The many joints in the sandstone beds prepared the rock for the cave-off. This illustrates a most common occurrence in nature, namely, that when slopes

FIG. 7-16 Breaking away of a mass of sandstone leaving an arch. Note rubble at foot. This is the beginning of the formation of a natural bridge such as shown in Fig. 7-17.

FIG. 7-17 Natural bridge in southern Utah.

FIG. 7-18 Creep of beds downslope.

they roll down the incline. In the high mountain slopes on a spring day a person will hear and see a good many rock fragments, small and large, tumble down the steep slopes. Here we see the slow process of "retreat of the slopes." Given time, profound changes occur, and there is much time in geology.

Note the cave and rubble pile shown in Fig. 7-16. The joints dictate here the arched shape of the cave left by the recent breaking away of the rock. This is the beginning of formation of a natural bridge, such as shown in Fig. 7-17.

In thin-bedded rocks that have been folded and turned up on end, the pull of gravity may slowly bend them downhill, such as shown in Fig. 7-18. Much rock, broken, loose, or in thin beds from the surface down to 5, 10, or 15 ft, moves slowly but conspicuously in places downslope, and the phenomenon is called *creep*. Tremendous volumes of rock are thus transported from higher to lower elevations. Frost actions generally causes heaving and settling, and each such cycle results in a small increment of movement downslope.

become too steep they become unstable and collapse. All slopes are susceptible, whether escarpments, headlands, or valley walls. Frost heave loosens particles individually, and then under pull of gravity

Suggested Aids

Readings
Kellog, Charles E.: "Soils," *Scientific American,* July, 1950.
"Soils," U.S. Department of Agriculture Yearbook, 1957.

Chapter 8

RIVERS AND MAN

Streams, small and large, have consumed man's attention and shaped his destiny in significant measure for many thousands of years. Stone Age man fished the streams and trapped along them. His villages were situated on them, and they were his routes of travel as well as his barriers. He was tied to them for drinking water; yet in flood time they devastated his villages and drove him away. The early Egyptians depended upon the spring floods for arable fields and later learned to divert the water for irrigation. Today man is harnessing the rivers with his greatest of engineering projects. He is building dams for water storage and flood control. Millions of dry acres are being irrigated. Electricity is being generated for new industry, and beautiful lakes are being created for recreation. He is also making the larger water ways more navigable and building many bridges across them. It is the purpose of this chapter to study streams in order to

Streams Fashion
The Landscape

 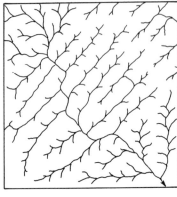

FIG. 8-1 Drainage patterns: left, arborescent, with local radial (*R*); right, trellis in central area with arborescent in upper and lower reaches.

understand how they operate, what they have done to the landscape in the geologic past, and to point out how the geologist and engineer use this knowledge in controlling and using them.

DRAINAGE PATTERNS

First, let us take a broad view of the continent and a map on which the rivers and tributary streams are well shown. We

FIG. 8-2 Arborescent drainage. Example in southwestern Montana. (Vertical aerial photograph.)

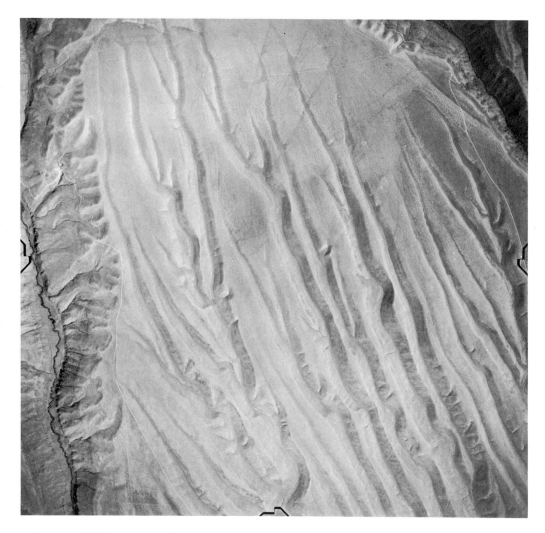

FIG. 8-3 Parallel drainage. Example in southwestern Montana. (Vertical aerial photograph.)

will see that most major streams with their tributaries have a pattern resembling an elm or an oak. The pattern is called *arborescent* or *dendritic*. See Figs. 8-1 and 8-2. In the Appalachian Mountains from Pennsylvania to Alabama, however, the tributaries and main streams take courses approximately at right angles to each other or make right angle jogs. This pattern is called *trellis* or *angular* (Fig. 8-1). In certain restricted areas we see that the drainage is radially outward, such as from a single high mountain, and this is referred to as *radial*. In certain restricted settings a number of tributaries are somewhat parallel, and the pattern is called *parallel* (Fig. 8-3).

STREAM FLOW

Immediate Observations

We should note at the beginning that streams are confined to channels with banks, they flow down hill only, they are often muddy, which means they are carrying particles of clay, silt, and sand, and their flow is turbulent and irregular.

Velocity of Flow

What Determines Velocity? Some streams flow slowly, some rapidly; the rate of flow varies along the course of any individual stream; they all flow more rapidly in high water times than in low.

Velocity of flow is determined principally by four factors: the gradient or slope of the channel, the shape of the channel, the volume of water flowing in the channel, and the roughness of the channels. If there were no retarding influences to flow, its velocity would accelerate to incredible speeds in a short distance. The steeper the gradient and the greater the amount of water, the faster the flow; but on the other hand shallow and rough channels hinder the flow and check the acceleration.

FIG. 8-4 Stream in the Rocky Mountains with steep gradient and cascading falls.

Gradient. In flowing a mile the lower Mississippi River loses only a few inches of elevation, whereas one of its distant tributaries in the Rocky Mountains falls several hundred feet in a mile (Fig. 8-4). Gradient of a stream is measured in inches or feet per mile in English-speaking countries and in centimeters or meters per kilometer in most other countries. Almost everyone has observed the constant attempt of the water to hurry along in mountain streams of high gradients where it plunges over waterfalls and rapids only to be obstructed by large boulders, fallen tree trunks, channel bends, and deep pools. Low gradients are generally synonymous with sluggish flow.

Roughness of Channel. As just mentioned, boulders on a stream bed obstruct the flow, especially at low-water stages. Roughness of the bedrock floor of the channel also hinders flow. A series of beaver dams slows the overall flow considerably. A winding or very crooked channel deters the flow. The factor of roughness is difficult to assess quantitatively, but its significance is most obvious.

Shape of Channel. The shape of a canal or flume in cross section which offers the least drag or resistance to flow and in which for a given gradient the water flows fastest is a half circle. See Fig. 8-5. This contains or passes the most water per area of channel surface and hence offers the least resistance to flow. A wide, shallow channel presents more surface area to less water and hence more drag on the water. Such channels are generally characteristic of low gradients. A deep, narrow channel, like the wide, shallow channel, retards the flow

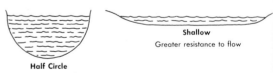

Half Circle
Least resistance to flow

Shallow
Greater resistance to flow

FIG. 8-5 Shapes of channels in relation to velocity of flow.

FIG. 8-6 Narrows of the Snake River below Jackson Hole. The channel here is about 20 ft wide and 60 ft deep with increased flow velocity.

more than the semicircular one, but the deep, narrow channels are generally full of water in mountainous areas and have steep gradients; hence the rather high velocities of flow. See Fig. 8-6.

Volume of Water Discharge. The more water in a given channel, the faster the flow. The quantity of water passing a given point on the stream bank in a unit of time is called *discharge* and is generally given in cubic feet per second. This measure is significant in comparing the activity of different streams.

The velocity of flow has been emphasized in the foregoing paragraphs because much of a stream's erosional and transportational power depends on velocity. This will be brought out in the following paragraphs.

STREAM LOADS (TRANSPORTATION)

Methods of Transport

A stream transports rock and mineral matter in three ways: in suspension, along the bottom of the bed or channel, and in solution.

Suspended Load

If you take a handful of dirt from the garden and drop it in a bucket full of water you will immediately perceive that there are different sizes of particles or grains and that the larger ones sink to the bottom rapidly, the intermediate-sized ones sink more slowly, and the small ones settle very slowly. In fact, some particles remain suspended and keep the water roily or turbid for hours.

Those particles which settle slowly and tend to remain suspended are the silt and clay-sized ones. Silt-sized particles will settle in a bucket of quiet water in an hour or so, but clay-sized particles may remain in suspension for hours or days. Now, as has been noted, stream flow is turbulent. There are eddies, vortices, and boils in the water's movement. It falls and tumbles and is deflected to the right and to the left by various obstacles. The upward eddies are forever lifting the silt and clay particles, and thus the particles never get a chance to settle out. Even considerable sand-sized particles are swept up in the eddies and move downstream an appreciable distance before settling out. Samples of the Missouri River water at Kansas City, for instance, were taken from top to bottom, and the particles that make the water muddy were analyzed for size. Fig. 8-7 shows the results. Clay-sized particles are in equal abundance from top to bottom; silt-sized particles become slightly more abundant near the bottom; but sand-sized particles increase conspicuously from top to bottom and are being moved in large amounts in the lower 3 ft of a stream some 11½ ft deep. It is evident that clay and silt are transported by suspension, and sand only partly.

Since stream flow is turbulent, the water remains roily or muddy for many miles. If just a small percentage of the weight of the water were suspended load, even a

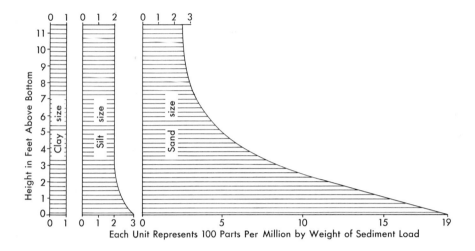

FIG. 8-7 Distribution of load in a stream, from top to bottom. The vertical scale shows the depth of water in the channel, and the horizontal scale indicates the amount of sediment being transported. Of the sand fraction the grains at the top are nearly all fine sand in size, but at the bottom of the channel they are half fine sand and half medium and coarse sand. This graph shows a sampling of the Missouri River at Kansas City. *(After Straub, in* Hydrology.*)*

small stream would transport a large amount of material. About 2 million tons of sediment is carried each day by the Mississippi River into the Gulf of Mexico.

Bed Load

If windows are constructed in experimental flumes and the movement of the grains observed on or near the bottom, it will be seen that only swiftly flowing streams develop enough turbulence to pick up sand grains from the bed of the stream. It is necessary here to distinguish fine, medium, and coarse sand grains, because much of the fine sand follows the silt in suspension, but almost all the medium and coarse sand grains roll along the bottom. As the velocity of flow is increased, we note a change from rolling and short leaps of a few grains to spasmodic movement of groups of grains to a smooth general streaming of many grains. It will be seen that there develops a transitional zone between bed-load transport and suspension transport of a few inches to a few feet,

depending on the velocity of the stream and the nature of the grains affected, in which it is difficult to distinguish the mode of transport. Undoubtedly the medium and coarse sand grains in this zone are proceeding by jumps.

Dissolved Load

Water that emerges as seeps and springs contains considerable material in solution, and such water contributes in good measure to almost all streams. The stream water also dissolves some material directly from its channel bottom and from the particles in mechanical transport. The chief compound in solution is calcium carbonate ($CaCO_3$), but ions other than those in $CaCO_3$ are common, such as Na^+, K^+, Mg^{++}, Cl^-, and SO_4^{--}. The major rivers carry only a few hundred parts per million of dissolved matter, but some of the smaller streams in arid regions carry several thousand parts per million and are distinctly saline to the taste. It has been estimated that more than half of all materials carried by river water from continent to ocean is dissolved load.

Velocity of flow, which is so important in the transportation of discrete grains of rocks and minerals, has little to do with solution. Once a material is in solution, except in unusual conditions, it stays there whether the stream flows rapidly or slowly.

Some streams are brown with organic acids in solution derived from the decay of plant material.

STREAM EROSION

Abrasion

The movement of rock particles along a stream bed accomplishes three things: the particles themselves are worn or abraded, the rock floor of the channel is abraded, and the banks are undercut and cave off into the stream.

The particles, whether sand grains, pebbles, cobbles, or boulders that are moved along, strike one another as well as the bottom and banks, and gradually their corners and sharp edges are chipped off, and they become rounded. The farther the particle has been transported, the rounder it gets.

At the same time the channel bottom is chipped and scratched as the particles tumble and bounce along. In mountain streams where the gradient is steep, large heavy boulders bash the bottom, especially in flood time, and abrasion is rapid. We note the effect in the downcutting of the stream channels (Fig. 8-8). Canyons or gorges that have near-vertical walls are clear examples of the stream's power to cut downward, almost as if a giant saw had been cutting through the bedrock. From gullies in a cornfield to the Grand Canyon of the Colorado a basic activity is downcutting, and in hard rock it is principally an abrasive phenomenon.

Although the chief activity is downcutting, the banks are undercut in places, and slabs and blocks of rock cave off to become

FIG. 8-8 Pot hole in hard rock of stream bed, worn by sand, pebbles, and cobbles being whirled around in eddies of the stream. Yosemite National Park. (Courtesy of U.S. Geological Survey and F. E. Matthes.)

part of the stream's load. Perhaps the blocks are too large to be moved by the stream, but in such event they themselves will be abraded by other passing particles, like the channel bottom, until they are small enough for some flood to move them on. Caving under waterfalls also helps along the general process of channel abrasion and downcutting. Study Fig. 8-9.

Solution

Channel erosion is helped by solution especially in limestone terranes. The limestone ($CaCO_3$) is taken into solution especially if the stream contains much carbon dioxide.

Abrasion, in producing small particles from large, helps the process of solution be-

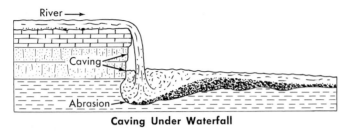

Caving Under Waterfall

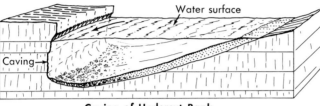

Caving of Undercut Bank

FIG. 8-9 Examples of erosion by caving. The lower diagram is a cut across an asymmetrical stream channel.

cause small particles present more face area per volume than large particles.

Source of Stream's Load

Downcutting soon produces such steep valley walls that caving occurs, and this adds to a stream's load. In fact, most arterial streams are busily engaged in transporting the material supplied by the tributaries, and the tributaries engaged in transporting the material brought to them by rainwash. Only part of the stream's energy can be expended in downcutting; in fact, downcutting is common only along steep gradients and relatively fast-flowing streams.

RELATION OF VELOCITY TO EROSION, TRANSPORTATION, AND DEPOSITION

Factors Determining Maximum Size of Particles

If a stream flowing at a certain velocity is just able to move coarse sand grains along the bottom, how much larger grains will it move if its bottom velocity is doubled? The answer is, Many times. There are several reasons. With twice the velocity each water particle hits twice as hard, and also twice as much water strikes the

face of the sand grain in each second. The water impact therefore increases as the square of the velocity. This means that, if the velocity is doubled, four of these particles placed end on end can be moved. This is shown by the use of cubes in Fig. 8-10. Now, if these four cubes, end on end, are built up to one large cube, which also can be moved by the doubled velocity flow, then the size of the particle is sixty-four-times as great; or, expressed in another way, the diameter of the particle is increased four times. It can also be shown

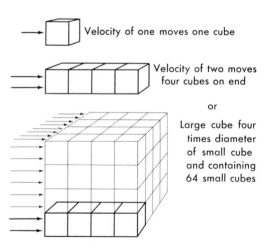

Velocity of one moves one cube

Velocity of two moves four cubes on end

or

Large cube four times diameter of small cube and containing 64 small cubes

FIG. 8-10 By doubling the velocity of flow, the impact is four times greater and theoretically the stream can move a particle having four times the diameter or sixty-four times the volume.

that, if the velocity is tripled, the diameter of the particle that the stream is able to move is increased nine times. This, of course, means that surprisingly large boulders can be moved if immersed in a rapidly flowing stream.

Add to the factor of impact the frictional drag of the water passing over the particle, a stream with increased velocity attains still more potency. Add, further, the factor of buoyancy, and we begin to appreciate the power of a raging stream. If a pebble of quartz weighs 2.7 g in air, it will weigh only 1.7 g in water, and hence, in the matter of buoyancy alone, running water has a much easier time than wind in moving rock particles.

Experimental Results

Figure 8-11 shows the results of experiments with running water and its ability to pick up, retain in transport, or to drop (deposit) the particles. It must be appreciated that the coordinates of the graph (velocity and grain size) are shown to increase logarithmically, and then it will be recognized that the size of the particles that a stream is able to move increases very much faster than the velocity increases.

Another point that is a bit surprising is that clay particles, once settled into a compact arrangement on the bottom, are hard to pick up and that the velocity must be increased to do so. Once in suspension they stay in suspension, however, with minimum velocities. The upper limit of the "transportation zone" marks the velocities necessary to pick up particles and to accomplish erosion. The lower limit represents those velocities which are just barely necessary to keep the particle in motion. If the velocity falls below this minimum, then the particle is dropped or stops rolling, and deposition results. All problems of erosion and deposition of rivers and canals must be considered in the framework of this basic graph.

Rivers in Flood Stage

Boulders 10 to 15 ft in diameter are rolled out of gullies in cloud-burst floods. Floods resulting from dam breaks have moved huge blocks of the ruptured con-

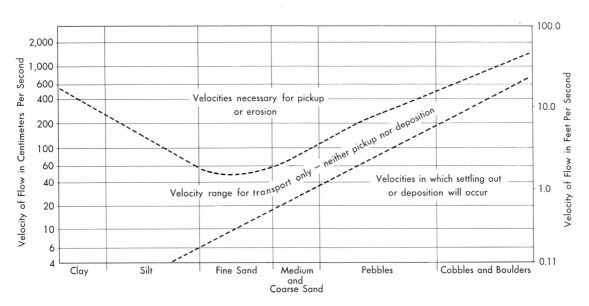

FIG. 8-11 Velocities necessary to erode, transport, or deposit grains of different sizes. Refer to Chap. 2 for size of clay, silt, sand, etc., particles. *(Compiled with simplification from Hjulstvom, Recent Marine Sediments, and Sundborg, Geografiska Annaler, 1956.)*

crete. The example is often cited of the St. Francis dam in southern California, which broke in 1928. The great mass of water, suddenly released, carried a block of concrete which measured 63 by 54 by 30 ft a half mile downstream. Floods with rapidly moving water are really monsters in their power to destroy.

The ability to move particles is called *competence*. The greater the velocity, the larger the particles moved, and hence we say the greater the competence. The total load carried, however, is a matter of a stream's *capacity*. Capacity depends on volume as well as velocity.

ANALYSIS OF STREAM ACTIVITY

Longitudinal Profile

If the gradient of a stream is charted from head to mouth, the graph obtained is called a *longitudinal profile*. The gradient is generally steepest at the head and gentlest at the mouth. Streams in the Rocky Mountains fall 5,000 to 7,000 ft in 50 to 100 miles, and then, on the Great Plains or other valley floors, fall only 500 ft in 200 miles. The entire profile approximates a smooth concave upward curve, which looks like a hyperbola. See upper curve of Fig.

8-12. Although every stream shows irregularities and departures from this hyperbola-like profile, the fact that almost all approach it must have real significance.

Graded Profile and Base Level

If faulting across a stream should suddenly drop the downstream block and elevate the upstream block, the stream's activity would be upset. Figure 8-12 shows the dislocated stream profile. The stream, in tumbling over the fault scarp, immediately gains velocity and starts to erode or deepen its channel at this point. The downcutting of the channel proceeds upstream through stages 1, 2, and 3, as indicated. Since the channel on the down-thrown block has had its gradient lessened, the stream there becomes sluggish and incompetent to transport the load it formerly handled. Not only this, but the channel deepening upstream from the fault will have added an additional load, which, under the circumstances, the stream below the fault is not able to carry away, so that sediment is dropped in the channel or valley bottom. This deposition will occur in stages 1, 2, and 3 downstream to match the progress of erosion upstream. And in the long run, a smoothly curved longitudinal profile is established as it was before faulting. A

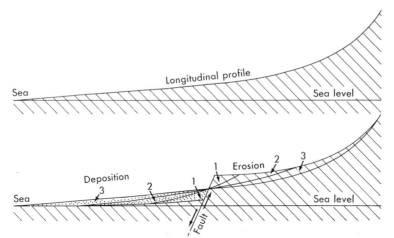

Sea   Longitudinal profile   Sea level

Deposition   Erosion

Sea   Fault   Sea level

FIG. 8-12   Longitudinal stream profiles.

FIG. 8-13 Headward erosion in the arid Colorado Plateau. *(Photograph by Hal Rumel, Salt Lake City.)*

stream that has established a smoothly curved concave profile is said to be *graded*, but this is probably an ideal condition toward which streams work. Every stream is attempting to achieve a gradient nicely adjusted to its volume, load, and the bedrock irregularities over which it flows.

In the profiles of Fig. 8-12, the stream is shown to empty into the ocean, and the horizontal datum line is at sea level. Any stream that empties into the ocean is controlled by the ocean level because the stream cannot erode its channel more than a few feet deeper than the ocean's surface. In fact, a moment's reflection will show that the profile approaches sea level as a base, and as this base is approached, the gradient of the lower part of the pro-

file becomes gentler, and downcutting slower. The ocean level is thus referred to as the stream's *base level*. If a stream empties into a lake, the lake is the stream's base level, or if a stream flows out onto an arid flat plain and dries up there, the plain is the stream's base level.

The concept of base level helps explain the hyperbolalike curve of the normal longitudinal profile.

Headward Erosion

Erosion is most vigorous in the steep upper reaches of a stream, and because of this, the longitudinal profile is lengthened. However, a smooth curve is maintained in the manner shown in the several stages of

FIG. 8-14 Headward erosion into a rolling upland. Book Cliffs, east-central Utah. (Vertical aerial photograph.) What is the meaning of the curving subparallel lines in the rolling upland?

Fig. 8-12. A photographic illustration of a stream extending itself by *headward erosion* into a fairly flat upland on a small scale is shown in Fig. 8-13, and on a larger scale in Fig. 8-14.

Natural and Artificial Base Levels

The Mississippi River lives a worried existence, attempting to keep adjusted to changing conditions. Undoubtedly, farm-ing of the many fertile acres of its drainage basin has added immensely to the load, and the river finds trouble in keeping its channels clear. Then there are the flood times and the low-water times, and the river under each condition finds itself out of kilter with the previous situation to which it was adjusting.

Not only this, but sea level, and hence base level, has fluctuated in the past. The ocean's level has risen and fallen as much

FIG. 8-15 Results of fluctuating base level: 1, original valley surface; 2, entrenched valley due to lowered base level; A, sediments deposited in entrenched valley with rising base level; 3, second entrenchment due to lowering of base level a second time; B, deposits with rising base level.

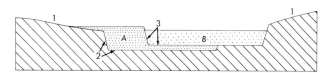

as 300 ft several times in the past half million years or so (during the climatic fluctuations of the ice age), and the river, frantically it would seem, trenched its valley during lower sea level in adjusting to the lower base level and filled up the trench with sediment again during the return to high sea level. Two cycles of downcutting followed by filling are shown diagrammatically in Fig. 8-15. The surface labeled 1 is the valley under graded conditions, presumably when the sea level was high or normal. Sea level dropped, and the river trenched its valley to surface 2. Later sea level rose, and the river filled the trench with sediments, labeled A. Sea level fell a second time, and the river trenched its valley again, but not necessarily in exactly the same place as the first. The new trench is labeled 3. Then sea level rose again, and the river followed suit by filling· in the second trench with sediments, called B. This time, perchance, the trench or valley fill was not built up quite so high as the first fill.

When man builds a dam across a river, such as the Boulder Dam on the Colorado near Las Vegas, Nevada, a lake (Lake Mead) is impounded back of the dam, and the lake creates a new base level for the river upstream from the lake. The lake becomes a settling tank for the river's sediments, and the dam thus creates an *artificial base level.*

It has been important to measure the volume of sediment that the Colorado River is carrying into Lake Mead, for in time, the sediment will fill the reservoir, and as this occurs, the water-storage capacity of the dam decreases. Here are some data on the Colorado River and Lake Mead:

✦ The water originally backed far up the Colorado River canyon into the narrow Lower Granite Gorge, but in the first 14 years (1935 to 1948) the river's sediments filled the gorge up to lake level for 43 miles downstream from the original point of entry into quiet water.

✦ The heavy turbid currents of the river dive under the clear water and flow along the old canyon bottom on occasion all the way to the dam, a distance of 120 miles. They thus carry the river's sediments along the entire length of the reservoir and particularly have filled the inner deep gorge.

✦ The sand particles settle out immediately, but the silt and clay particles are

FIG. 8-16 Deposits by the Colorado River in Lake Mead back of Boulder Dam. *(After Gould, S. E. P. & M., 1951.)*

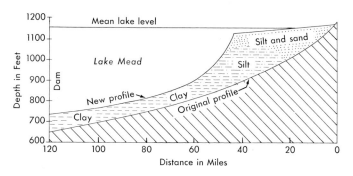

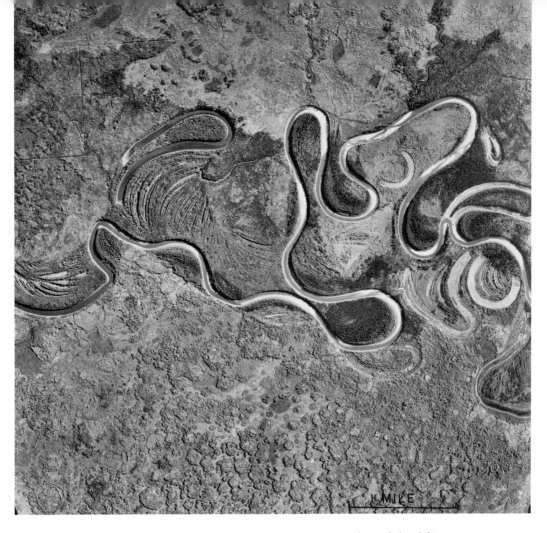

FIG. 8-17 Meandering Hay River, northwestern Alberta. Note the crescentic bars of the shifting meanders, meander cutoffs, and oxbow lakes. *(Courtesy of Geological Survey of Canada and Ed Schiller.)*

carried by the turbidity currents the entire length of the reservoir. See Fig. 8-16.

✦ In the first 14-year period of the reservoir's existence some 2 billion tons of sediment was deposited in the lake. About half is deposited immediately at the point of entry of the river into still water, but half is spread out along the entire deep bottom by the turbidity currents. The total water-storage capacity has thus been reduced by about 5 per cent.

✦ If 5 per cent of the storage capacity is lost in 14 years because of sediment fill, then half of the storage capacity will be lost in 140 years, and by this time, the useful-

ness of the great dam and reservoir will be seriously impaired.

Grain, Size, Load and Longitudinal Profile

Studies of several large rivers have resulted in the generalization that the size of the grains transported gradually decreases downstream. This fact helps to explain the decrease in gradient of the longitudinal profile, because the load, reduced to smaller particles by constant wear, is more easily transported or can be transported at lower velocities.

Meandering Streams

Streams seldom pursue straight courses. Even in short stretches they seem to disdain the straight-away channel and develop a sinuous or winding path. The bends are generally picturesquely rounded and curved. Such streams are said to be *meandering*. Study Figs. 8-17 and 8-18. From many observations and experiments it is concluded that the streams given most to intricately meandering courses are those whose banks and bed are in unconsolidated alluvium. For instance, during the postglacial rise of sea level the Mississippi River deposited a thick layer of sand and silt across the floor of its broad valley, and now this sand and silt material fosters the tendency of the great river to meander. It is true that some

streams pursue meandering courses in hard rock, such as the Green, Colorado, and San Juan Rivers in places in Utah, but such examples usually reflect complicated geologic histories that will be taken up later.

Leonardo da Vinci, about 450 years ago, perceived the activity of meandering streams and pointed out in connection with the River Arno that erosion and deposition were occurring and where. Representative of Newton's first law of motion, moving water particles tend to keep in the direction in which they are going and hence, in rounding a bend, the current impinges upon the outer bank. Refer to Fig. 8-19. Here, undercutting of the bank occurs. Small cuts by small rivers and large cuts by large rivers are numerous and obvious wherever the rivers follow meandering

FIG. 8-18 Meander scars of the Yukon River in the Bethel area. *(Courtesy of H. N. Fisk, and with the permission of Fairchild Aerial Surveys, Inc.)*

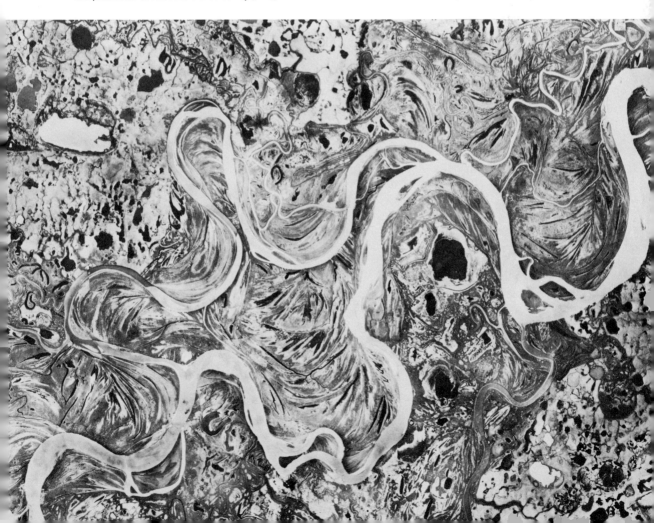

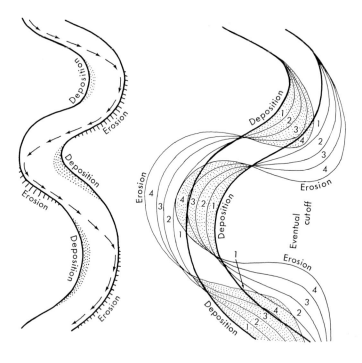

FIG. 8-19 The process of meandering by erosion and deposition (left), and successive stages in the development of meanders (right).

courses. Observe the freshly cut and slumping banks of the small meandering stream in Yellowstone Park (Fig. 8-20) and the imposing banks on the Yukon (Fig. 8-21).

Now the sediment eroded from the bank is carried downstream by the current and most of it comes to repose in the slack water of the inside of the next lower bend (Fig. 8-19). See also the bars deposited by the Yukon on the inside of a great curve

FIG. 8-20 Meandering stream in Yellowstone Park showing freshly cut bank.

FIG. 8-21 Bank erosion on the outside of a large meander bend on the Yukon River, Alaska.

floods. The stream overflows its banks, with the overflow taking the direct course to the adjacent bend and eroding out a direct chute or channel.

If the base level of a meandering stream is lowered and the gradient and velocity thus increased, then the stream erodes its bed, and the meanders become *entrenched*. Study Figs. 8-23 and 8-24.

Braided Streams

Meandering streams are basically eroding streams, but under certain conditions a stream's major activity is turned to deposition, and the channel or valley is filled with sediment. If, for some reason, a stream's tributaries start bringing in more load than it can transport, it then drops part of its load. The channel fills up, and the stream overflows its banks. It may find several low spillways over the banks and break into as many *distributaries*. Each small branch channel soon becomes filled, and its flow spills over to form more branches. Such a stream is shown in Figs. 8-25 and 8-26. It is said to be *braided*. The easily eroded soil from a newly plowed grassy turf may overload the stream and result in a braided condition. The melt waters from a glacier are generally so heavily laden with debris that the stream is not able to carry the material along the gradient to which it was adjusted before the glacier formed, and a braided condition results.

(Fig. 8-22). The cutting and filling proceeds to such an extent that the channel migrates here and there across the entire river flood plain.

Small rivers have small meanders, and large rivers have large meanders. In fact the radius of curvature of the meander bends is two to three times the width of the river. This ratio is not determined by the load, it is believed, but to the dynamics of flow, which is so complicated that the complete solution is not yet at hand. As the meanders developed into more complete circles some of the meanders eventually intersect, and cutoffs occurs. The stream, encountering a small but sharp drop at the cutoff, follows this more direct course and forsakes the horseshoe-shaped channel, which stands partially full of quiet water. The ends of the cutoff channel become silted up, and thus a lake that is called an *oxbow lake* is born. The cutting across meander bends is often hurried along by

FIG. 8-22 Meander bend on Yukon River, showing bar deposition on inside of curve. Large rivers have large meander bends.

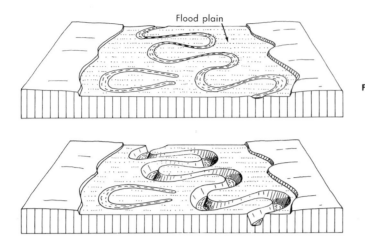

Flood plain

FIG. 8-23 Meandering stream with oxbow lake above, adjusted to base level. Below, base level lowered suddenly with entrenchment of stream in meandering course.

Natural Levees and Flood Plains

A common association is flood plain and natural levee. Low ridges border each side of the river channel and stand a few feet higher than the flood plain. Flood stage is reached when the river rises to overflow the levee and to pour out over the flood plain.

The levee is built at flood times of the coarsest material that the river is carrying. At the moment that the channel-confined current spreads in a thin sheet over the bank, the velocity drops and so also the coarsest particles of its load. The finer particles are carried out over the flood plain, but almost all the material is deposited immediately adjacent to the channel, and hence a levee is built. Levee building and channel fill continues in places to such an extent that the river surface is above the flood-plain elevation. In this condition if the river in flood spills over the levee, it might

FIG. 8-24 Entrenched meandering stream. Hoback River, western Wyoming.

cut a channel through the levee, and the much of the flow would then debouch on the flood plain, with dire results.

The levees built by the river are called natural, in contrast to any artificial embankment that man might build to confine the river in high-flood stage.

Deltas

The deposit of the Colorado River in Lake Mead is called a *delta*. The term refers generally to the part of the deposit at the river mouth and not to the turbidity current deposit far out in deep water.

Great deltas like the Mississippi are fairly complex. The river divides into distributaries, with each distributary building its own smaller delta, and in total a pattern remindful of a bird's foot is formed. In modern analysis, the water of each distributary jets into the quiet water of the Gulf, and deposits of clay, silt, and sand, so controlled, result. See Fig. 8-27.

The coarsest particles, here sand, are dropped at the point where the current enters still water. This deposit forms a base over which the current then flows, only to deposit more sand at the new point of entry. A tongue of sand is thus built out by each distributary, and as you might deduce, each distributary is immediately underlain by a tongue or bar of sand. On the sides and underneath is silt, and out still farther in deeper water the finer clay particles settle.

Terraces

Stream terraces are benches along the sides of river valleys. Good examples occur on either side of Madison Valley in southwestern Montana (Fig. 8-28). They are common along almost all rivers that have reached fair adjustment but then have been energized or *rejuvenated* by uplift of the land. Entrenchment ensues, then broadening of the entrenched meanders until a new valley floor is established with terraces on either side. Rising and lowering of base

FIG. 8-25   Braided stream in Mount McKinley National Park, Alaska.

level in several cycles cause rather complex sets of terraces. See Fig. 8-15.

Valley Widening

When the land is uplifted in respect to the sea or lake into which the stream flows, the stream will cut a sharp, V-shaped valley into the uplifted terrane. Downcutting is the chief process. As the longitudinal profile becomes graded, downcutting becomes slow or minimized, and the processes of valley widening become dominant. The processes of frost action and talus formation, landslides, and rainwash, such as described in Chap. 7 erode away the valley

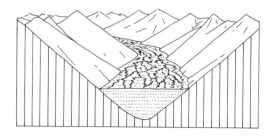

FIG. 8-26   Braided stream and its deposits in a mountainous V-shaped valley. Compare with Fig. 8-25.

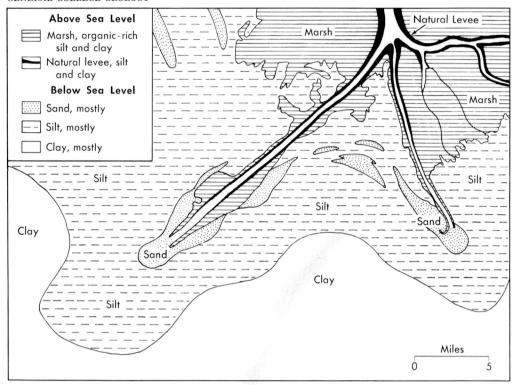

FIG. 8–27 Southwest part of Mississippi birdfoot delta, showing distribution of sand, silt, and clay deposits. *(Simplified from Fisk et al., 1954.)*

sides. In arid regions the valley walls generally retreat in the manner illustrated in Fig. 8-29. The slope remains fairly constant, and a distinct angular break in cross profile between valley wall and valley floor is maintained (Fig. 8-30). In many places of our Western arid and semiarid regions changes in climate in the past 25,000 years (during and following the last ice age) and overgrazing in the past 75 years have resulted in vigorous changes in the streams' regimen. At times filling (alluviation) of valley bottoms and at other times entrenchment of the streams in the previous deposits have resulted in complex terraces and have contrived to obliterate the simplicity

FIG. 8-28 Terraces along the Madison River near Varney, southwestern Montana.

FIG. 8-29 Process of valley widening in arid lands.

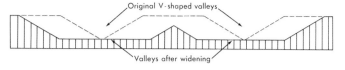

Original V-shaped valleys

Valleys after widening

of the valley forms, such as portrayed in Fig. 8-29, which might otherwise exist.

In humid climates the valley sides become rounded with the upland, and a more rolling and less angular topography results.

INFLUENCE OF BEDROCK VARIATIONS ON STREAM ACTIVITY

Erosion Patterns in Flat-lying Beds

The drainage pattern in a region of flat-lying beds will be arborescent, such as shown in Fig. 8-31. If the beds have been cut and displaced by a fault some of the tributaries may develop along the fault, owing to the broken nature of the rock on either side of the fault or, perhaps, to harder rocks on one side against softer rocks on the other. The valley walls, especially in arid regions, will consist of steps such as shown in Fig. 2-21.

An aborescent drainage is also characteristic of a terrane of granite or some other fairly homogenous rock.

Erosion Forms in Folded Beds

If sedimentary strata have been folded or tipped up to a steep angle, such as seen in Fig. 2-23, then beds resistant to erosion alternate with beds more easily eroded, and a trellis pattern of drainage results (Fig. 8-1). Attention to the details of a trellis pattern may enable a person to recognize anticlines and synclines in the folded beds. You will need to study topographic maps with different drainage patterns in the laboratory and be furnished collateral information on the bedrock structures in order to understand this subject better.

Fault Scarp Features

Erosion attacks the uplifted block of a fault vigorously and soon cuts a number of V-shaped clefts in it, in the manner shown in Fig. 8-32. If the fault displacement amounts to several thousand feet, as is the case in many ranges of the Great Basin of Utah, Nevada, and eastern California, then the clefts become canyons, deepest at the

FIG. 8-30 Angular break (knick point) between valley wall and valley floor. Badlands of South Dakota. *(Courtesy of Kenneth G. Smith.)*

FIG. 8-31 Arborescent drainage developed in flat-lying beds. Green River formation of the Uinta Basin, Utah. (Vertical photograph.)

front of the uplifted block. As erosion proceeds, the canyons extend headward into the uplifted block, and the old land surface becomes much dissected. Eventually, there are no remnants of the old surface, but a series of nicely aligned triangular faces mark the fault scarp. Such a mountain front is pictured in Fig. 8-33.

Another example of block faulting on a large scale is Jackson Hole, Wyoming. The Teton Range has been lifted up and dissected into a series of deep canyons, and the downdropped block has been covered with the debris eroded from the uplifted block. Figure 8-34 shows a scarp, only mildly dissected, of a subsidiary fault within the major downdropped block. The major fault is along the front of the mountains beyond.

The deposits at the foot of a fault scarp are cone- or fan-shaped, with the apex of each fan at the mouth of the canyon or gully in the uplifted block. It is clear that the debris has spewed or flooded from the canyon. These deposits are called *alluvial fans* (Figs. 8-32, 8-35, and 8-36). They occur in all climates but are especially clear and impressive in arid regions where block faulting has occurred. Like deltas their rock fragments are coarsest at the top or apex and finest at the periphery, and also like deltas this general distribution is altered by long radiating channels of coarse debris encased in fine material. The debris of alluvial fans is not so well sorted as in deltas and contains large boulders. Alluvial fans, however, are good reservoirs for underground water, and considerable atten-

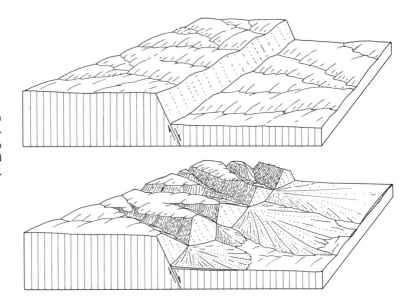

FIG. 8-32 Forms resulting from dissection of a fault scarp. Note remnants of upland surface, V-shaped gorges in uplifted block, triangular faces, and alluvial fans on downfaulted block.

tion has been given to their structure and "plumbing system."

DISSECTED EROSION SURFACES

Many of the high ranges of the Rocky Mountains display nearly flat, gently rolling, or inclined surfaces at high elevations. See Fig. 8-37. These are generally remnants of erosion surfaces fashioned by streams as wide valleys or piedmont slopes before the range was uplifted. With uplift, vigorous headward erosion sets in, which dis-

sects the range and, perhaps, leaves remnants of the old surface here and there, generally at the drainage divides. See Fig. 8-37 again.

The flat-topped ridges of the Appalachian Mountains are classic examples of such an old erosion surface. The history there has been as follows: first, folding; second, extensive erosion across the folded strata to form a surface with only gentle, low divides and wide valley bottoms (a *peneplain*); and third, uplift of the entire region with dissection and entrenchment of the streams. Parallel ridges and valleys were etched

FIG. 8-33 Aligned triangular faces marking a fault scarp. East of Salt Lake City, Utah.

FIG. 8-34 Jackson, Wyoming, at foot of fault scarp. A transverse valley, which existed before faulting, appears just beyond the town.

out of the parallel hard and soft upturned or folded strata, but the flat tops of the parallel ridges reflect the old erosion surface.

RATES OF UPLIFT AND RATES OF EROSION

Progress of Erosion in the Face of Uplift

Students of geology were well aware many years ago that mountainous areas, although of considerable relief today, have suffered thousands of feet of erosion. The mountains usually are only stumps of the mighty uplifts. In some it is quite evident that 10,000 to 20,000 ft of rock or even more has been removed by erosion. One of the ranges in the Rocky Mountains that became known to geologists around the world for its evident great uplift and subsequent great reduction by erosion is the Uinta Mountains of northern Utah. The first director of the U.S. Geological Survey, John Wesley Powell, reported on the structure of this range and portrayed it as a large anticline with marginal faults. The total amplitude of the crest of the original

anticline related to the troughs of the adjacent basins is about 30,000 ft. The present erosion surface truncates the anticline and exposes rocks in the core that were once possibly 20,000 ft below the surface. At this stage we must consider some quantitative data on rates of erosion and rates of uplift.

Rates of Denudation

The term "denudation" refers to the lowering of a land surface by erosion. In the filling of reservoirs by sediments, the rates of sediment influx can be accurately measured, and geologists of the U.S. Geological Survey have transformed these rates of sediment accumulation into rates of denudation. A number of types of drainage basins were studied, and various measurements of actual denudation have also been made by observing the loss of soil from around benchmarks of steel and concrete. It was concluded that the average rate of denudation is about 0.25 ft per 1,000 years and that the maximum rate is 3 ft per 1,000 years. The most rapid rates occur in areas of semiarid climate that are underlain by sedimentary rocks. Also, the higher

FIG. 8-35 Mountain front largely due to faulting. Note alluvial fans and small scarp at base of mountain front. Southern Wasatch Mountains, Utah.

FIG. 8-36 Vertical aerial photograph of dissected fault scarp and alluvial fans near Dillon, southwestern Montana.

FIG. 8-37 Continental Divide in Estes Park, Colorado, showing remnant of high, old erosion surface.

the elevation, the greater the rate of denudation. The effect of elevation on the rate of denudation is charted in Fig. 8-38.

The rate of denudation slows as the climate becomes more humid than semiarid, and also it slows on the other hand as the climate becomes more arid than semiarid. So the figures given above are for semiarid countries and are likely to be greater than those of many drainage basins.

Rates of Uplift

The Coast Ranges of California are noted as an example of vigorous mountain building going on today. Survey bench marks have been reoccupied several times in the past fifty years and the progress of uplift definitely detected. Figures are numerous and substantial and indicate an average rate of uplift of 25 ft per 1,000 years. Compare this with an average rate of denudation of 0.25 ft and a maximum rate of 3 ft per 1,000 years, and you are immediately struck with the fact that uplift, or mountain building, is a number of times faster than denudation. In certain small areas underlain by easily eroded shale and silt the rate of denudation is as high as the rate of uplift in parts of the Coast Ranges, but such examples are certainly exceptional.

The average rate of uplift in the central part of Fennoscandia in the past 7,000

Uinta Mountains, but this is very instructive.

Uplift of the Uinta Mountains

The second diagram in Fig. 8-39 shows three separate uplifts that have combined to produce the Uinta Mountains. The first occurred about 65 million years ago, the second about 40 million years ago, and the third started about 20 million years ago and may still be slowly continuing. The first two episodes of uplift were rather sharp and are estimated to have occurred at about the rates of 5 to 10 ft per 1,000 years. These rates are indicated by vertical bars in the lowest diagram of Fig. 8-39.

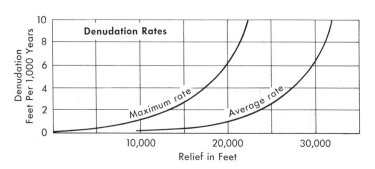

FIG. 8-38   Rates of denudation of land surfaces. (After Schumm, 1963.)

years has been measured to be 48 ft per 1,000 years. This is a region where a thick and extensive ice cap had previously depressed the crust, and the crust is now recovering. Chapters 12 and 21 take up the subject. The Lake Superior region is rising at the rate of 16 ft per 1,000 years for the same reason. Many other examples of rates of uplift are known, and each demands individual consideration, but it is evident that the rates of uplift, for a while at least, are apt to be much greater than the processes of erosion can reduce the uplift. How, then, does erosion operate in the face of uplift, and what kind of erosion forms develop? Obviously this is a complex study, with examples on every hand of varying conditions. We will have to confine our attention to the one example, the

The third uplift was undoubtedly at a slower rate and is estimated at 0.5 ft per 1,000 years. You will have to accept these figures and statements without evidence or explanation for the time being. Later chapters, particularly 15 and 17, will present some of the basic considerations and reasoning. Suffice it to say that the large anticline and marginal faults were formed in the first two uplifts and then the entire Rocky Mountain region was uplifted, to produce the present setting.

Denudation of the Uinta Mountains

Assuming maximum rates of erosion after each uplift (about 3 ft per 1,000 years), it is obvious that the mountain mass rose faster than it was denuded at these times.

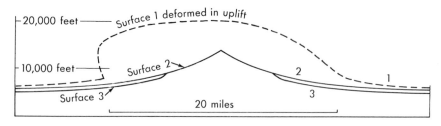

Idealized Erosion Surfaces of Uinta Mountains

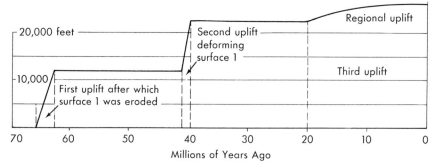

History of Uplifts of Uinta Mountains

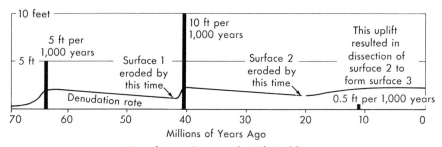

Denudation Compared With Uplifts

FIG. 8-39 Rise of Uinta Mountains anticline and analysis of stages of uplift and stages of denudation. (See Bradley, 1936, and Schumm, 1963.)

This relationship is shown in the lower diagram of Fig. 8-39. Now, the history of the range before and immediately after the first uplift is beyond the scope of the present book, but if we begin with the culmination of the first cycle of erosion in the development of surface 1, then we can proceed with good understanding. The second anticlinal uplift deformed erosion surface 1 approximately as shown in the top diagram. This uplift is estimated to have occurred in the course of about 1 million years at a rate of 10 ft per 1,000 years. Erosion set in at about 3 ft per 1,000

years, but as the relief of the uplift was reduced, the rate of erosion fell off. After about 20 million years the uplift was reduced to surface 2. Assuming that about 7,000 ft of rock was removed from the uplift, the average rate of erosion would then have been about 0.35 ft per 1,000 years, which is just slightly more than the average rate deduced from modern measurements.

The third uplift resulted in rejuvenation of the streams and dissection of valleys in surface 1 about 500 ft deep. The floors of these valleys are labeled surface 3. Erosion below surface 2 has been rather extensive, and the remnants of surface 2 stand very conspicuously as a high erosion surface on either side of the crest of the range. The gradient of the surface and a thin cover of gravel suggest that it developed as a pediment. The gravel contains fossils of Miocene age (Chap. 20).

Suggested Aids

Readings

Bradley, W. H.: *Geomorphology of the North Flank of the Uinta Mountains,* U.S. Geological Survey Professional Paper 185-I, 1936.

Leopold, L. B., and W. B. Langbein: *A Primer on Water,* U.S. Geological Survey Miscellaneous Report, 1960.

————and M. G. Wolman: "River Meanders," *Bulletin of the Geological Society of America,* vol. 71, 1960.

Schumm, S. A.: *Disparity between Present Rates of Denudation and Orogeny,* U.S. Geological Survey Professional Paper 454-H, 1963.

Filmstrip

The Story of Rivers, Encyclopaedia Britannica, FSC-479.

Movies

Work of Rivers, Encyclopaedia Britannica, 16 mm, 15 min.
Understanding our Earth, Planet Earth Series, US-42.

Chapter 9

DEFINITION AND SIGNIFICANCE

Ground water is water that fills, or partially fills, the openings in the rocks below the surface.

There are vast stores of water underground, and now, more than ever before, man is making good use of it. The rapidly growing communities in the arid west are partly or largely dependent on it, and many cities and towns in the more humid parts of the country have found a convenient source of their culinary water in the underground. It has been estimated that much more water is in storage underground than in all the surface reservoirs and lakes, including the Great Lakes. The total usable ground water in the United States is of the order of ten years of annual precipitation. How does water occur below the surface, and how much is available for use in any particular place? Can we consider the underground supply a reservoir that can be

Ground Water

managed like a surface reservoir? These and other questions will be taken up in the following pages.

THE HYDROLOGIC CYCLE

Water that falls to the earth as rain or snow has a varied history. Part of it drains off the surface to form the streams and rivers. This is called *runoff*. Part of it is returned fairly promptly to the atmosphere by *evaporation* or through the agency of plants that lose water to the air through their leaves. This is called *transpiration*. The last part of the water that falls as precipitation seeps into the soil and rocks below to become ground water. Eventually the ground water finds its way back to the surface as springs to become part of the runoff or as seeps into lakes and even into the oceans. The oceans, through evaporation, replenish the moisture in the atmosphere and thus prepare the way for more precipitation on land. This is the *hydrologic cycle*.

Wells that are drilled for oil often tap flows of salt water or brine in porous sandstone. This water has probably been locked up in the pore spaces between the sand grains since the grains originally accumulated, and it is called *connate water*. Connate water is distinguished from the ground water of the hydrologic cycle described above, which is called *meteoric water*. Meteoric water is generally in a state of slow circulation and is fresh unless it has mixed with salty connate water, such as exists in some of the basins of the arid west.

In the chapter on volcanoes we say that the release of water vapor from the magmas is the chief cause of explosive eruptions and that large volumes of such water reach the atmosphere in this way. In most eruptions, it is believed, this water has come from within the earth and has not previously been part of the hydrologic cycle. Such is called *juvenile water*. Much juvenile water is also released by cooling and crystallizing magmas underground.

This water has carried metalliferous compounds gained from the magma upward and has deposited them as minerals in nearby and cooler rocks.

The present chapter will be concerned only with meteoric ground water as part of the hydrologic cycle.

WATER IN THE PORES OF ROCKS

Kinds of Pores

Ground water occurs in the cracks, crevices, and pores of the rocks. All consolidated rocks are riven by joints (Chap. 3), and the amount of water depends on the abundance of the joints and the degree to which they are open. Generally such joints do not provide much room or storage capacity, but the water can move through them fairly well, even if they are only slightly open.

When water moves along joints in limestone it usually dissolves out passage ways of considerable size, sometimes to the extent of large subterranean caves. These will be taken up later.

The chief space for water is in granular aggregates, such as sand and gravel or their cemented equivalents, sandstone and conglomerate. In these rocks from 12 to 45 per cent of the total volume may be pore space. The maximum pore space is present in well-sorted grains, such as shown in Fig. 9-1, top left and right. If small grains are present along with larger ones they will partially fill the voids and reduce the amount of space that water might otherwise occupy (Fig. 9-1, bottom left).

If the grains are bonded together with cement, the pore space is again reduced, so porosity is chiefly a result of the degree of sorting and the extent of cementing (Fig. 9-1, bottom right). Another factor, less easily perceived, is the degree of compaction. For instance, given the same sand, there may exist a loose arrangement with

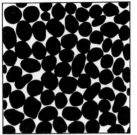

Sand

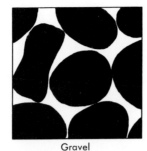

Gravel

Different Size but Each Well Sorted and
of About Equal Porosity

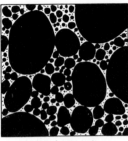

Poorly Sorted,
Low Porosity

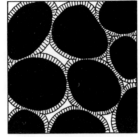

Porosity Decreased
by Cement

FIG. 9-1 Variable porosity in assemblages of rounded grains.

high porosity or a compact arrangement with lower porosity.

Movement of Water through Pores

Porosity is defined as the percentage of pore space in a rock. This, then, is a measure of the water-storage capacity in a rock. Even though all the pores are interconnected and all filled with water, not all the water thus held is available for use; not all can be taken from or will drain out of the rock. For instance, if a piece of porous sandstone is submerged in water, in time the water will penetrate and fill all the connected pores. Now, if the block is taken out of the water and allowed to drain, only a part of the water held in the rock will drain out. The coarser the sandstone, the more water will be lost; the finer, the more will be retained. It is retained as attracted films on the surface of the grains. (they are said to be wetted)

and as filling in the narrow spaces between grains. We have seen water rise in a glass tube with a needle-sized opening and stay there in spite of the pull of gravity downward. The power of small openings to draw a liquid into them is called *capillary attraction.*

Capillary attraction is a very real influence to consider in the movement of water through porous materials. Water will penetrate and moisten a shale or clay, but none of the water will drain out, nor can it be forced out except under high differential pressure. About the same is true with silt and siltstone. But water does move through sand or poorly cemented sandstone, and under a little pressure the flow is appreciable. Since springs and wells are fed by water moving through pores, we are much concerned with the ease or difficulty with which the flow occurs. The measure of the facility of flow through porous rock is called *permeability;* the percentage of pore space is called *porosity.* The capacity to hold water is determined by the rock's porosity, but its capacity to yield water is determined by its permeability.

Commonly, good porosity goes along with good permeability, especially if coarse sediments are involved, but we must appreciate that a rock like pumice or scoria has a high porosity, but poor permeability, because the pores are not connected. Also certain clays have moderately high porosities but very low permeabilities.

If a sandstone, for instance, has a porosity of 20 per cent but will yield only half of this water, then the rock is said to have a *specific yield* of 10 per cent. A specific yield of 10 per cent, however, represents a great volume of available water in storage.

Take, for example, a valley or basin that is 10 miles long and 5 miles wide. It has an area of 50 sq miles. Each square mile has 640 acres, so that we are dealing with an area of 32,000 acres. If the porous sediments are 500 ft thick and have a specific yield of 10 per cent, the available water content should be equivalent to a layer 50 ft thick. Therefore, $50 \times 32,000$ equals 1,600,000 acre-feet of water, or 432,000,000,000 gal. The equation used is

Area in acres × depth of porous alluvium × specific yield × 270,000 (gal per acre-foot) = gallons of available water in storage below the surface

All we need to do is drill wells and pump out the water. We should know a little more about ground water than this, however, before expensive wells are drilled, or before we misuse a valuable natural resource, so that the next paragraphs will concern the features that geologists have found significant.

GROUND WATER IN ROCKS WITHOUT BARRIERS TO MOVEMENT

Ground Water Table

In porous and permeable rocks such that water can move from the surface downward and laterally without restrain other than that imposed by the capillarity of the pores, a certain distribution always occurs. There is the zone immediately below the surface in which the pores are filled with both air and water, and below this is a second zone in which all the pores are completely filled with water. The upper one is called the *zone of aeration* and the lower one the *zone of saturation*. Rain and stream water filters into the soil and downward through the zone of aeration and becomes part of the water of the zone of saturation. See Fig. 9-2. The upper limit of the zone of saturation is the *water table*. If an open hole or well is dug through the zone of aeration into the zone of saturation, such as shown in Fig. 9-2, then the well will fill with water up to the water table. The ground may be moist in the zone of aeration, but the chances are that very little water will ooze out of its pores into the well. On the other hand, the pres-

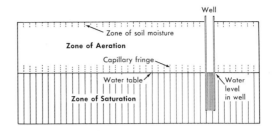

FIG. 9-2 Distribution of ground water in permeable, homogeneous rock or unconsolidated sediment.

sures are hydrostatic in the zone of saturation, and water will flow out of the pores into the well and fill it up to the water table. The water level in a series of wells in an area, in other words, marks the upper limit of the zone of saturation.

In detail we see in places and at times a thin *zone of soil moisture* derived from a recent rain. Any excess water beyond that necessary to fill the small capillary openings will work on down through the zone of aeration. Then there is the *capillary fringe* just above the water table, in which water is drawn up into the capillary openings. See Fig. 9-2 again.

If the water table is studied in a hilly terrane it will rise and fall, reflecting the topography, but in a subdued way. It will rise under the hills, but not so much as the surface, and fall under the valleys. The zone of aeration will be thickest under the hill tops. If a lake exists in a topographic depression, the water table will meet the lake level. See Fig. 9-3. If the water table were below the lake, then the water of the lake would settle through the permeable

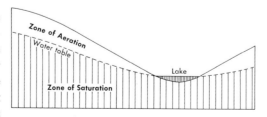

FIG. 9-3 Relation of water table to land surface.

sediments and rocks and become part of the zone of saturation, and the lake would disappear. If, on the other hand, the water table rose, then the lake level would rise. During seasons of high precipitation, the water table rises, and during seasons of low precipitation it falls. This fluctuation is readily observed in wells and is a result of recharge and discharge of the underground reservoir. Before proceeding further, let it be emphasized that ground water flows slowly through the openings in rocks because of the friction between the water particles and the rock surfaces (capillary attraction), and it always moves under the influence of gravity toward the lower area or point of natural or artificial discharge.

Discharge

First, water may be pumped from the reservoir through wells. This is an artificial discharge. Second, the ground water may leak out into stream beds and lakes. Third, the ground water may emerge at the surface as a spring, which, in a homogenous rock, is much the same situation as in the bed of a stream. Fourth, plants with long roots may reach to the zone of saturation and use some of the ground water.

Recharge

The reservoir is recharged by infiltration in general from surface precipitation and from streams. The amount of stream recharge may be measured in some basins by gauging a stream's flow before entering a basin and then by gauging its flow as it leaves the basin across which it flows. If the flow is less upon leaving the basin, then the difference is the amount that has filtered into the rocks or sediments of the basin.

A stream which receives water from the underground and whose flow is increased is said to be *effluent*, whereas one that loses water to the underground is said to be *influent*. See Fig. 9-4.

Recharge may also be figured by recording total rainfall in a watershed and by measuring the runoff, transpiration, and evaporation. Then, by the equation

$$\text{Precipitation} = \text{runoff} + \text{transpiration} + \text{evaporation} + \text{infiltration}$$

the amount of water that seeps into the underground may be calculated. Of course, it is quite a problem to measure transpiration and evaporation, but techniques to do this have been developed.

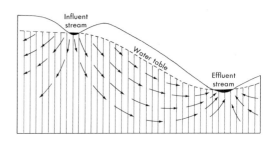

FIG. 9-4   Movement of ground water in permeable homogeneous rock. The stream at higher elevation loses water, and the lower stream gains water. The flow is treated by ground-water specialists mathematically like an electric current. Permeability is like resistance, and gradient is like voltage.

It should now become evident that a ground water reservoir may be managed like a surface reservoir if the geological framework of the reservoir is understood and all the aspects of recharge and discharge are known. For instance, consider a surface reservoir. We determine its size or capacity, we measure the water that the stream brings into it, and we compute the increase in storage as the surface of the reservoir water rises. Finally, the level reaches the spillway, and water overflows and is lost. Only that which is held back of the dam remains to be used. Likewise we assess the capacity of the underground reservoir; we measure the recharge and watch the water level rise. Finally we see springs start up and streams enlarge or dry stream beds start to flow water. This is the overflow that is the equivalent of the water in the dam that goes over the spillway and is lost.

Now, in the case of the dam, if it only took one year to fill to overflowing, we would judge that we could use all the water, say for summer irrigation, and that the supply would be replenished during the fall, winter, and spring. However, if it took five years to fill the reservoir, then we had probably better use only one-fifth of its capacity in one year; otherwise it would not fill up in the next year. Likewise with underground reservoirs, we should not take out each year more than nature puts back in during the following year. But we do not know right off how long it took nature to fill up the underground reservoir. If, however, the water table does not return to its former elevation, then more water has been pumped out than has been put in. It may be possible in this event to augment the recharge. This again takes a professional geological knowledge of the basin, the recharge area, and the management of runoff.

Considerable water is added to the underground by irrigation, because more water is generally applied to the soil than is needed to meet the demands of evaporation and crop growth. This is necessary to keep the soil flushed of salts that would otherwise accumulate, especially if the irrigation water were slightly saline. The "excess irrigation water" seeps downward to the water table and adds to the supply there.

In the impounding of water back of dams, considerable surface water may be fed into the underground, and in certain dams this has been deliberately planned. In others, without planning and careful geological work beforehand, most of the water has disappeared into the underground, and the surface storage facility has been a failure. This happens particularly in cavernous limestone regions.

The Water Supply Papers of the U.S. Geological Survey are the great store of information on the principles of ground water occurrence and the many ground water regions of the country, and should be referred to for information about your local ground water conditions, and particularly about recharge.

Effect of Well on Water Table

If a well is pumped heavily the water table is drawn down around it in the shape of a cone. The *drawdown* is called the *cone of depression*. See Fig. 9-5. If now, for

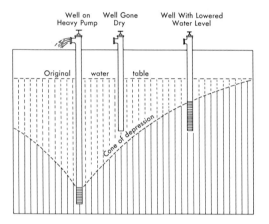

FIG. 9-5 Cone of depression.

instance, a city or industrial plant has a well with a wide-diameter casing, such that a large flow can be pumped from it, and if the well is pumped heavily, the cone of depression of the water table in time will spread hundreds of feet away from the well. Perhaps the area affected will be a mile in diameter, with the big well in the center. Now, other wells around will be affected. All wells within the cone of depression will experience a lowering of the water level in them, and possibly in some of the shallow wells the water table will drop below their bottoms. In this event they will have gone dry. See Fig. 9-5 again. This situation is a common cause of law suits. Since ground water moves and is not fixed in place like a mineral deposit, who owns it? Various interpretations have been made in the courts, but basic to any worthwhile settlement is an understanding of the geology and hydrology of ground water. One of the best services of a geologist is to prepare charts and diagrams so that judges, attorneys, city fathers, and businessmen can be brought to understand the facts of ground water occurrence and the special geological conditions that exist in each particular area at point.

GROUND WATER IN STRATIFIED ROCKS

Pervious and Impervious Beds

So far ground water has been considered in rock bodies that are homogeneous as far as porosity and permeability are concerned. When, however, ground water in sedimentary rocks is investigated, we deal with some beds that are pervious and transmit water freely and some that are impervious and serve as barriers to movement. Sand and sandstone beds are generally good carriers of water, but clay and shale are barriers to flow. When a sandstone bed, for instance, is underlain and overlain by a shale bed then it is clear that we have to deal with *confined water*, much like in a conduit. When confined, hydrostatic pressures may build up and cause some surprising conditions, as we shall see presently.

A stratum that transmits ground water

well, that is, has sufficient permeability to pass commercially valuable amounts of water through it, is called an *aquifer*. A bed that prevents the flow of ground water through or across it is called an *aquiclude*. Since sediments and sedimentary rocks are extremely variable in permeability, it follows that there are many variations between very permeable aquifers and completely impervious aquicludes. Not only is the permeability of a bed above or below different, but the permeability of a given bed may change from place to place. Considering these conditions and also that sedimentary rocks are in places tilted, folded, and faulted, we can see that nature has fashioned some rather complex "plumbing systems."

Artesian Pressure

Let us take a structure consisting of inclined pervious and impervious beds cropping out at the surface, as shown in Fig. 9-6. The sandstone bed is assumed to be a good aquifer between two shale beds or aquicludes. Streams draining from the mountainous area on the left flow across the beveled edge of the sandstone bed, and considerable water filters into it. This is the recharge area. If wells are drilled into the sandstone bed such as shown, we find that water will rise in them above the sandstone bed. This is due to the fact that the water is confined in the sandstone and under pressure. The well serves as one arm of a U tube and the sandstone bed, from

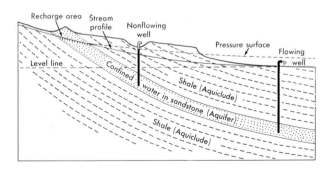

FIG. 9-6 Structural and hydrological conditions necessary for a flowing well. The nonflowing well, as pictured, is not in the main valley labeled "Stream profile," but some distance away in a tributary valley.

the surface down to the well, as the other. This illustrates the well-known principle that water in a U tube seeks a common level on both sides.

Water that rises in a well above the aquifer from which it comes is called artesian. If it rises to the land surface where the well is drilled, as it does in a good many places, then a flowing well exists. In Fig. 9-6, one well flows and one well does not, but both are artesian wells.

If the pressure is gauged in artesian wells in a certain area, or in other words if the level is noted to which the water rises in the well, then we have defined the artesian *pressure surface*. Where the pressure surface is above the land surface, flowing wells will occur, but where it is below the land surface, the wells will be nonflowing. The artesian pressures in wells in a basin can be contoured in the same manner as a land surface is contoured, and an area-wide map is at hand, not merely a cross section, as in Fig. 9-6. With such a map the level to which water will rise in a new well to be drilled anywhere in the area can be determined.

Now, the pressure surface is not a level one. If there were no resistance to flow through the pores of the aquifer and if there were no leaks in the underground plumbing system, then the pressure surface would be horizontal. Since both these factors are very real, the pressure surface is a sloping one away from the recharge area. Its gradient varies from basin to basin, and also it changes as water is artificially withdrawn from the aquifer.

Nature works out a balance of recharge and discharge in these confined water systems, but man upsets the balance by adding new discharge in the form of wells. If more water is withdrawn than is recharged, then the pressure surface falls, and where it falls below the land surface, the wells cease to flow. They must then be put on pump. This is a common story in many of our artesian basins. It is possible that recharge increases as the pres-

sure surface drops and that with a steady rate of discharge a new but lower surface will become established. However, if the pressure surface continues to drop, the users of ground water in the area are due for a shortage eventually.

ADVANTAGES OF GROUND WATER OVER SURFACE WATER

Now that the main elements of ground water occurrence are understood, it may be emphasized that certain advantages accrue to the users of ground water over surface water. These are as follows:

✦ Ground water may be reached within a few hundred feet of the place where it is used, and on the same property, whereas surface water may require pipelines and rights-of-way over stretches of several miles.

✦ Ground water may be available for use in areas where the water in streams and lakes has already been appropriated by other users.

✦ Yield from wells and springs generally fluctuates less than stream flow in alternating wet and dry periods.

✦ Ground water is more uniform in temperature and soluble mineral load than surface water and is generally free of turbidity and pollution by pathologic organisms. Commonly the ground water is cold and clear.

✦ There is little or no evaporation loss from underground reservoirs, whereas surface reservoirs lose a tremendous amount in arid regions.

✦ Underground reservoirs are ready-made.

On the other side of the ledger, however, it must be said that many ground waters are rather hard, and need to be run through softening plants before the water is suitable for culinary use, particularly for washing purposes.

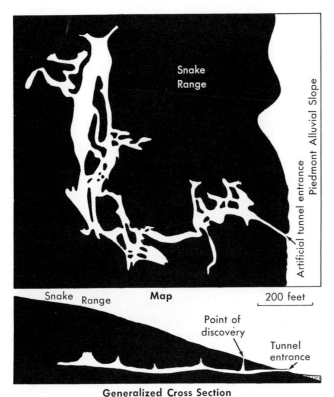

Snake
Range

Piedmont Alluvial Slope

Artificial tunnel entrance

Map

200 feet

Snake Range

Generalized Cross Section

Point of discovery

Tunnel entrance

FIG. 9-7   Lehman Caves, Nevada. The large north-south caverns are dissolved out of badly shattered limestone along faults.

GROUND WATER IN CARBONATE ROCKS

Solution Effects

The regimen of ground water in limestone and dolomite terranes is somewhat unusual and needs special consideration. This is because the carbonate rocks are fairly soluble in water charged with carbon dioxide. It has been pointed out in Chap. 7 that carbon dioxide gas gets into the ground water chiefly as rain water passes through the soil where plants are decaying. Then as the water continues downward through the joints in the limestone and dolomite it dissolves away the surfaces along which it passes and creates irregular passage ways. Circulation follows the joints that cut across beds and along bedding surfaces between beds. The rock may be badly broken or shattered along a fault, and this zone particularly would be one of circulation and con-

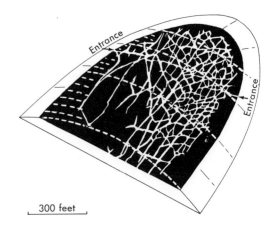

Entrance

Entrance

300 feet

FIG. 9-8   Cavernous system in limestone developed by solution along intersecting sets of joints. Part of Cameron Cave, Missouri. The level of the cave system is midway up a hill. *(After Bretz, Caves of Missouri, 1956.)*

sequently of solution. In time, cavernous openings are dissolved out of the rock, some of considerable height and some of long and devious horizontal extent. Some of the cavernous passages are large and continuous enough to conduct streams of water that can truly be called underground rivers. In the Ozark Mountains of Missouri and in parts of the Allegheny Plateau and Appalachian Mountains certain rivers flow into the underground and others emerge from it.

Limestone Caves

Most caves are in limestone and there are literally thousands of them in the United States. Among a few well-known ones that might be listed are the Mammoth Cave of Kentucky, the Shenandoah Caverns of Virginia, the Carlsbad Caverns of New Mexico, and the Lehman Cave of Nevada. The only other kind of natural cave of significance is the tubular opening that develops in some basalt flows, previously described.

Limestone caves may develop as single- or multiple-story structures. The plan of a single-level one may show a long winding and branching opening with enlarged chambers along it (Fig. 9-7) or a maze of openings controlled by intersecting sets of joints (Fig. 9-8). Where solution ways are developed on several levels, then vertical or near-vertical shafts connect the levels. In mountainous regions where thick limestone formations occur, the solution channels may have more of a vertical direction than horizontal. There are three main levels in the Carlsbad Caverns so far explored, and these extend to 1,320 ft below the surface. Several caves in the Rocky Mountains

FIG. 9-9 Poorly drained area with many swamps and lakes (dark) between grass lands (light) in Orange County, Florida. The depressions may be in part due to the solution of limestone by waters seeping into the underground. *(Courtesy of W. W. Doeringsfeld, Jr.)*

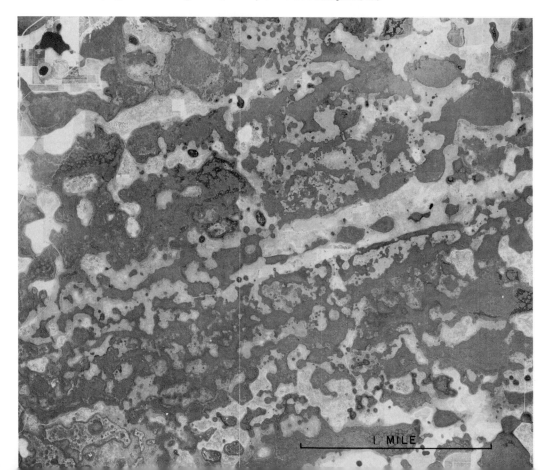

FIG. 9-10 Meramec Caverns, Franklin County, Missouri, showing profusion of stalactites. *(Courtesy of Massie-Missouri Commerce.)*

FIG. 9-11 Stalactites and stalagmites in Lehman Cave, Nevada.

are known to extend to depths greater than 1,000 ft. Certain individuals find it exhilarating and fascinating to explore and map caves, and they are called speleologists. They are generally more interested in the techniques of descent, ascent, mapping, and survival than in the geological aspects.

Karst Topography

A limestone terrane (the Karst region) in Yugoslavia is pitted with depressions that drink up all the precipitation. These are solution and caved structures that lead downward into systems of solution channels like those shown in Fig. 9-8. These pits are called sink holes. In wet seasons small ponds may exist in their bottoms, and in dry seasons the pond water flows away underground. Many of the sink holes are the result of roof falls of underground chambers. Eventually the caving of the roof rock reaches to the surface, and a pit with broken rock in its bottom results. A landscape pitted with sink holes is said to have a *karst* topography. There are a number of such areas in the United States, especially in Florida, southern Indiana, Kentucky, and Missouri. Figure 9-9 is a photograph of a karst region.

Depositional Forms

It seems that caves in limestone are no sooner dissolved out than the chemical process is reversed and calcium carbonate is precipitated. The depositional forms are some of nature's fancy work, but in total, they contrive to fill up the cave openings. What causes the drastic change?

The change from solution to precipitation of calcium carbonate is now known to be caused by a lowering of the water table. The main solution process occurs in the zone of saturation, where the openings are filled with water. Solution etchings are just as pronounced on the ceilings as on the floors of some caves, because the en-

FIG. 9-12 Bridal Cave, Camden County, Missouri, showing principally stalagmites. (Courtesy of Massie-Missouri Commerce.)

internal tube through which the drip water flows, but some water may run down the outside as well. They are called *stalactites*. See Figs. 9-10 and 9-11.

The water that falls from the ends of the stalactites builds mounds on the floor. These are generally stockier than the stalactites and are slightly cupped at the top. They grow by accretion of layers of $CaCO_3$ on their surfaces, where the drip water splashes and runs. They are called *stalagmites*. See Figs. 9-12 and 9-13. Stalactites and stalagmites grow in a great variety of forms and sizes. If, by chance, a stalactite and its complementary stalagmite grow until they meet, the resulting form is called a *column*, (Fig. 9-14).

Water running out of cracks sometimes builds fluted forms called *draperies* (Figs. 9-15 and 9-16). On inclined slopes various

tire passage way or chamber was full of water when the solution was occurring. Now, with a lowering of the water table, some or even all of the solution channels come to be in the zone of aeration and are therefore drained of most of their water. Only that water which seeps from the surface downward and passes through the zone of aeration drips into the caves, generally entering from the roof. With air in the caverns, and generally circulating a little, the dripping water looses some of its carbon dioxide, and some of it evaporates, and consequently calcium carbonate is precipitated. Considerable water runs as thin sheets or films down the walls and is thus particularly susceptible to evaporation and loss of CO_2

Two principal deposits form as a result of dripping. Iciclelike forms grow downward from the ceilings. They maintain an

FIG. 9-13 River Cave, Camden County, Missouri, showing giant stalagmite. (Courtesy of Massie-Missouri Commerce.)

FIG. 9-14   Columns in Lehman Cave, Nevada.

calcium carbonate dams are built that retain beautiful pools of water back of them. This produces a terraced affect (Fig. 9-17). Nearly every cave has unique forms, and many people are fascinated by the end-less variety of depositional forms and see in them such varied things as heads, faces, dogs, broncos, deer antlers, cathedrals, queens, angels, cowboys, and other strange phenomena.

FIG. 9-15   Draperies in Lehman Cave, Nevada.

FIG. 9-16   Peculiar drip and flow stone deposit in Lehman Cave, Nevada.

FIG. 9-17   Onadaga Cave, Crawford County, Missouri, showing particularly beautiful terraced pools. *(Courtesy of Massie-Missouri Commerce.)*

SPRINGS AND SEEPS

Causes

Ground water finds natural outlet to the surface in several basic geologic settings. Examine Fig. 9-18. In unconsolidated sediments a typical situation is provided by an impervious clay overlain by a pervious sand or gravel deposit, with each cropping out on a hill side (Fig. 9-18, top). In consolidated rocks the setting might be such that a pervious bed of sandstone or limestone conducts water from a higher place of intake to a lower place of discharge (Fig. 9-18, second from top).

Faulting produces shatter zones in the rock, and if confined water, such as in (Fig. 9-18, third from top) is tapped by the shatter zone, the water will rise to the surface. Some faults are marked by a series of springs along them. Large faults that cut deeply into the crust sometimes bring hot mineral waters to the surface, part of which may be juvenile (Fig. 9-19).

The Snake River in southern Idaho has cut a valley through lava flows, as illustrated in (Fig. 9-18, bottom). The basal part of some flows is porous and conducts the water from mountain streams, from canal water used for irrigation, and from direct precipitation freely to the Snake

River valley wall. Along a certain stretch of the valley wall the water gushes out in what is called "Thousand Springs," and the flow has been gauged at 600 cu ft per sec (Fig. 9-20).

Deposits

Springs that issue from limestone formations are heavily charged with calcium carbonate, part of which is promptly dropped where the spring emerges. This builds sizable, and in places picturesque, deposits called travertine (Fig. 9-21). The term is particularly appropriate to those deposits which are quarried and used as building stone. Travertine is usually a porous rock, cuts easily, and has a soft cream, tan, or rusty color. The ancient coloseum in Rome is built of a travertine that was quarried nearby. It is a very popular interior decoration stone in public and industrial buildings today.

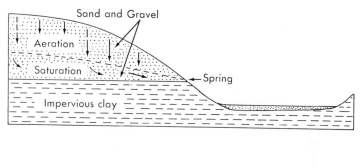

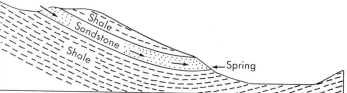

FIG. 9-18 Typical geologic settings in which springs occur.

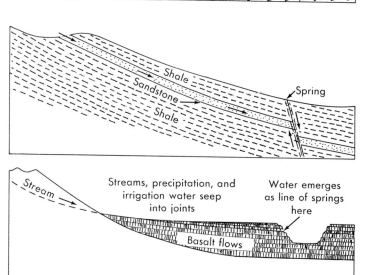

FIG. 9-19 Spring on left side of Hoback River, Wyoming, discharging hydrogen sulfide gas and colloidal sulphur into river water.

EXAMPLES OF GROUND WATER OCCURRENCE

Alluvial Fans

Much ground water is obtained from alluvial fans in eastern California, Nevada, Utah, Arizona, and New Mexico. The setting of an alluvial-fan piedmont is depicted in Fig. 8-32. The idealized structure of an alluvial fan is given in Fig. 9-22, and the position of confined water in the coarse and porous wedges noted. The water table will be deep in the upper part of the fan, and drilling and pumping costs too high to be profitable. The intermediate slopes will be those under which confined water will exist, and here the wells will have artesian pressures. Some of the wells may flow. Farther out in the valley the sediments are too fine and the permeability too low to make good wells. Nearly every alluvial-fan piedmont at the foot of a high mountain range has a zone of flowing wells. Owens Valley at the east foot of the Sierra Nevada is a notable example of the yield of

FIG. 9-20 View of some of the springs of Thousand Springs and collecting canal on the valley wall of the Snake River Canyon, near Twin Falls, Idaho.

FIG. 9-21   Travertine spring deposit at Thermopolis, Wyoming.

large quantities of cold, clear, and potable water. Much of it is piped in aqueducts to Los Angeles and the surrounding area.

Glacial Deposits

Many of the cities, villages, and farms of the Great Lakes States are supplied in part or whole by well water from glacial deposits. These will be studied in a later chapter, but suffice it to say that they are unconsolidated sands, gravels, boulderclay, and clay deposits in an array of forms and arrangements. Some of the porous material was deposited along lake shores, some exists as outwash sheets, and others as river channel sands. See Fig. 9-23. Some water is confined and rises in the wells, but generally the wells must be pumped. Some yield excellent flows without much drawdown of the pressure surface. Wells in other places may not penetrate very porous material, and the yield is small.

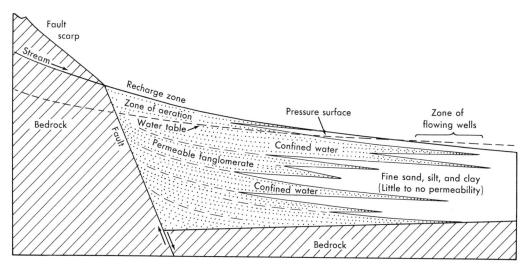

FIG. 9-22   Idealized structure of alluvial fan and distribution of ground water in it. The fan here is built on the downfaulted block, and the sediments have been derived by erosion of the upfaulted block.

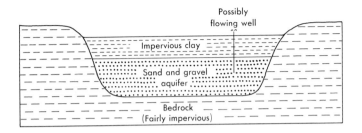

FIG. 9-23 An old filled river valley and the conditions necessary for artesian or flowing wells.

Sandstone Aquifers

The Great Plains of South Dakota, east of the Black Hills, has been one of the most prolific flowing-well regions on the continent. The Dakota sandstone is upturned along the east front of the Black Hills but flattens out under the Plains. It is overlain and underlain by impervious shales and hence serves as an aquifer to conduct water many miles to the east. Probably the

was a critical situation for the farmers, but what could be done? The U.S. Geological Survey made a thorough study of the geology and water wells and instituted a program of controls with implemented recharge, but reservoir pressures have not increased much to date. It is an example of wasteful use of a great natural reservoir that might have been better managed. The moral is, except for very pressing and expedient reasons, more water should not be

FIG. 9-24 The Great Plains east of the Black Hills and an example of a sandstone aquifer and flowing wells.

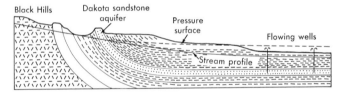

sandstone becomes silty and impervious toward its easternmost extent, and hence the confined water in it is sealed off. See Fig. 9-24. Streams draining from the Black Hills flow across the bevelled edges of the sandstone and supply it with water. In the early farming and ranching days wells drilled into the sandstone spouted over 100 ft in the air. Many of them were left open and flowed continuously, forming small lakes in low areas around. After a few years the pressures began to drop, and eventually many wells ceased to flow. This

taken from an underground reservoir than nature, with our help, perhaps, can put in.

Coastal Plains

The Atlantic and Gulf Coastal Plains constitute the most productive ground water province in the United States. This is the margin of the continent over which the Atlantic Ocean and Gulf of Mexico have spread and, with fluctuations, have gradually withdrawn, leaving bottom deposits as a testament. The deposits consist of

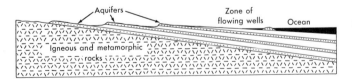

FIG. 9-25 Idealized section of Atlantic Coastal Plain showing ground-water conditions.

FIG. 9-26 Old Faithful in eruption, Yellowstone National Park.

sand, silt, clay, and limestone, and only the limestone is consolidated. The beds dip gently toward the ocean, as shown in Fig. 9-25, and because of the favorable structure of coastward-dipping permeable sand and limestone beds alternating with aquicludes of clays and marls, artesian conditions prevail throughout most of the vast region. Flowing wells can be obtained almost everywhere along the coast and in the valleys extending back from it. Since the sediments were deposited in sea water they were originally charged with salt water, but following the retreat of the seas

much rain has fallen on the sediments during the last era of geologic time, and they have been flushed fairly well of any salt water. Only in a few places is somewhat salty water found. Heavy pumping of wells could bring salt water up the aquifer.

The Tamiami limestone of southeastern Florida, part of the Coastal Plain sediments, is the most permeable aquifer ever investigated by the U.S Geological Survey, and the Edwards limestone of Texas supplies the largest known flowing well in the world at San Antonio, yielding nearly 25 million gal per day.

FIG. 9-27 Geyserite deposits around geyser and hot springs in Upper Geyser Basin, Yellowstone National Park.

LEGAL ASPECTS OF GROUND WATER USE

Since ground water is mobile and can be drawn from beneath one person's property by wells in an adjacent person's property, it is easy to see that lawsuits can result. More basically, the intimate relation of surface waters to ground waters makes it necessary to consider both in adjudicating the rights of the owners of each. Many court decisions have been based on erroneous concepts or a lack of understanding of ground water, and hence much confusion exists in the laws pertaining to rights and ownership.

Some states have made significant advances in determining rules and administering them in the management of ground water reservoirs, and this has come by the recognition of the courts of the work and understanding of geologists and engineers on the specific reservoirs in question.

GEYSERS IN VOLCANIC REGIONS

Geysers are hot water springs that erupt by the blowing off of steam. They are really rare in occurrence, but because of their attractive character in Yellowstone National Park most people are aware of them. They occur in Iceland and New Zealand in lesser number and in milder eruptive form but are practically wanting elsewhere. Some erupt mildly every few seconds or minutes, others jet water and steam over a hundred feet skyward regularly every hour or so, and others burst into activity at irregular and longer intervals. They all occur in volcanic regions, and it is clear that the heat that turns the water to steam is from the still hot volcanic rocks.

The prerequisites for geyser eruption are first, ground water circulating in the openings of heated volcanic rocks and, second, a narrow irregular conduit to the surface. The rocks must be hot enough to turn the water to steam even under pressure of a column of water over a hundred feet long. The vent to the surface must be so narrow, so crooked, or so restricted in places that convection circulation cannot take place and bring the heated water to the surface. Under these conditions the water at depth will reach the boiling temperature before the water in the upper part of the conduit does, and when this occurs, the column of water is lifted, water spills over at the surface, the pressure is lessened on the water at the boiling temperature below (perhaps even superheated), and the geyser springs into a major eruption. See Fig. 9-26.

The geysers and associated hot springs of Yellowstone National Park build cones and terraced deposits around their orifices, but the material is not travertine ($CaCO_3$), but *geyserite*, composed of silica (SiO_2). Chemical studies have demonstrated that meteoric waters percolating through the volcanic rocks in Yellowstone National Park become alkaline or basic and in such condition take up appreciable silica in solution. Then, when they cool upon reaching the surface, the silica is dropped as a spongy amorphous material. See Fig. 9-27.

Suggested Aids

Readings

Sayre, A. N.: "Ground Water," *Scientific American*, November, 1950.

Tolman, C. F.: *Ground Water*, McGraw-Hill Book Company, Inc., New York, 1937.

Filmstrip

The Story of Underground Water, Encyclopaedia Britannica, FSC-480.

Chapter 10

WAVES AS A GEOLOGIC AGENT

Accomplishments

The waves of the oceans and lakes are the fundamental force operative along shores and they expend a tremendous energy in eroding, transporting, depositing, and in general, fashioning the exquisite scenery of our lake shores and ocean coast lines. Beaches often change rapidly. Extensive sand deposits are there one season and gone the next. Beaches change so rapidly that maps of one decade are of little use the next. Man's efforts to stay the effects of the waves on certain shores have been inconsequential.

The short-time changes are conspicuous, but if a long-time view is taken, we perceive a profound remaking of the shore topography, and this will be the theme of our study in the present chapter.

Shore Processes
and Forms

Definitions

At this point it might be well to define a few terms. By *beach* is meant the loose material upon which the waves play. The zone extends from the upper limit of storm wave wash on land to a point seaward under water to a depth where the waves have little or no effect on loose particles. On small lakes this depth is a few feet, whereas along ocean shore lines it may be 50 to 100 ft.

By *coast* is meant the general terrane landward of the ocean and includes the vegetation, climate, topographic features, and any human culture related to the water body. Coast is generally not used in connection with lakes.

Shore, like coast, is a general term for the belt of land bordering on the water body, and it has applicability to both lakes and oceans. Some writers limit shore to the zone between low tide and the upper reach of storm waves.

Shore line is the line, as nearly as it can be defined, between water and land.

FACTORS AFFECTING THE BEACH

The type of coastal features in any place, with emphasis on the beach, depends on four factors:

✦ The *waves*, their size, their direction of impact on the shore, and the frequency of storms.

✦ The *tides*. A beach with a constant sea level (tideless) and with the expenditure of wave energy within the range of normal and storm activity will have characteristics different from one in which the water falls, say 20 to 40 ft twice a day. Also tides are conducive to currents in certain inlets and estuaries that help shape the beach features.

✦ The *topography* of the coast upon which the waves and currents come to act. There are several basic kinds of coast

topography, and the waves and currents develop different features on each in their erosional, transportational, and depositional activity.

✦ The *material* of the coast upon which the waves spend their energy. It is quite a different matter if the waves work on a loose sand and gravel deposit on the one hand and on a mass of granite on the other.

WAVES AND THEIR ACTIVITY

Wave Form

Waves in the open water are oscillatory and represent a transfer of form but not mass. This means that, as a wave sweeps

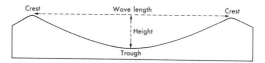

FIG. 10-1 Parts of wave.

by, there is no rush of water but simply a passage of form. If you are in a small boat on a lake, say where 2-ft waves are rolling, your boat will simply rise and fall as each crest and trough passes.

The ideal wave is symmetrical, and its parts are called the *crest* and the *trough*. The distance from successive crest to crest is a wave length, and the vertical distance from trough to crest is the wave height. See Fig. 10-1.

The period is the time taken for the wave form to move the distance of one wave length. In deep water the wave length, velocity, and period are related by the simple equation $L = VP$, where L is the length, V is the velocity, and P is the period. For any one velocity in deep water (deeper than ½ wave length) there is only one appropriate wave length and period. If the period, therefore, is measured, which can be done easily, the wave length and velocity can be obtained. On the other hand, length and velocity cannot be measured easily in the open sea. Velocity and length are related by the formula $V = \sqrt{gL/2\pi}$, where g is the force of gravity. The relation of wave length in feet to the period in seconds is shown by the formula $L = 5.12P^2$. The height of the wave is not considered in these formulas, but it can be shown that height to length (H/L) does not effect the velocity much. Even the steepest waves travel only 10 per cent faster than the low waves.[1]

When the height of a wave becomes greater than 1/7 of the length, then the

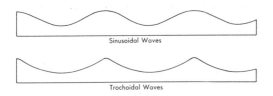

Sinusoidal Waves

Trochoidal Waves

FIG. 10-2 Ideal wave forms.

wave becomes unstable and breaks, but this condition is rarely reached in nature, for a steep wave in the open ocean is 10 ft high and 184 ft long. This has an H/L ratio of 1/18.

The ideal wave, perhaps only theoretically possible, is either sinusoidal or trochoidal. See Fig. 10-2. The sinusoidal form has equal curvature in the crest and trough, whereas the trochoidal has sharper crest and flatter trough and is a "curve swept by a point within a circle which is rolled along a straight line."[2]

Waves in the open sea are more complex than the ideal waves, especially in the area where they are being generated by the wind. It is the frictional drag of the wind over the water surface that creates the waves, and part of the wind energy is im-

parted to the waves. In this generating area a number of wave systems are generally superimposed on one another, not only of different lengths but of different directions, and this gives the water surface a most confused appearance. It is an area known as the *sea* to mariners, but as the waves move out of this area into one of relative calm they resolve into *swell*. Here the pattern and form assume some measure of order. The shorter waves have been left behind, and we have to deal with regular, long-crested waves.

Pyramidal or short-crested waves are common in a sea, and their cause as well as that of deep troughs is depicted in Fig. 10-3. Here two wave trains traveling in slightly different directions are superimposed. They determine a pattern of zones of amplified waves with short but high crests and basinlike deep troughs, as well as zones where crest has canceled trough. Visualization of this situation, plus the addition of other wave trains, will lead to the understanding of the complexity of waves in the area of generation and shifting winds.

Water Particle Movement

As the wave form passes by, what motion does each water particle describe? In the ideal wave, such as described above, the water particles follow the paths of orbits that are nearly circular. By reference to Fig. 10-4 it can be seen how a wave form is transmitted while adjacent water particles move in circular orbits. The crest of the wave moves ahead as each succeeding water particle rises to the top of its orbit. Each particle at the surface completes one orbit during the wave period. Also the diameter of the orbit is equal to the height of the wave.

Beneath the surface the orbits decrease in diameter progressively downward. For every 1/9 of the wave length the orbit in depth is halved. For practical purposes, therefore, the water can be considered still

[1] C. A. M. King, *Beaches and Coasts*, Edward Arnold (Publishers) Ltd., London, 1959.
[2] *Ibid.*

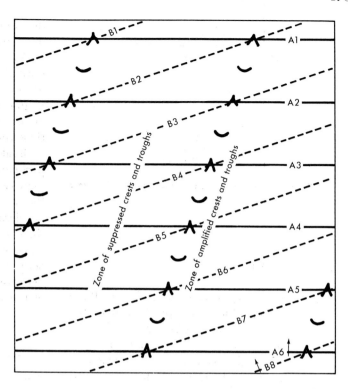

FIG. 10-3 Two interfering trains of waves, A and B. The crest of each wave is numbered. Where the crests are superimposed, the greatest height will obtain (∧); where the troughs are superimposed, the greatest depressions will be formed (∪). Elsewhere, where trough intersects crest, the two will nullify each other. (After C. A. M. King, Beaches and Coasts, E. Arnold, 1959.)

at a depth equal to about ½ the wave length.

The drag of the wind on the water surface causes the water particles to advance slightly in the direction of wave advance, and the circles are said to be open. See Fig. 10-5. This amounts to a slight forward movement of the water, which is known as *mass transport*. Such slow movement of the surface layer is more significant in high waves than in low and results in the piling up of water on certain leeward shores during wind storms and the complementary return of water as a bottom current. An easterly wind on Lake Erie may cause a 4-ft rise of the lake at the west end, and likewise a strong northwesterly wind over Great Salt Lake will cause the level on the southeast end to rise about 2 ft. Combinations of running waves, wind, and tide all working strongly together cause the disastrous high-water storms that irregularly strike certain coasts.

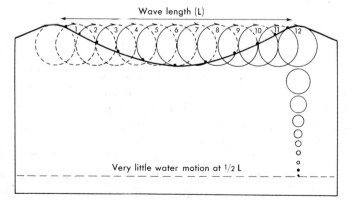

FIG. 10-4 Particle motion as wave form passes from left to right.

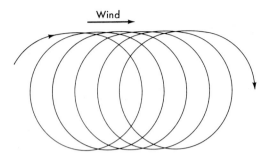

FIG. 10-5 Open circles and mass transfer of surface water.

Size of Waves

The size of waves depends on three factors: first, the wind speed; second, the wind duration; and third, the fetch. The fetch is the length of the body of water over which the wind blows. For instance, no matter how hard or how long the wind blows, if the fetch is short, large waves cannot develop.

As the waves move from sea to swell, the height decreases, the sharp crests of the storm area change to rounded, and the wave length increases. The swell becomes almost sinusoidal. Although the waves are said to decay as they travel away from the storm, they transmit great energy long distances and, as they approach a shore, become the dominant, and sometimes very destructive, waves.

Changes in Shallow Water

Length, Height, and Steepness. As waves run into shallow water, as depicted in the top diagram of Fig. 10-6, two changes occur. The wave length becomes shorter, and the height increases. Wave shortening begins when the depth to bottom equals ½ wave length (wave length as measured in the deep water). By the time the depth is 1/20 of an original wave length, the wave has shortened to ½ of what it was. See Fig. 10-7. The period, however, remains

the same. This means that the velocity of the wave motion decreases.

Wave height does not start to increase until the depth of water is about 1/20 of an original wave length; thereafter the height and the sharpness of the crest increase rapidly (Fig. 10-7). At the same time the trough becomes flatter.

Breakers. The orbital paths of the water particles become open ellipses as the height increases, with the long axes horizontal. In the sharp crest there is a rapid landward acceleration, while under the flat trough there is a retarded seaward movement. A wave will break when the increasing velocity of the water at the crest exceeds the decreased velocity of wave form. The top of the wave falls forward in a picturesque

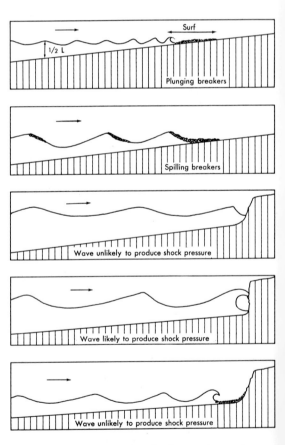

FIG. 10-6 Waves transgressing the shore under varying conditions. *(Partly after King, 1959.)*

circle without enough water to make up the central part, and the wave collapses, or is said to break. Refer to top diagram of Fig. 10-6 again, and to Fig. 10-8. Breaking will occur when the wave height is a little less than the depth to bottom.

There are two types of breakers: the *plunging* and the *spilling*. The type just depicted, in which the crest describes an arc while falling forward and enclosing a pocket of air, is the plunging breaker. It occurs when a fairly low wave approaches

creases in height until it becomes swash on the beach. Such waves are often fairly steep in deep water and advance over a gently sloping, usually sandy beach. It is these waves that produce several rows of breakers advancing shoreward simultaneously. These are the surf waves down the advancing front of which the surf board riders glide. The best place for surf waves on Waikiki Beach, Honolulu, is where the water shoals over a coral reef about a half mile from shore. The waves increase in

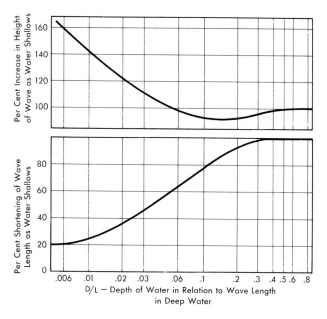

FIG. 10-7   Increase in wave height and decrease in wave length as the wave moves into water less than one half-wave length in depth. *(After C. A. M. King, Beaches and coasts, E. Arnold, 1959.)*

a steep beach. The form of the wave is entirely lost upon breaking, and the energy is converted into a current of tumbling water that rushes up on the sandy beach. This is called the *swash*. The falling of the breaker water and the swash sweep the bottom sand up the beach 10 to 40 ft, depending on the size of the breaker. With the return runoff or backwash the sand is carried downslope, only to be caught up in a new breaker swash.

The spilling breaker advances with a foaming or tumbling crest. The wave does not lose its identity but gradually de-

height upon approaching the reef area, and it is here that the surf riders rendezvous to catch a wave for the ride in. The waves on occasion may reach heights of 30 ft. At first, the wave is steep-fronted and generally glisteningly smooth; then as it rolls shoreward its crest begins to foam, first here and then there, and the surf rider steers obliquely down the front to avoid the foam. The crest actually plunges somewhat at times, but the wave holds its identity and rolls on in. If he is caught in too much foam he usually capsizes. If successful he rides the wave to within 100 ft or

FIG. 10-8 Plunging breaker and swash on Waikiki Beach, Hawaii.

so of shore. The wave decreases in height from the time that the foaming starts until it is a mere 4 or 5 ft high when the rider abandons it, or vice versa. The spilling represents a loss of the wave's energy, and hence the decrease in height. Finally, within 20 ft or so of shore, the wave may finally dissipate in a small plunging breaker.

Breaking on Walls and Cliffs. Under the right conditions storm waves impacting on cliff faces produce what is called *shock pressure*. Three variations of waves impinging against steep faces are shown in Fig. 10-6. The central sketch shows a large plunging breaker enclosing a pocket of air against a cliff face. Undercut cliffs with caves provide a very favorable situation for the compressing of a pocket of air. The force will be approximately proportional to the wave velocity where the wave breaks, and thus the enclosed air becomes compressed considerably. The water, air, and spray are driven into the cracks and joints repeatedly, leading to considerable damage. In the case of abutments or breakwaters, the depth of water should be controlled so as to cause the wave to break before striking the structure, if possible. This is one of the ways in which the waves erode hard rock in places along steep shores.

Refraction. The energy that waves spend in eroding shores is attenuated in some places and concentrated in others. Oncoming waves at right angles to the general shore line are shown in Fig. 10-9. They bend around the headlands and drape shoreward around the bay. The headland, therefore, gets a concentrated beating, whereas the bay receives the effect of stretched or weakened waves. The bending of the waves as they run into shallow water is called *refraction*.

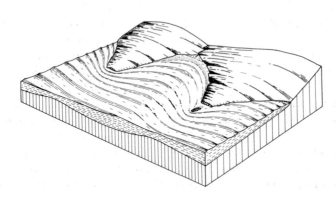

FIG. 10-9 Refracted waves with energy concentrated on headlands.

FIG. 10-10 Crossing sets of refracted waves off the east end of San Nicolas Island, California. *(Courtesy of U.S. Geological Survey and John G. Vedder.)*

Study the refracted wave patterns of Fig. 10-10 and 10-11.

Alongshore Transport. In the case of waves approaching shore at an oblique angle the waves are bent or refracted as shown in Fig. 10-12. Breakers play against the beach but also sweep along it. The swash rushes the sand and silt particles obliquely up the beach. They return in the backwash down the steepest slope, or normal to the beach. These same particles are caught up by the next swash and again carried obliquely up the slope, to return downward again in the backwash. This process, repeated many times, although only affecting a few pounds of sediment in any small stretch of the beach, and transporting it only a foot or two lengthwise of the beach in each swash cycle, results in time in the movement along shore of enormous volumes of sediment. Many beach features, as we shall see, are built by the transport of material along shore by the process described.

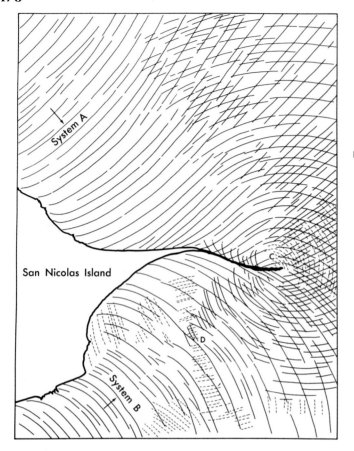

San Nicolas Island

FIG. 10-11 Diagram of waves visible in Fig. 10.10. System A and System B are refracted waves coming from a single system approaching the island from the left and intersecting each other. System C is a diffracted group of waves originating at the point of the spit and proceeding outward concentrically. System D seems to be originating as reflected waves from a small island at point D.

Alongshore currents are set up by waves rolling in obliquely to shore. In the process of breaker swash and backwash there is a slow transfer of water alongshore, and also in the zone of breakers there is a pulsating propagation of water in the same direction.

In the mass transfer of water in wave action water piles up along the shore. Sometimes there is a gentle return bottom current to compensate (the *undertow*), but at other times a local, restricted seaward current carries the hydrologically unstable water back to the sea. This is called a *rip current*, particularly because it may obtain speeds of 2 to 3 miles per hr where concentrated in the surf zone. Once through the surf they tend to spread out and dissipate. See Fig. 10-13.

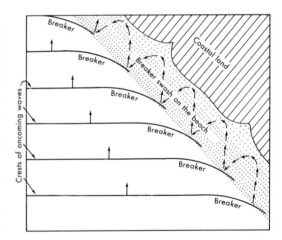

FIG. 10-12 Transportation of sand along the beach by waves approaching at an oblique angle. Note also the bending (refraction) of the waves as they roll into shallow water. Material is moved by the breaker swash on the beach and in the turbid surf zone.

TIDES

Whereas the variation of wave intensity is irregular and unpredictable, the rise and fall of the tide, every 12 hr, is normally both regular and predictable. Sometimes meteorological conditions conspire to compound tides with high waves and prolonged high winds; these are generally not predictable but at the same time are very destructive.

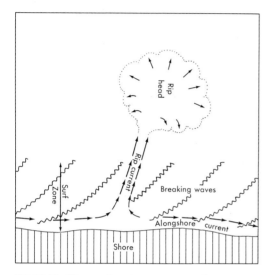

FIG. 10-13 Waves, alongshore current, and rip current. (After R. S. Arthur, "Dynamics of Rip Currents," Jour. Geophys. Research, vol. 67, 1962.)

On a tideless coast the beach coming under wave activity is limited by the size of the waves and is generally not very broad. The constancy of position of the breaker activity will produce a certain beach profile and also a certain distribution of materials. Now, if the tidal range is great (30 to 50 ft) then the break point of the waves is never fixed, and a different distribution results at high tide than at low. This has a definite bearing on wave-cut and wave-built features, which will now be described.

In regard to tidal currents it is recognized that *flood current* flows in one direc-

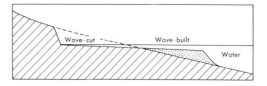

FIG. 10-14 Wave-cut and wave-built terrace.

tion and the *ebb current* in the other, thus somewhat negating each other. On the other hand, the flood currents affect the shore at higher elevations than the ebb currents, and therefore some changes in beach forms may occur.

PROFILES OF BEACHES

The waves both erode and deposit, and are said to be constructive and destructive. In ideal form on a steep shore the waves fashion a terrace, part of which is erosional and part depositional. The rock-cut platform is continuous in a gently seaward dipping plain with the deposit. See Fig. 10-14. It has been supposed that the waves strive to build a stable beach profile that is neither too steep nor too gentle and that, once attained, it remains. This is called the profile of equilibrium. But because of the varying height, steepness, and length of the waves and because of the general progress of erosion, certain beaches in particular are characterized as mobile. In Fig. 10-15 it will be seen that with the progress of erosion the beach becomes broader and flatter, with the wave energy being more largely spent in crossing the platform and hence progressively less ef-

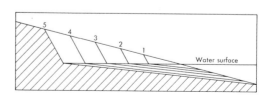

FIG. 10-15 Progressive cutting of rock platform.

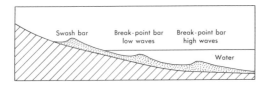

FIG. 10-16 Kinds of bars along the beach.

fective in further erosion. In this sense a profile of equilibrium is being attained.

In detail the beach may develop a bar at the breaker point and another at the head of the swash. See Fig. 10-16. The breakpoint bar forms at the point of breaking of the waves, and its position depends on the height of the wave. Two bars may be built if small waves follow large waves. Such shallow ridges are often experienced by swimmers on lake beaches. With a falling water level (ebb tide) the break-point bar is destroyed.

Swash bars may be built above the mean water level. They form particularly under the influence of flat waves, which have been found to move sand at depths both inside and outside the break point toward the land. During storms such bars may be built by the throwing landward of the sand and flotsam several feet above the swash of normal waves. The bars are called *storm beaches* by some, and *berms* by others. The leeward face is in places an angle of repose slope. The storm beaches dry out after the waves that built them subside and then furnish sand in the face of onshore winds to the coastal sand dunes, described in the next chapter.

EROSION ALONG SHORES

The waves not only remove loose material from the shore but attack the solid rock. In doing so, rock-cut platforms (Figs. 10-17 and 10-18) and cliffs are formed. The retreat of the cliffs is intimately related to the cutting of the platform, and both processes are dependent on the waves reaching the rocks.

The processes involved are solution, corrasion, attrition, and hydraulic action. Solution by water, as pointed out in previous chapters, is particularly significant in limestone, and where the cliffs are eroded in limestone, various solution etching effects are prominent. Corrasion implies the direct striking and rubbing of the rocks by sand grains, pebbles, and boulders. In time of ocean storm waves huge blocks of rock are hurled around with great force. Fine sand and silt exert little corrasive action, however. At the same time that the platform and cliff are being corraded, the particles themselves are being worn down. They become rounded and smaller.

After the cliff is formed the other erosional processes may become active, such as frost action, chemical decay, and gravity, and fragments fall to the base of the cliff. These are broken up by the wave action and are used as tools for corrasion; they eventually are carried away.

We have learned of the hydraulic pressures and shock pressures of pockets of air enclosed in breakers striking a steep cliff face. For a wave 10 ft high and 150 ft long the hydraulic pressure against the cliff is about 1,200 lb per sq ft. A very high

FIG. 10-17 Wave-cut platform across inclined limestone and chert beds, near St. Jean de Luz, Bay of Biscay, France.

FIG. 10-18 Wave-cut cliff at Acapulco, Mexico. (Photograph by Hal Rumel, Salt Lake City.)

shock pressure was measured in a cliff cave at Dieppe, France, of 12,700 lb per sq ft.[3] These pressures seem sufficient to pry apart and dislodge rock fragments. In badly jointed rock formations the effect is undoubtedly great, and the process is possibly more significant than corrasion.

The rock-cut platform at Santa Cruz, California, is instructive (Fig. 10-19). It slopes seaward at an angle of less than 1° and is carved in the Monterey formation, which consists of bedded porcelanites and shales. Porcelanites are hard shales that have a texture and break like porcelain. At times the platform is bare, but at other times it is mantled by a thin layer of loose sand. The platform extends seaward to a

depth of 65 ft and is over 1½ miles broad. See Fig. 10-20. W. C. Bradley[4] has concluded that:

✦ Abrasion (corrasion) is restricted to the surf zone, which has a maximum depth of 30 feet.

✦ Sediments are transported to depths beyond the surf zone but are too fine and the water movement too slow to accomplish any abrasion there.

✦ Since the rock-cut platform extends out to a depth of 65 feet, it is concluded that the coast has been sinking, or the water level rising, and that the deeper outer

[3] *Ibid.*

[4] "Submarine Abrasions and Wave-cut Platforms," *Bulletin of the Geological Society of America,* vol. 69, 1958.

FIG. 10-19 Elevated platform cut below water near Santa Cruz, California. *(Courtesy of W. C. Bradley.)*

part of the platform was eroded during a lower water level.

✦ If the sea level is stationary relative to the land, erosion of a platform about one-third of a mile wide is all that may be expected. The shaping of a continuously smooth platform of greater breadth than this requires the slow submergence of the land.

The maximum depth of affective erosion is called *wave base*.

Headlands are particularly susceptible

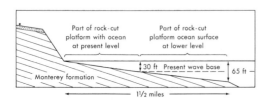

FIG. 10-20 Rock-cut platform at Santa Cruz, California. *(After W. C. Bradley, G. S. A., vol. 69, 1959.)*

to platform and cliff cutting because the waves are refracted around them and the energy concentrated on them. They appear in many variations like that shown in Fig. 10-21. Incident to such erosion, pedestal-like remnants are often left for a while. They are called *stacks* (Fig. 10-22). They soon are worn away, however. Other forms are caves and arches, as the irregularities in resistance and fracturing of the rocks allow the erosional processes various irregular avenues of penetration.

DEPOSITS ALONG SHORES

So far we have thought of deposits along shores in cross section. Now, when we take the map view and consider the significance of alongshore transportation, some of the most striking features come into focus. The deposits generally produce straight or gently curved beaches. In the attainment of this kind of beach the waves often trim off cer-

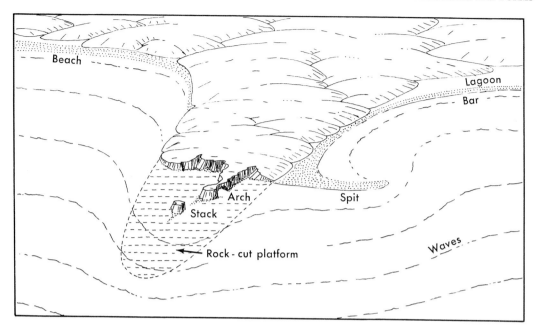

FIG. 10-21 Typical features of a headland undergoing wave erosion.

tain prominences as they fill in between with sand. See Figs. 10-21 and 10-23.

The alongshore currents commonly build sand and shingle (gravel) projections out from eroded headlands. These are called spits. See Figs. 10-21 and 10-24. If spits from headlands on either side of a bay are joined, the deposit is called a bar, and this kind, a bay-mouth bar. In the course of spit building the end may become hooked, which always occurs toward land. Possibly strong onshore waves during a storm accomplish the turn. Successive new hooks may form as the alongshore currents continue to unload sand at the end of the spit (Fig. 10-25). There are many irregularities in shore topography, and thus the erosional and depositional forms incident to the work of the waves and currents are quite varied, but almost always the waves and currents conspire to smooth out the shore. This we should look for on our next visit to a large lake shore or the ocean coast.

In the large plan certain coasts for hundreds of miles are remarkably straight or smoothly curved. Spits and bars across bays are generally smaller features, but much of the coast of the eastern and southeastern United States has been remade by the waves on a scale dwarfing all engineering projects of man. The straightening of an originally irregular coast has been accom-

FIG. 10-22 Sea cliffs and stack near Cheticamp, Nova Scotia. *(Courtesy of Geological Survey of Canada and R. F. Block.)*

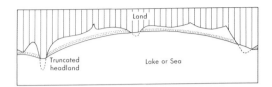

FIG. 10-23 Smoothly curved beach formed by trimming off headlands and deposition of sand in recesses or across embayments.

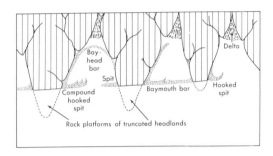

FIG. 10-24 Spits, bars, and truncated headlands.

plished chiefly by the building of great bars in shallow water some distance in places from the shore line. These are called *barriers*, *barrier bars*, or *barrier beaches*. They enclose a swampy lagoon between them and the mainland. A large and detailed map of the eastern seaboard should be examined, and it will be seen that long stretches of the shore are formed by the barrier beaches beginning with Long Island

and extending to the Florida Keys. There are also long and smooth barrier beaches west of the Mississippi delta along the coast of Texas and Mexico. At Atlantic City, New Jersey, one of several cities built on the barrier beaches, a southward movement of 400,000 cu yd of sand per year has been estimated. The barrier ends south-

FIG. 10-25 Hooked spit at Cape Kellett, Banks Island, Canada. *(Courtesy of U.S. Navy and James A. Whelan.)*

ward at Great Egg Inlet to Great Egg Bay only to take up on the south in another barrier on which Ocean City is located. Here, however, the sand is drifting northward along shore at the rate of about 50,000 cu yd per year and is building the barrier northward into the inlet. See Fig. 10-26.

It will probably be surmised by now that some of our harbor breakwaters have interferred with the beach-forming process, and there are a number of noted examples where this interference has resulted in unexpected deposition in places and erosion in others. We have succeeded, at least temporarily, in some of our engineering projects along the coasts but have lost in the struggle against the sea in others. It is no wonder that wave action has been investigated extensively, and the literature on this complex subject is rather technical and mathematical.[5]

The origin of the long barrier beaches is a controversial subject, but the theory that they are built by sand thrown up from the seaward bottom seems to have preference. A slope or profile is presumed to have existed that is gentler than the equilibrium gradient for the waves that play upon the beach. The waves rectify the situation by throwing up sand from the bottom into a bar and thus making the slope greater and more agreeable (Fig. 10-27). There is no doubt that alongshore transportation of sand occurs after the barrier is built, but this is not considered very important at the beginning of building.

SHORES OF EMERGENCE

The crust of the earth is restless, and in some places geologists note uplift and in others subsidence. Particularly along shores is it easy to recognize these movements. For instance, if a coast has been rising, we

[5] See C. M. A. King, *Beaches and Coasts*, Edward Arnold (Publishers) Ltd., London, 1959.

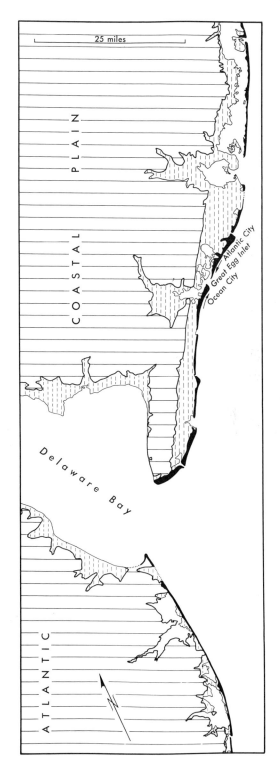

FIG. 10-26 Barrier beaches (black) of the Atlantic seaboard, near Atlantic City, and Delaware Bay. Lagonal areas are in dashed lines.

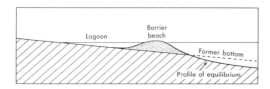

FIG. 10-27   Origin of barrier beach.

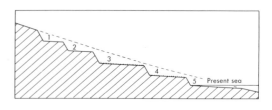

FIG. 10-28   Platforms cut as coast emerged.

should note a succession of wave-fashioned beaches above the present one (Fig. 10-28). On the west side of Ben Lomond Mountain near Santa Cruz, California, there are five main terraces and several indistinct intermediate ones that give the appearance of a crude gigantic staircase from sea level up to an elevation of 850 ft. They are all rock-cut platforms and attest to the rise of this section of the coast of

FIG. 10-29   Raised beaches on the south shore of Victoria Island. *(Courtesy of Geological Survey of Canada and Ed Schiller.)*

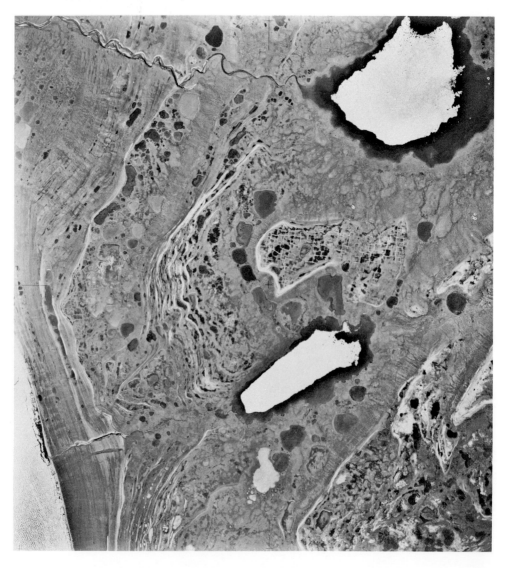

FIG. 10-30 Multiple beaches fashioned by Lake Bonneville as it fell. View is at Lakeside station.

850 ft in rather recent geologic time. Note the raised beaches on Victoria Island (Fig. 10-29). The same effect is obtained when the level of a body of water falls, such as was the history of old Lake Bonneville in the Great Basin. As it fell it left a series of erosional and depositional beaches, as shown in Fig. 10-30.

Shores of emergence are usually fairly steep and straight and have only a few harbors.

SHORES OF SUBMERGENCE

If a coastal area subsides, the lower part of the valleys of rivers that flow into the sea will be flooded, with the development

FIG. 10-31 Seven Sisters of the Chalk Cliffs of England, showing shore line straightened by erosion.

of estuaries like those of Chesapeake and Delaware Bays. Such valleys are said to be drowned. In fact, the entire coast from North Carolina to Newfoundland is one of fairly recent submergence, geologically speaking in point of time. The Gulf of St. Lawrence is another great drowned river valley. Needless to say, the strong waves of the Atlantic have worked over the irregular relief features as the seas have advanced on the land but have not had time to straighten out the shore much from Long Island northward. There are thousands of truncated headlands, bars, spits, and curved beaches, but all on a much smaller scale than the barrier beaches to the south.

In a submerged beach of headlands and bays the process of erosion of the headlands has been imagined from the early inception to an advanced stage, where they have all been worn back to a straight coast line. Such may be the case along the Chalk Cliffs of England (see Fig. 10-31).

Suggested Aids

Readings

Bascom, Willard: "Ocean Waves," *Scientific American,* August, 1959.

Bradley, W. C.: "Submarine Abrasions and Wave-cut Platforms," *Bulletin of the Geological Society of America,* vol. 69, 1958.

King, C. A. M.: *Beaches and Coasts,* Edward Arnold (Publishers) Ltd., London, 1959.

Chapter 11

WIND AS A GEOLOGIC AGENT

Wind, like running water and waves, erodes, transports, and deposits. These accomplishments are the subject of the present chapter.

Wherever clay, silt, or sand particles are dry and loose and exposed at the surface they are subject to wind transportation. These conditions are general in deserts, but in more humid regions they are locally present. For instance, along ocean and lake shores dry sand is left by storm waves, and there it drifts into sizable accumulations by the force of the wind.

Rivers are confined to channels; the wind sweeps across the entire countryside. Rivers erode and transport in downhill courses; wind may transport particles uphill and hence erode out depressions. Water, besides transporting discrete particles of matter, can take compounds into solution; wind is limited as a geologic agent to physical

Work of the Wind

action expended on particles or grains of rock, mineral, or plant and animal matter.

WIND EROSION AND TRANSPORT

Bed Load and Suspended Load

Particles are moved by the wind, first, along or near the surface and, second, considerably above the surface in temporary suspension. Sand grains particularly within the size range of 0.15 to 1.0 mm are confined in normal winds to within a few feet

During the great dust storm of March 20 to 22, 1935, the geology department of the University of Wichita, Wichita, Kansas, "weighed" the atmosphere on Wednesday, March 20, and estimated that at 11:00 a.m. 5,000,000 tons of dust were suspended over the 30 square miles of the Wichita area within one mile of the ground. The dust extended upward to a height of more than 12,000 feet, so the above estimate appears to be very conservative. The source area for most of the dust of this storm was in southeastern Colorado, more than 250 miles west of Wichita. Dust from this area seems to have been deposited, at least to some extent, at most places across Kansas and eastward, and the great dust cloud eventually reached

FIG. 11-1   Front of severe dust storm coming over a town in northeastern New Mexico.

of the surface, chiefly below 18 in., whereas silt and clay particles are carried in suspension and make up the dust clouds or storms. Sand-sized grains are not part of the dust in dust storms. The difference between bed load and suspended load is generally striking and is illustrated by certain examples. During the drought in the thirties the Great Plains became a dust bowl because the grassy sod had been ploughed under, and the silty loam, now exposed and dry and loose, was picked up by the winds. The dust rose in dense clouds to heights of several thousand feet and obscured the sun for hours at a time (see Fig. 11-1):[1]

the Atlantic coast, nearly 1,500 miles from the source area.

Much loam was removed from certain areas and dropped many miles away.

On the other hand:[2]

In an erosion desert, the only free dust consists of these fine rock particles which have been loosened by weathering since the last wind blew, and have therefore not been carried away. In such country the wind produces for the first hour or so a mist consisting of both dust and sand. Later, although the wind may have shown no signs of slackening, the mist disappears. But the sand still continues to drive across the country as a thick, low-flying cloud with a clearly marked upper surface. The air above the sand cloud becomes clear, the sun

[1] A. L. Lugn, *The Origin and Sources of Loess,* University of Nebraska Press, Lincoln, Nebr., 1962.

[2] R. A. Bagnold, *The Physics of Blown Sand and Desert Dunes,* William Morrow and Company, Inc., New York, 1942.

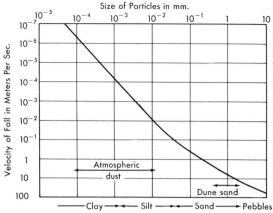

Size of Particles in mm.

FIG. 11-2 Relative size and rate of fall of small particles. The arrows indicate size of atmospheric dust particles and dune sand generally observed. See Chap. 2 for discussion of silt and sand. *(After Bagnold, The Physics of Blown Sand and Desert Dunes, 1942.)*

velocity of an updraft eddy of air that might pick up a particle from the surface. We can conclude that, when the velocity of fall becomes less than the upward eddy currents within the average surface wind, the particle will be picked up and carried in suspension, but if the velocity of fall is greater, then the grain will only be driven in a horizontal direction. The maximum size limit for a wind of given velocity for bed-load transport is defined by a grain resting on the surface that ceases to be moved either by the direct pressure of the wind or by the impact of other moving grains against it.

Now, if we measure the grains of sand in the bed load or in sand dunes they usually range from 0.15 to 0.3 mm in diameter. The maximum upward eddies in a wind of 5 m per sec (11 miles per hr) are about 1 m per sec, and it will be seen in Fig. 11-2 that grains having this velocity of fall are 0.2 mm in diameter. We might, therefore, expect that at somewhere about this size there will be a noticeable change in the character of small loose particles either carried in suspension for some time or drifted along the surface, and such is the case.

When winds reach velocities of about 10 miles per hr near the surface, it has generally been observed that a few sand

shines again, and people's heads and shoulders can often be seen projecting above. . . .

When the wind subsides, the sand movement disappears with it.

The reason for the fairly sharp boundary between dust storms and sand bed load with little intermediate material will be understood if an experiment of Bagnold (cited above) is considered, in which he measured the rate of fall of grains of various silt and sand sizes through the air. See Fig. 11-2. The rate of fall is in effect the same as the

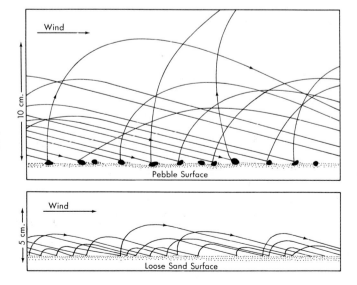

FIG. 11-3 Paths of bounding sand grains over surface strewn with pebbles and over loose sand surface. *(After Bagnold, 1942.)*

FIG. 11-4 Desert pavement, near Crossing of the Fathers, southern Utah. Pebbles and cobbles are shiny with desert varnish.

FIG. 11-5 Desert pavement. Pebbles of limestone and dolomite cover soft tuffaceous shales. Silver Island Mountains, western Utah. (Courtesy of Walter Sadlick.)

grains start to roll, and when the grains have gathered enough speed they begin to jump. The paths of the bouncing sand grains are pictured in Fig. 11-3. Upon striking other grains, these in turn are set in motion, and soon a sand cloud develops and moves to the leeward. Most of the bounces or jumps are less than 10 cm (4 in.) high in normal winds, and hence the greatest density of sand movement is close to the surface. Wind velocities necessary to start sand moving are somewhat greater than required to keep it moving once the bouncing and impact of falling sand grains has started.

In summary we recognize that sand grains in general are too large to be carried in true suspension by the wind. The great bulk of them moves by *saltation* (jumps), but some never leave the ground because they are too large. Those slightly larger than sand may creep along because they are driven by the impact of smaller grains.

We should note also that the wind is a remarkable sorter of grains. The silt- and clay-sized particles are removed entirely and blown many miles to leeward. Often they do not settle until brought down by rain. The medium and fine sand is concentrated into dunes, as we shall see, and the coarser particles are left as a residue or protective cover of the surface and are referred to as *desert pavement* (Figs. 11-4 and 11-5).

It should also be recognized that moisture bonds the silt and sand grains sufficiently together so that winds are not generally able to move or pick them up, and with moisture comes vegetation to cover, hold, and fix the small grains in place. Therefore, the wind is most effective in arid and semi-arid climates, and only significant in humid climates along shore lines where a supply of loose, dry sand is afforded.

Deflation

Deflation is the process of removal of rock waste from a land surface by the wind.

If the material underlying the surface is a mixture of silt, sand, and gravel, then sufficient silt and sand will be transported away until a protective cover of gravel remains, and this about ends the cycle of deflation. But if the area is underlain by friable sandstones, siltstones, and shales, the process of deflation may go on for a long time until even a basin of considerable proportions has been sculptured out in the rocks. The lower limit of deflation will be the capillary fringe of the water table, and under the circumstances of a desert region the zone of saturation will lose water and slowly fall, thus allowing the wind to erode a little deeper.

Wyoming, New Mexico, Colorado, and Texas have wind-carved basins or pans a few to several hundred feet deep and a fraction to 15 miles across. The writer estimates that the eastern margin of the Great Salt Lake Desert has been deflated about 10 ft over many square miles. The upper half inch or so of the moist silts and clays of the old lake bottom dry out in the hot summer sun and are partly removed by the wind. The lake dried up completely about 11,000 years ago, according to carbon-14 dates; yet the sediments deposited at that time have been removed down to those that yield carbon-14 dates of about 25,000 years in the eastern part of the desert.

The oases of north Africa in Egypt and Libya are situated in large depressions, such as the Qattara of World War II battles, and these have been fashioned, most probably, largely by wind erosion. Some have bottoms below sea level.

Abrasion

The surface movement of sand grains is sufficient to act as a blast, and objects in the way are sometimes mechanically worn and etched by the sand blast. Ledges and rock columns may be undercut, and the

FIG. 11-6 Dreikanter (three edger), abraded on desert floor by sand blast. Vertical view, top; end view, bottom.

fact that the abrasion is greatest at the ground surface and fades out a few inches above ground attests to the restriction of movement of sand grains to and near the surface.

Sometimes cobbles on the desert floor become etched or faceted by the sand blast, and fairly sharp edges between the etched faces result. The etched cobbles commonly develop three sharp edges, for some reason not clear, and they are known by the German word *dreikanter*. See Fig. 11-6.

WIND DEPOSITION IN DESERTS

Collecting of Sand in Dunes

The drifting sand, freed of the finer silt particles, and with the coarse sand granules and pebbles left behind, collects into dunes. The reasons for the accumulations are, first, obstacles that cause deterent eddies,

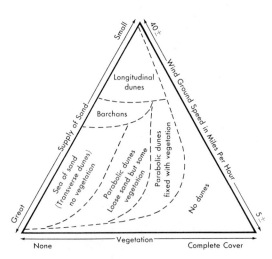

FIG. 11-7 Dune forms in relation to supply of sand, wind velocity, and aggressiveness of vegetation. (Modified from J. T. Hack, "Dunes of the Western Navajo Country," Geographical Review, vol. 31, p. 240, 1941.)

second, rise of moisture into the sand if the grains are driven into a swamp or on moist ground, third, the mastery of vegetation over the drifting sand, holding and fixing it in place, and fourth, the flow of turbulent air that tends to sweep the sand grains together and build them into streamlined forms.

Dunes take a number of characteristic forms that are repeated in many places the world over. The chief factors which determine the shape and size are, first, supply of sand, second, wind speed, and third, the amount of vegetation. These three factors are related in Fig. 11-7, with the various kinds of common dunes known.

The Basic Dune Form

The cross section of a dune in the direction of wind blow reveals a gentle slope to windward up which the sand grains are rolled and a steep slope to leeward down which the grains tumble when drifted over the crest. This is the steepest angle at which the sand will stand without slumping and is called the *angle of repose slope* or the *slip face*. See Fig. 11-8.

Now, the size and ground plan of dunes varies considerably, but the longitudinal section remains fairly constant, in shape at least. A basic design is exemplified by the *barchan* in Figs. 11-9 and 11-10. A barchan is a crescent-shaped dune with slip face and "wings" to leeward. The crests of measured barchans range in height from 12 to 100 ft, and their breadth and length are about ten to twelve times their height. Observation confirms the obvious, that the sand grains are propelled up the gentle slope by the wind and then slide down the steep slip face. The wind movement over the dune is as an elliptical mound, with the space within the bite of the slip face an almost perfect wind shadow. The air is stagnant there. Even in storm periods there is hardly enough movement to cause the sand grains to stir. No sand is ever blown away from the barchan that reaches the slip face.

It is interesting to examine the sand budget of a barchan. Sand is added and sand is lost. Is the mass of the dune held constant or is it growing or shrinking?

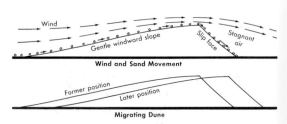

FIG. 11-8 Basic sand dune profile.

FIG. 11-9 Barchan dunes in Monument Valley, northern Arizona. *(Photo by Hal Rummel, Salt Lake City.)*

Sand is added to the periphery of the dune windward of the transverse profile *AB*. Since it is trapped on the slip face, the only places of loss are the outer wing surfaces to the leeward, from *A* to *E* and *B* to *F*. This means that the sand, if any, streams away to leeward from the wing tips. In places where the sand supply is abundant, according to Bagnold,[3] the barchans tend to pile up or merge, but as the sand forms migrate to leeward and the supply becomes less abundant, separate barchans take shape and progressively become farther separated from each other. See Fig. 11-11. Theoretically the size of the barchans should diminish as they migrate away from

[3] *Ibid.*

the sand source, but commonly other circumstances enter the picture, such as new sand supplies or topographic hindrances, and the diminution is not clearly recognizable.

The rate of "march" of the barchans of the Kharga Oasis, Egypt, has been measured to range from 35 to 60 ft per year. Bagnold relates that belts of barchans trail out from this and other depressions of southern Egypt and the northern Sudan for 50 to 175 miles and that, with the velocity of march given above, it has taken about 7,000 years for the front-running dunes in a 50-mile belt to reach their present positions. "This brings us to 5000 B.C., which is a not unreasonable date for the

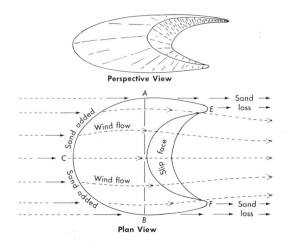

Perspective View

Plan View

FIG. 11-10 Barchan dune, ideally-developed.

abandonment of the Libyan Desert by the pre-Dynastic folk who are known to have migrated to the Nile Valley."[4]

Perfectly developed barchans seem to form on a featureless plain, with moderate winds, and most important, with one-directional winds. It must be obvious that as soon as the wind shifts, a new streamlining

[4] *Ibid.*

of the previously built dunes will start, and in the transition, many complex and difficultly understood shapes will appear.

Sand Seas of Northern Africa

Parts of the Sahara Desert are vast seas of sand, with almost a total absence of vegetation. See Fig. 11-12. Gentle windward slopes and leeward slip faces are everywhere in evidence. The slip slopes are commonly crescent-shaped, reminding one of the barchan form. Some of the individual dunes may rise nearly 1,000 ft above their bedrock floors. (Fig. 11-13).

Various kinds of dunes have been described in connection with the sand seas,

FIG. 11-11 A belt of barchans. The source of greatest sand supply is to the left. (From Bagnold, 1942.)

FIG. 11-12 Sand sea of the Sahara Desert in Southern Morocco. (Photograph by Cecil B. Jacobsen, U.S. Bureau of Reclamation.)

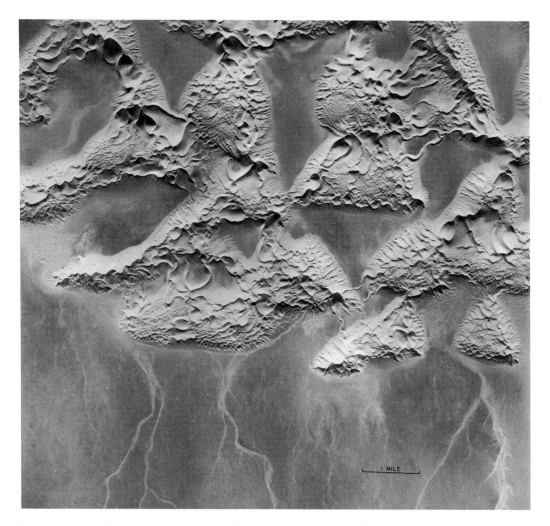

FIG. 11-13 Giant dunes of the Murzuch, southwest-central Libya. These dunes are certainly among the largest of the world. They approach 300 m (1,000 ft) in height and, as may be seen, are in great triangles 1 to $2\frac{1}{2}$ miles along a side, with the floor of the desert swept clean in between. The dry desert "washes" grade from south to north, and the present march of the dunes is from north to south. There appears to be absolutely no vegetation to impede the drifting of the sand. Such dunes are not described in the literature and do not find a place readily in current classifications. They probably belong to the lower left-hand corner of Fig. 11-7. (Courtesy of William E. Humphrey and American International Oil Company.)

particularly in the Egyptian Desert, and for particulars the student is referred to Bagnold's book, previously cited.

Dunes of the Colorado Plateau

In the Colorado Plateau, and particularly in the Navajo country, dunes are profuse and three varieties have been recognized:

transverse, parabolic, and longitudinal.[5] The sand is derived from the old friable sandstones that form many of the cliffs and escarpments of the plateau and in places is blown up the escarpment faces onto the plateau surfaces above and also blown from the high flat surfaces down over the

[5] J. T. Hack, "Dunes of the Western Navajo Country," *Geographical Review*, vol. 31, p. 258, 1941.

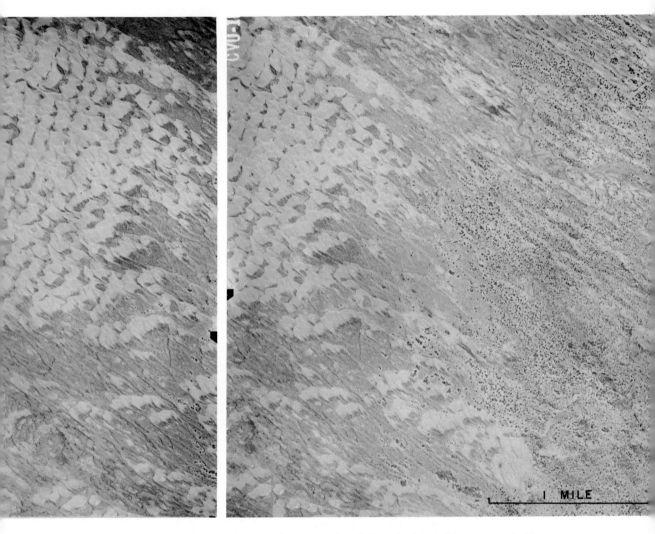

FIG. 11-14 Sand dune complex in southwestern Utah. Left is north, and wind is northeasterly. The light gray dunes are vegetation-free and tend to take barchan forms, but where closely packed, they build a transverse fabric. The juniper trees (clots) and desert grasses and brush (medium gray areas) have fixed the dunes fairly well, and in these areas longitudinal and parabolic dunes are the rule.

escarpments. The sand trains are intriguing in places as well as very scenic, for they inherit in delicate hues the colors of the sandstones from which they were derived. The coral sands, the red sands, and the white sands are common appelatives. The shape and relation to wind direction are the result of three interacting influences, namely, amount of sand, extent of vegetation, and wind speed.

Transverse dunes, as the term is used by Hack, are fairly extensive, barren sand zones transverse to the wind direction. There are sand-free places in the zones, and some forms resemble barchans (Fig. 11-14). They develop where the source of supply of sand is abundant and the winds are low to moderate. The sands drift, and the dunes are said to be active.

Parabolic dunes, as the name implies,

have a parabolic shape, with the wings of the parabola to windward, just opposite to the barchan, but the gentle windward slope and steep slip slope to leeward prevail, as would be expected. Figure 11-15 is a sketch of a cluster of parabolic dunes as they might develop in the desert. They form by the wind removal of sand from the windward hollows and its transport to the crest and over to the slip slope. They are always associated with vegetation cover, and it is a constant struggle of the plants to prevail against the wind, which blows away the sand in which the roots are embedded. Where the wind gets the upperhand, blowouts or deflation hollows form. Elsewhere,

FIG. 11-15 Parabolic dunes on Antelope Mesa, Navajo Country, Arizona. Some vegetation tends to fix sand, but dunes are kept alive by sand blown from a small sand sea of transverse dunes nearby. *(Sketched from vertical photograph in Hack, 1941.)*

FIG. 11-16 Longitudinal dune ridges on the Moenkopi Plateau in north-central Arizona. Sand is blown up the escarpment and strings out on the plateau.

FIG. 11-17 Sand-dune chain or ribbon in the Copiapo area of northern Chile. The sand originates here in an uplifted marine stand (terrace) just inland from the present beach. The view is toward the high Andes. (*Courtesy of Kenneth Sagerstrom and U.S. Air Force.*)

the sand is somewhat held in place by the vegetation and low ridges between hollows develop. Refer again to Fig. 11-14.

Where the wind is strong and the supply of loose sand scarce, long parallel lanes of sand string out over the plateau surface. The lanes or *longitudinal dunes* are only 6 to 30 ft high and 25 to 100 ft wide, and some extend for several miles. They are about 300 ft apart. The zones between the sand ridges, as well as the flanks of the ridges, are covered with vegetation; only the long ridge tops are bare. Longitudinal dunes may also be completely stabilized by the encroachment of vegetation. See Fig. 11-16.

DUNES ALONG SHORES

Source of Sand

The sand produced by the waves along shores is a good source of dune sand in many places. The extreme desert coast of northern Chile and southern Peru as well as the temperate but humid coast of the Bay of Biscay, of southwestern France, supply large quantities of sand to the wind, and in either climate, large dunes complexes develop. A source of loose sand is unusual in humid climates, and the waves are the chief fabricators of such a supply. But the plants along humid shores, particularly dune grass, mount an immediate attack on any wind-driven sand and usually do an effective job of preventing further drift. The vegetation is hardly a factor, however, in such intensely dry deserts as those of northern Chile and southern Peru.

Coastal Dunes of Desert Climates

From an airplane over coastal Peru and northern Chile one can see long ribbons of sand starting from the shore line and draped over hills and depressions but gradually climbing to points inland possibly 20 miles away and 3,000 ft above sea level. See Fig. 11-17. After noting the long belts of sand dunes in north Africa, we do not find the distance of 20 miles so remarkable, but the elevation to which the sand has been blown does pique the imagination. The ribbons are mostly variations of belts of barchans and longitudinal dunes, previously described. Topographic constrictions through which the sand is blown detract from the development of perfect forms of one type or the other.

Coastal Dunes of Humid Climates

The coastal areas of the Great Lakes are marked by dunes in a number of places,

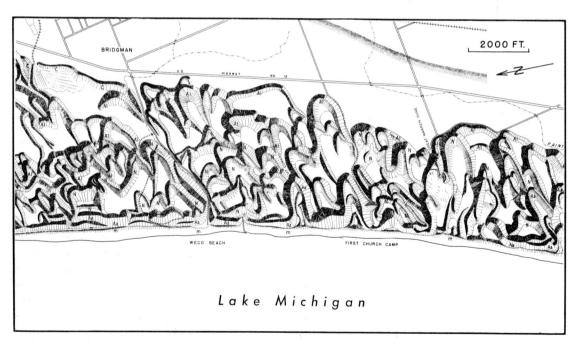

FIG. 11-18 Parabolic dunes of the Grand Marais Embayment, Michigan. (*Reproduced from G. C. Tague, Post Glacial Geology of the Grand Marais Embayment in Berrien County, Michigan, Occasional Papers for 1946, Michigan Geological Survey.*)

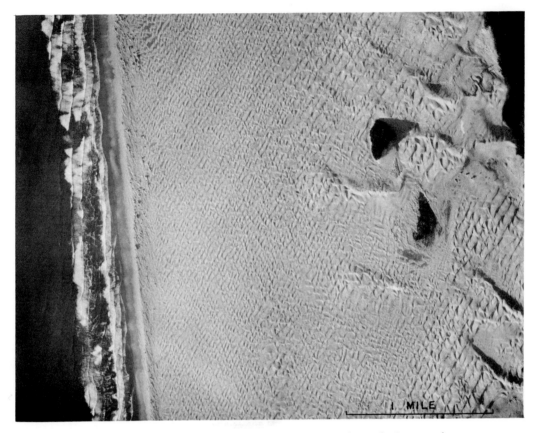

FIG. 11-19 Transverse dune complex along the coast of Oregon. Note breaker surf. *(Courtesy of W. S. Cooper.)*

and particularly the east side of Lake Michigan and the south side of Lake Superior are noted for their impressive dune complexes.

The waves derive the sand by erosion of glacial deposits and then carry the sand by alongshore currents to indentations, where it accumulates in large amounts. During storms with large waves beating on the shore, sand ridges are thrown up, called storm beaches. The sand in the storm beach is above and beyond the reach of the normal-sized waves and hence has a chance to dry out after the storm. Without a storm beach there would be no supply of loose dry sand for the wind. Another requisite for coastal dunes is onshore winds, because offshore winds simply return the sand to the waves.

The onshore winds drift the sand im-

mediately back of the storm beach to build the first true dune, which is sometimes refered to as the *foredune*. It is a ridge 10 to 30 ft high parallel with the storm beach. See m, Fig. 11-18. Dune grass immediately starts to grow but it generally fails to stabilize or fix the sand completely, and spots develop where the sand is rapidly removed in a second step inland. These spots grow into pockets or *blowouts*.

In the second stage of transport the sand builds and drifts into parabolic dunes, about as described in the Colorado Plateau. Here, too, a partial stabilization of the sand by vegetation is the key to the parabolic form. An example of a group of parabolic dunes along the shore of Lake Michigan is given in Fig. 11-18. It will be noted that some parabolic dunes are labeled *Al*, some *N*, and some *Aa*. These were built when the lake stood at higher levels than the present. The letter *m* indicates the modern foredune ridge, which is younger than the rest and is in the process of formation. Some of its sand undoubtedly is blown back into the adjacent parabolic dunes.

The coast of Washington and Oregon is one of extensive dune development. A narrow strip of lowland adjacent to the ocean contains the dunes, back of which is the mountain front. Stabilized older dunes of complex habit and history are succeeded in places by active dunes whose dominant element is transverse ridges. Here the summer wind, while the sand is dry, is from the north and northwest, and the sand is driven southward in waves where crests are normal to the wind with gentle slopes to north and steep slip face to south. See Fig. 11-19. The dune waves range from 100 to 120 ft from crest to crest, and in plan view in some places are sinuous. According to W. S. Cooper, who has studied them extensively, the subparallel sand ridges form where there is a heavy accumulation of sand

unencumbered by vegetation and the wind is constant in direction. He contends that this is the basic form of dune, not the barchan. Study also Figs. 11-20 and 11-21.

LOESS

Nature and Origin

Deposits of silt, called *loess*, that mantle the uplands are very extensive in the Missouri and Mississippi Valleys of Nebraska, Kansas, Iowa, Missouri, Illinois, Indiana, Tennessee, and Mississippi. Geologists early recognized that the loess was made of dust falls because of its position generally above the river courses, because it lacks the bedding characteristic of river flood-plain deposits, and because it consists of particles, such as the wind transports, in suspension. There were those geologists who contended that the source of the silt was in our Western deserts and was brought to the moister lower Mississippi Valley by the prevailing

FIG. 11-20 Dune complex surrounding forested hills on the coast of Oregon. (Courtesy of W. S. Cooper.)

FIG. 11-21 Dune advancing on forest along the coast of Oregon (Courtesy of W. S. Cooper.)

westerly winds. The rains help to clear the atmosphere of the dust in a more humid climate. However, later mapping of the silt deposits showed most of them closely tied to the old courses of the Mississippi-Mis-

souri River system, and it has been concluded by some that the loess was derived from the dried-out flood-plain deposits of the rivers nearby. During the last ice age, the Mississippi and its tributaries were

FIG. 11-22 Silt being caught up and transported by wind from braided river flood plain in Alaska Range, Alaska.

FIG. 11-23   Loess exposure, U.S. Highway 61 bypass, 5 miles east of Vicksburg, Mississippi. This is a very fresh road cut, and weathering has not yet revealed the vertical joints. (Courtesy of Harold Fisk.)

much swollen by the melt waters of the glaciers (Chap. 21) and had spread sand and silt widely over their flood plains. This, when dried out here and there, afforded the wind a fine opportunity to create a major dust storm, and the surrounding silt deposits are the result (Fig. 11-22).

Detailed studies in Nebraska and adjacent states by Lugn[6] led him to conclude

[6] *Op cit.*

that extensive dry sand-dune areas of northeastern Colorado and western Nebraska were the source of much of the loess. The sand dunes are the residue left behind from river flood plains and from the Ogallala formation, which lies at the surface over wide areas. The formation consists of mudstone and sandstone and is rather crumbly when very dry. It, itself, is chiefly an ancient river flood-plain deposit.

FIG. 11-24   Additional road cuts in Mississippi in which weathering has revealed the vertical joints in the loess. (Courtesy of Harold Fisk.)

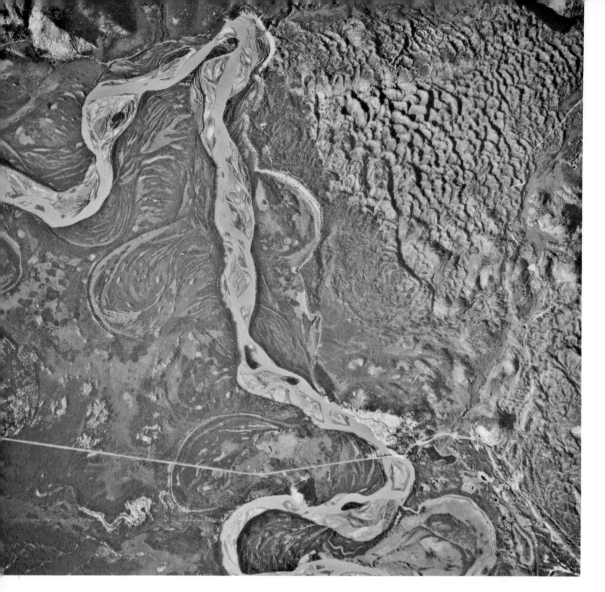

FIG. 11-25   Sand dunes adjacent to Tanana River at Tetlin Junction, Alaska. The Tanana River freezes over in winter. It is generally low in spring and high in summer during melting of glaciers and rains. In low periods it presents a braided appearance, as seen here. (Courtesy of Helen Foster.)

Loess generally develops columnar joints as it compacts and consolidates and erodes into vertical banks or bluffs, as illustrated in Figs. 11-23 and 11-24.

Parts of Alaska, especially the Yukon Valley, are blanketed with silt that has settled out of the air. We observe here today real dust storms on the braided river flood plains (Fig. 11-22) and recognize clearly the source and mode of origin of the silt blankets on the hills and mountain slopes up to 1,000 ft or more in elevation.

In places the silt blankets are 50 ft thick. Sand dunes also originate from the river flood plains (Fig. 11-25).

Loess Soils

Soils formed on loess are some of our very best. Witness the wonderfully productive soils of Iowa, Illinois, and Indiana. This is due to two characteristics: first the silt particles are made up of a number of different minerals and hence furnish the elements necessary for plant growth; second, the silty or loamy nature of the soils holds water; yet it renders them loose enough for easy plowing. They do not clod up like clay, nor are they like sand, from which the soil moisture drains. See Fig. 11-26.

TRANSPORT OF OCEAN SALT TO CONTINENTAL AREAS

Salt, like water, follows the hydrologic cycle. It is picked up from white caps as spray from the ocean surface by the winds and transported many miles inland over the continents. It falls to the land surface in the rains and then proceeds to drain off in the rivers to the sea again. Part, of course, gets into the ground water, but since the amount is very small, we hardly recognize it in either surface or ground waters. However, in those parts of the continents where interior drainage occurs, such as the Great Basin of the western United States, the salt collects year after year, and our numerous salt pans and lakes result. The Bonneville salt crust and Great Salt Lake are the most noted examples.

Weathering of rocks in the form of chemical decay undoubtedly yields some salt to the streams, but we are now disposed to

FIG. 11-26 Soil developed on Peoria loess in Doniphan County, Kansas. (Courtesy of John Frye.)

think that most of the salt comes from the atmosphere. Sodium chloride ($NaCl$) is the chief salt, but other common ions are K^+, Mg^{++}, and SO_4^{--}. The reasons for the atmospheric source are first, that measurable amounts of salt are contained in the atmosphere and rain waters; second, that the rivers gain consistently in salt content as they flow toward the sea regardless of the rocks over which they flow; and third, the salt content of the rivers is similar to the salt content of the atmosphere.[7]

[7] For further information see Junge and Gustefson, "On the Distribution of Sea Salt over the United States and Its Removal by Precipitation," *Tellus*, vol. 9, p. 164, 1957.

Suggested Aids

Readings
Bagnold, R. A.: *Physics of Blown Sand and Desert Dunes*, William Morrow and Company, Inc., New York, 1942.

Hack, J. T.: "Dunes of the Western Navajo Country," *Geographical Review*, vol. 31, p. 258, 1941.

Lugn, A. L.: *Origin and Sources of Loess*, University of Nebraska Press, Lincoln, Nebr., 1962.

Movie
Succession from Sand Dune to Forest, Planet Earth Series, SSC-313.

Map
Pleistocene Eolian Deposits of the United States, Alaska, and parts of Canada, edited by James Thorp and H. T. U. Smith, 1952. Sold by Geological Society of America, New York.

Chapter 12

DEFINITION OF GLACIER

Ice is a brittle substance when struck sharply, but in large masses it behaves like a viscous liquid. The ice in many glaciers is over 1,000 ft thick, and when such a mass is unconfined, such as on a mountain slope, it starts to flow. Gravity is the sole force acting on it and causing it to flow. The streaming of ice in glaciers is an extremely obvious phenomenon and has been measured in many places. Thus, a glacier may be defined as any mass of ice on land sufficiently large to flow.

TYPES OF GLACIERS

There are two principal types of glaciers: the continental and the valley. The continental glaciers are great sheets of ice, called ice caps, that cover parts of continents. The earth has two continental glaciers at present: one spreads

Glaciers and Their Work

over most of Greenland and one over all of Antarctica save for a small window of rock and the peaks of several ranges. See Fig. 12-1. The Greenland ice sheet is over 10,000 ft thick in the central part and covers an area of about 650,000 sq miles. The Antarctic sheet has been sounded, in one place at least, to a depth of 14,000 ft, and it spreads over an area of 5,500,000 sq miles. This is larger than conterminous United States in the proportion of 5½:3. It is calculated to store 7 million cu miles of ice, which if melted would raise the ocean level 250 ft.

Valley glaciers are ice streams that originate in the high snow fields of mountain ranges and flow down valleys to warmer climates, where they melt (Fig. 12-2). Some flow all the way to the sea, where they break up into icebergs and eventually melt in the ocean (Figs. 12-3 and 12-4). In certain places the valley glaciers flow down the mountain valleys to adjacent plains and there spread out as lobate feet (Fig. 12-5). These are called *expanded-foot glaciers*. Generally the sprawling feet of several valley glaciers coalesce to form one major sheet, and this is called a *piedmont glacier*.

Valley glaciers range in length from a few hundred feet to streams 50 miles long. Some of the streaming glaciers of Antarctica, nourished by the vast ice cap, are much longer still. During the past ice age many of the ranges of western United States supported valley glaciers 10 to 30 miles long, but now there are only shrunken remnants, or the glaciers are gone entirely.

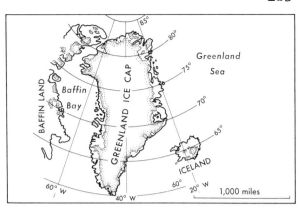

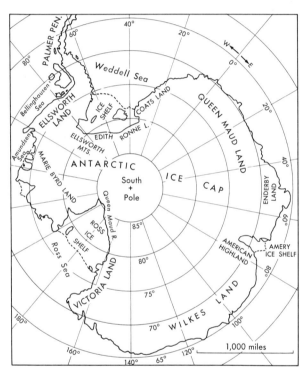

FIG. 12-1 Continental glaciers of Greenland and Antarctica. The ice cap of Greenland extends to the dotted line. Antarctica is all ice except for the peaks and ridges of a number of mountain ranges.

THE GLACIAL REGIMEN

Nourishment of Valley Glaciers

If more snow falls in the winter in the high parts of a mountain range than melts in the summer, then, year after year, an accumulation builds up. The snow of one year, buried under the snow of the next,

turns granular, and after a few years and under the weight of snow falls of several years turns to ice. This ice, when in sufficient volume, starts to flow downhill under the pull of gravity. It does not take much ice before flowage starts, as may be seen from the cascading ice masses in Fig. 12-6 and from small glaciers in Fig. 12-7.

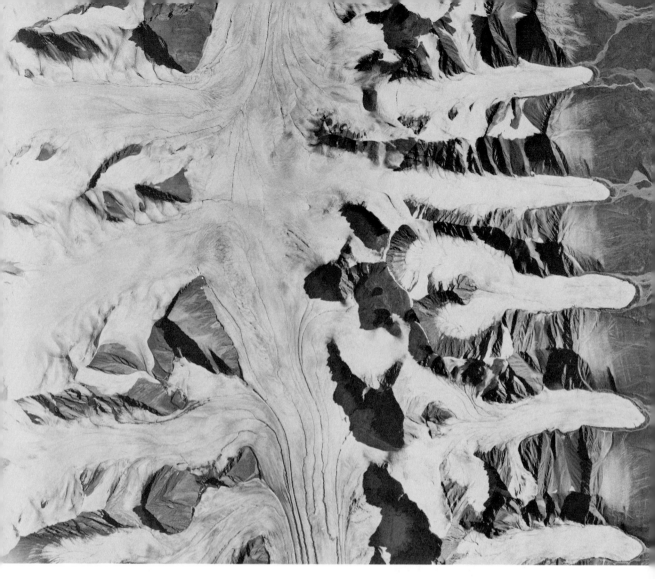

FIG. 12-2 Glaciers of Ellesmere Island. These are polar type and are frozen tight at bottom. Hence melt water runs as streams on surface. Note also that glacial fronts nestle in terminal moraines, indicating that glaciers are at most advanced position. Note also outwash streams. *(Courtesy of Geological Survey of Canada and Ed Schiller.)*

Important in the nourishment of a glacier is a good-sized catchment basin. This is a setting at the head of a mountain valley or canyon in which a large area is made up of slopes that drain into the valley head. Here the snow over a large area will feed into one valley. A number of small valley heads, all tributary to a main valley, may have their own snow fields and small glaciers, and these may flow together to form one major ice stream a number of miles long.

It is evident that, if the number of inches of snowfall is the same in two catchment basins, the largest basin will nourish the largest, and probably longest glacier. Snowfall depends on three principal factors: first, the higher the range, generally the greater the snowfall; second, the farther north and south from the equator, generally the greater the snowfall for the same altitude; and third, proximity to the ocean means notably greater precipitation in certain places. For instance, at an altitude of

FIG. 12-3   Hubbard Glacier, Alaska. *(Courtesy of Bradford Washburn and Duncan Stewart.)*

FIG. 12-4   Wasting front of the Columbia Glacier, Alaska. Slides of broken ice are frequent on the front, and occasionally large blocks break off and float away as icebergs.

FIG. 12-5 Expanded foot glaciers of eastern Baffin Island. Glaciers are at maximum stage of advance Note extensive rolling upland surface that is dissected by stream valleys and etched by cirques. *(Courtesy of Geological Survey of Canada and Ed Schiller.)*

FIG. 12-6   Northwest slope of Mount Sanford, showing snow and ice starting to move down the steep slopes. (Courtesy of Bradford Washburn and Duncan Stewart.)

FIG. 12-7   Glaciers from Mount Marcus Baker literally cascading down steep slopes. (Courtesy of Bradford Washburn and Duncan Stewart.)

FIG. 12-8 The long Nizina Glacier, Alaska. Note wasting front or snout of glacier. *(Courtesy of Bradford Washburn and Duncan Stewart.)*

12,000 ft along the 40° N latitude in Colorado and Utah only small snowfields last through summer, but at 6,000 ft in 50° N latitude in the Canadian Rockies glaciers several miles long occur. Also along the Pacific Coast from the Olympic Mountains in Washington to Mount Saint Elias in Alaska, precipitation is especially heavy, although the temperatures are not particularly low, and this results in great snowfields and extensive glaciers, especially in British Columbia and Alaska (Fig. 12-8).

Rate of Flow

Numerous measurements of the rate of flow of glaciers have been made. The procedure is to drive a line of stakes across a glacier and then chart their position each day, each month, or each year thereafter, depending on the rate of movement. In all cases the center of the flow moves the

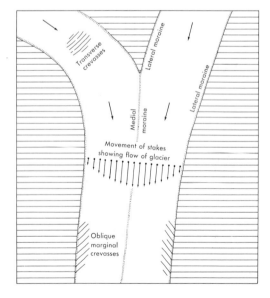

FIG. 12-9 Nature of flow, crevasses, and moraines of a valley glacier.

FIG. 12-10 Glaciers of Mount Saint Elias Range, Canada. The main glacier has stagnated and melted away, leaving only rock debris, once in transport. Note moraines of receding tributary glaciers. *(Courtesy of Geological Survey of Canada and Ed Schiller.)*

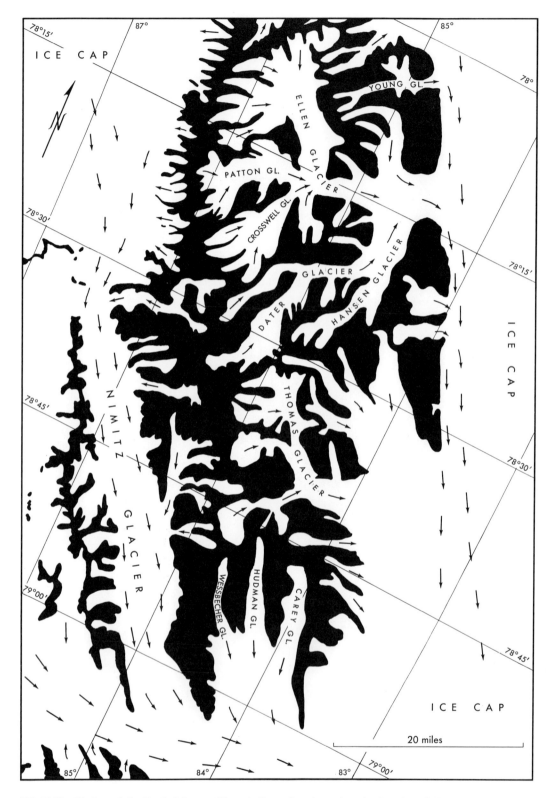

FIG. 12-11 Glaciers of the Sentinel Range, Ellsworth Mountains, Antarctica, showing the relation of valley glaciers to the ice cap. The ice cap contributes to the flow of the Nimitz Glacier. *(Taken from the Vinson Massif and Nimitz Glacier Maps of the U.S. Geological Survey, 1960.)*

fastest, and in time the straight row of stakes is bent into a curve, convex downstream. The centers of different glaciers measured have been observed to flow a few inches to more than 150 ft per day. See Fig. 12-9.

It will be seen in later paragraphs that glaciers transport large tonnages of rock fragments from high along their courses to their lower ends because of their slow flowage downstream. An unusual example of transportation is found in the Bossons Glacier of the Alps. Two climbers plunged to their death in a crevass, their bodies were frozen in the ice, and owing to the flow of the ice the bodies were released forty-one-years later at the melting end of the glacier several miles below.

Melting

The glacier is nourished by snowfall in the higher elevations, flows to lower and warmer climates, and there melts. Meltwater or thaw-water streams discharge from the glacier (Figs. 12-5 and 12-8) from the surface, from passage ways within, and from the bottom. The lower mile or two of the large glaciers are generally in a state of dissipation owing to melting, and the front or snout of some glaciers appears tattered and irregular (Fig. 12-10).

The water discharged is laden with silt and clay particles, free of organic material, and is light gray. The fine particles are commonly called *rock flour,* and the light, chalky melt water is called *glacial milk.*

FIG. 12-12 Glacial striations of several directions on bedrock in northern Manitoba. *(Courtesy of Geological Survey of Canada and Ed Schiller.)*

FIG. 12-13   Scratched and faceted boulders used as abrading tools by the glaciers. Each about $1\frac{1}{2}$ ft long. (Courtesy of Dr. Duncan Stewart.)

You may be driving along a mountain stream, not knowing that it is melt water from a glacier, but such can be surmised readily by the chalky color of the water. Once seen, the tone will be remembered.

FIG. 12-14   Ice-abraded outcrops of limestone on the Athabaska River of northern British Columbia along the Alaskan Highway. Ice moved from right to left.

The terminus of the glacier is not just the place of final melting of the ice but the site of unloading of much debris that the glacier has carried down from higher altitudes. This will be considered presently.

The front of a glacier remains in the same place if the rate of forward flow is equal to the rate of backward melting. Corollary statements may be made, namely, that if the forward flow exceeds the melting, then the front or toe of the glacier advances, and if the forward flow is less than the melting, then the front of the glacier recedes. Valley glaciers in almost all mountains have been receding consistently in historical times, and the mean ocean level the world over has gone up a few inches in the last century, undoubtedly owing to the release of water stored in the glaciers. The near world-wide recession of valley glaciers is taken to mean a slight warming up of the earth's annual temperature.

Features of Continental Glaciers

Continental glaciers are fed by snow that forms extensive annual layers. The layers compact into granular ice and then solid ice within a depth of 50 ft or so. The annual layers are still evident in the solid ice.

Studies during the International Geophysical Year show that in Antarctica the accumulating snowfall in terms of water per year is greatest in the coastal or marginal areas and becomes progressively less toward the high interior plateaus. At the South Pole the accumulation is 6 to 7 cm of water per year ($2\frac{1}{2}$ in.), whereas on the Ross Ice Shelf it ranges from 14 to 21 cm per year. The average across Marie Byrd Land and Ellsworth Land is about 18 cm per year, and in the coastal area just south of the Bellinghausen Sea it may be as much as 60 cm per year, or $23\frac{1}{2}$ in.[1] Ice has accumulated in the interior plateaus until

[1] M. B. Giovinetto, *Mass accumulation in West Antarctica, Transactions of the American Geophysical Union*, vol. 42, no. 3, p. 386, 1961.

FIG. 12-15 Sheep backs, or glacial-abraded hard rock hills, just west of Whitehorse, Yukon Territory. Also called *roches moutonnées*, from the French, meaning sheep rocks.

FIG. 12-16 Plucking effect of glacier. It moved toward viewer, abraded the top slope smooth, but plucked blocks from the leeward slope. Granite in Wasatch Mountains, Utah.

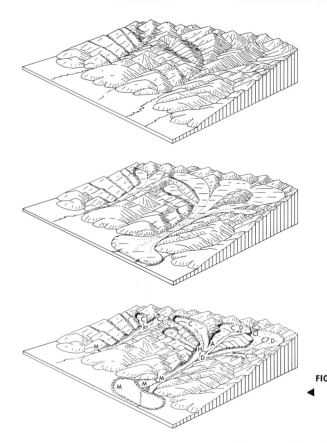

great streams pour down through the gaps in the Queen Maud Range into the Ross Ice Shelf. The Leverett, Robert Scott, Amundsen, Liv, Shackleton, and Beardmore Glaciers are some of these streams that have been charted, with the Beardmore probably the largest. It is 140 miles long and in places 25 miles wide. Some recent maps made from vertical aerial photographs of an area at the base of the Palmer Peninsula in the Ellsworth Mountains show many typical valley glaciers heading in snow fields in the crest of the range. The valley glaciers flow into the vast ice cap field, from which some major ice streams resolve and flow probably toward the Weddell Sea. The Nimitz Glacier is one of these (Fig. 12-11),

◀ **FIG. 12-17** Valley glaciers and glacial features: top, before glaciation; middle, during glaciation; bottom, after glaciation. C, cirques; D, rock basin lakes; H, hanging valley; A, arête ridge; M, terminal moraines; C1, Col.

FIG. 12-18 Little Cottonwood Canyon (left) in Wasatch Mountains is a smoothly curved, U-shaped valley, owing to glacial erosion. Bell Canyon (right) is also one of glacial erosion, with a spoon-shaped terminal ▼ moraine at the base.

and it is about 10 miles wide and at least 55 miles long. It appears to be nourished partly by ice from the ice cap and partly from the valley glaciers of the Sentinel Range (part of the Ellsworth Mountains).

The Greenland ice cap is hemmed in by marginal ranges, through the passes of which the ice pours in great valleylike glaciers. Their appearance and activity is the same as valley glaciers, but they are fed by ice from the interior ice cap. Some reach the sea and discharge angular icebergs, which float with jagged peaks above water.

The nourishment of the continental glacier of Antarctica, as described, with numerous ranges jutting up through the ice, and with many large and small topographic irregularities below the ice, must give rise to a very complex flow pattern. In the last

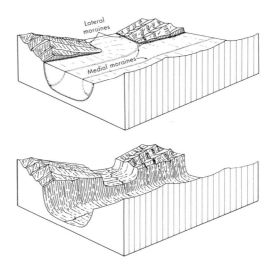

FIG. 12-19 Relation of tributary glacier to main valley glacier, showing particularly the origin of the hanging valley.

FIG. 12-20 Hanging valley and waterfall in Yosemite Valley, California. View is up the U-shaped glaciated valley with El Capitan on left and Bridal Veil Falls on right. Half Dome is in the center distance. (*Photograph by F. E. Mathes and courtesy U.S. Geological Survey.*) ▼

FIG. 12-21 Bergschrund near the head of a catchment basin. Mount Deception, Alaska. (Courtesy of Bradford Washburn and Duncan Stewart.)

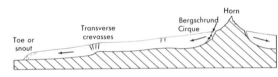

FIG. 12-22 Longitudinal section of valley glacier from bergschrund to snout.

analysis the ice reaches the sea, where it dissipates. The major problem of Antarctic glaciology is that of the ice budget. How much is being added each year? How much is being lost each year? Is the great ice cap decreasing or increasing in size? These questions have only been partially answered to date.

A recent report by Péwé and Church[2] summarizes the condition of the glacier margins at several places and concludes that from the period 1911 to 1958 the ice flow is about in equilibrium; the fronts are neither advancing nor retreating. This suggests that the ice budget is at present in balance and that the great ice cap is neither building up nor wasting away.

GLACIAL EROSION

Processes

Blocks of rock, commonly large and angular, are frozen in the ice and, thus firmly gripped, are ground against the bed-

[2] T. L. Péwé and E. Church, *Glacial Regimen in Antarctica, etc.*, University of Alaska, Department of Geology, Reprint Series, no. 15, 1962.

FIG. 12-23 Cirque wall with much talus that has accumulated since the ice melted. Uinta Mountains, Utah.

FIG. 12-24 Rock basin lakes due to glacial erosion in Snaring River Forks, Alberta. *(Courtesy of Geological Survey of Canada and E. W. Mountjoy.)*

FIG. 12-25 Fiord in southeastern Alaska. ▶

rock over which the glacier moves. This has been likened to a filing or rasping action. Where glacier snouts have retreated in historical times, the gouged, grooved, striated, and polished surfaces of rock over which the ice formerly flowed may be seen. More than this, the abrasion effects of the extensive glaciers that existed during the ice age are plain to see on every hand. Figure 12-12 is an example.

The blocks of rock that the glacier uses as tools to grind the bedrock away are themselves abraded. They develop grooved and striated faces. See Fig. 12-13. Such boulders are common in the terminal de-

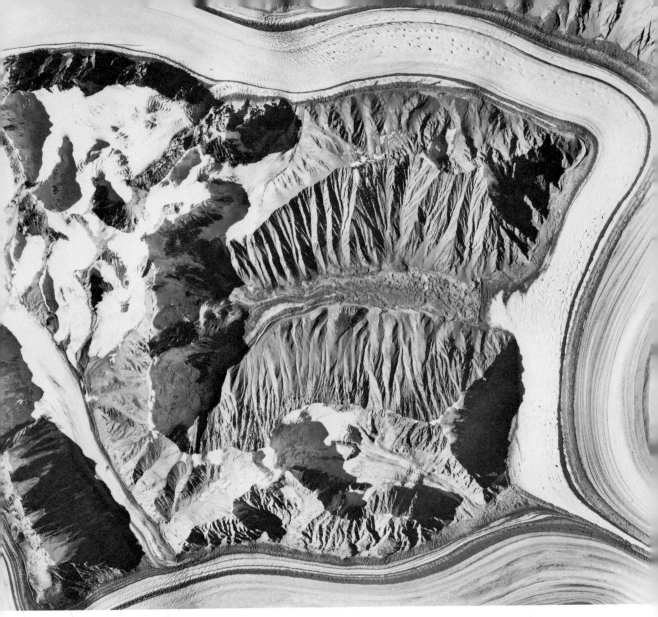

FIG. 12-26 Glaciers of Mount Saint Elias Range, Canada and Alaska, showing lateral and medial moraines, crevasses, and small stagnant glacier (center). This is a steroscopic pair, and

posits of the glaciers. Rivers, the wind, and the waves do not have the particular ability to use rock fragments as rasps or to fashion faceted and striated boulders. Such features are trademarks of glacial action.

As a glacier passes over a bedrock hill or protuberance it grinds away on the side of approach in the manner described, Figs. 12-14 and 12-15), but it is said to "pluck" rock fragments from the leeward side. The ice penetrates the open fractures and in effect freezes around the fragments. Then,

as it moves on ahead, the fragments are pulled or plucked from their place, and a jagged steep leeward slope results. See Fig. 12-16. In the following description of glacial erosional forms the processes of abrasion and plucking will be further elaborated.

Features Formed by Glacial Erosion

The most conspicuous form developed by a valley glacier is the U-shaped valley.

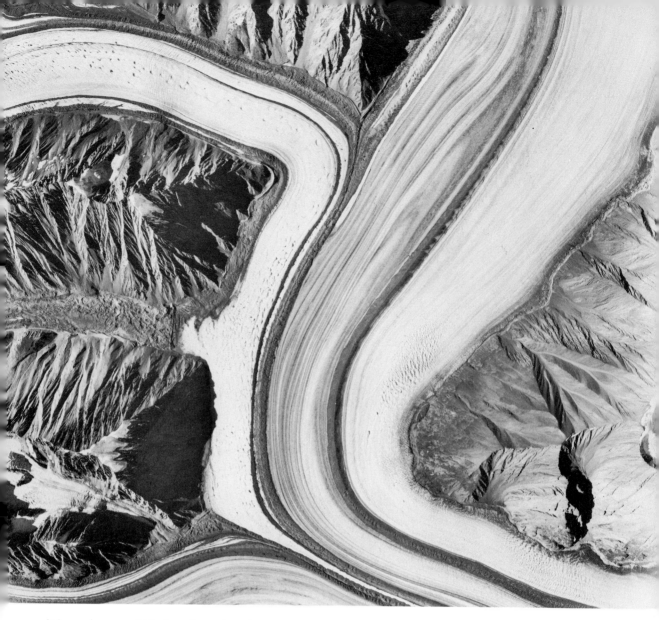

relief may be seen vividly by using a lens stereoscope.
(Courtesy of Geological Survey of Canada and Ed Schiller.)

Mountain valleys due primarily to stream erosion are V-shaped with a zig-zag course. See upper diagram of Fig. 12-17. After a glacier has flowed down a valley for some time it will have abraded a U-shape in the bottom of the V, as indicated in the bottom diagram. Also the jutting side ridges around which the stream made its zig-zag course will have been truncated and the canyon straightened out to one with a smoothly curving course. See bottom diagram again. Figure 12-18 is an example of a U-shaped valley with a broadly curved course. It acquired this form because a valley glacier flowed down the canyon during the ice age. The valleys of the Alps of Switzerland are classic examples, and there the processes and forms of glaciation were first recognized. Many of our mountain valleys in New England and in the western Rockies are U-shaped, at least in their headward sections, and attest to one or more episodes of glaciation sometime in the past.

In a mountain region that has been gla-

FIG. 12-27 Outwash gravels from glaciers upstream. Note the terminal-moraine ridge around the snout of the glacier just beyond the wooded spur.

ciated the tributary valleys may enter the main valleys over a cliff face and are called *hanging valleys*. See Figs. 12-19 and 12-20. Although the surface of the tributary glacier and the main glacier are confluent, that is, flow together at a common elevation, the floor of the main canyon is abraded more deeply than the floor of the tributary glacier. Hence, when the glaciers are melted, the tributary U-shaped valley is suspended above the main valley.

In the catchment area of a valley glacier

FIG. 12-28 Till in Granite Creek, Gros Ventre Mountains, Wyoming.

near the upper limit of the snow field a gaping fissure or crevasse commonly forms. This is the *bergschrund* of the Alpine geologist and mountain climber (Fig. 12-21). It is a dangerous crevasse because snow cornices commonly develop and even bridge across it, and it is through these thin bridges that climbers may fall.

The bergschrund separates bedrock and ice in the manner illustrated in Fig. 12-22. There is much thaw water in a summer day dripping down the crevasse, and undoubtedly rock fragments are pried loose by frost action, but it is also believed that there is considerable plucking going on. At any rate, a near-vertical wall is eroded that curves around the upper edge of the catchment basin, and when the glacier melts, we find a large amphitheaterlike basin with very steep walls around three sides at the head of the U-shaped valley. See Fig. 12-17, lower diagram. This basin is called the *cirque*. Figure 12-23 represents a cirque wall etched into a gently sloping upland surface.

From the cirque on down the glaciated U-shaped valley, pockets or small basins may have been ground out of the bedrock by the ice with its tools, and these are later filled with water when the glacier has melted. The small lakes are called *bedrock lakes,* and those within the cirque are called

FIG. 12-29   Terminal moraines of the Iliamma Glacier, Alaska. *(Courtesy of Bradford Washburn and Duncan Stewart.)*

FIG. 12-30   Terminal moraine of present Teton Glacier, Western Wyoming.

FIG. 12-31   Vertical aerial photograph of terminal moraines of piedmont glacier in western Montana. Note also the lake impounded back of the second moraine.

cirque-basin lakes (Fig. 12-24). Some people use the Scottish word *tarn* for the rock-floored lakes in cirques.

In some glaciated mountains a central high peak is surrounded by cirques that feed radiating glaciers. The cirque walls have sharpened the slopes of the peak on all sides until it stands as the commanding buttress or sentinel of the region. Such a peak is called a *horn*, after the Matter-horn, of Switzerland.

Two glaciers or cirques may erode toward each other to the extent that the dividing ridge becomes knife-sharp and marked by jagged spikes of rock. Such a ridge is called both a *comb ridge* or an *arête*. See *A*, Fig. 12-17.

Where two crescent-shaped cirque walls have been eroded to the point of inter-section (*Cl*, Fig. 12-17) a pass between the two may have developed. This is called a *col*.

The valley glaciers of certain coastal ranges, in flowing down to the sea, may have eroded the lower parts of their U-shaped valleys below sea level, and with the melting of the glaciers these parts be-come flooded with sea water. They are, of course, characterized by the steep valley walls rising directly from the water and are called *fiords*. Figure 12-25 is a woodcut of one of the many scenic fiords of the Coast Range of British Columbia and southeastern Alaska. The exquisite coast of Norway also has many fiords.

GLACIAL TRANSPORTATION

Rock and mineral fragments are transported directly by the ice and also by the melt waters from it. The most evident material in transport is along the margins of valley glaciers, where angular fragments, large and small, pried loose by frost action on the steep slopes above, collect as talus on the ice. This makes up the *lateral moraine*, as shown in Figs. 12-9 and 12-26. At the

juncture of two valley glaciers, or the tributary with the main ice stream, the two lateral moraines merge to form a train of debris near the center of the glacier. This is called a medial moraine. There will be as many medial moraines as there are tributaries, and all are being transported to the terminus of the glacier.

Continental glaciers, in flowing around a peak, pick up lateral moraines. Such an island of rock in a sea of ice is called a *nunatak*. Continental glaciers, such as those in Greenland, which flow through mountain passes, also acquire some lateral morainal material.

Both valley and continental glaciers take up great volumes of loose material from the surface over which they flow and trans-

FIG. 12-32 V-shaped cut through moraine. Note the braided stream back of the moraine and beyond this a glacier terminus. Near Columbia ice field on the highway between Banff and Jasper.

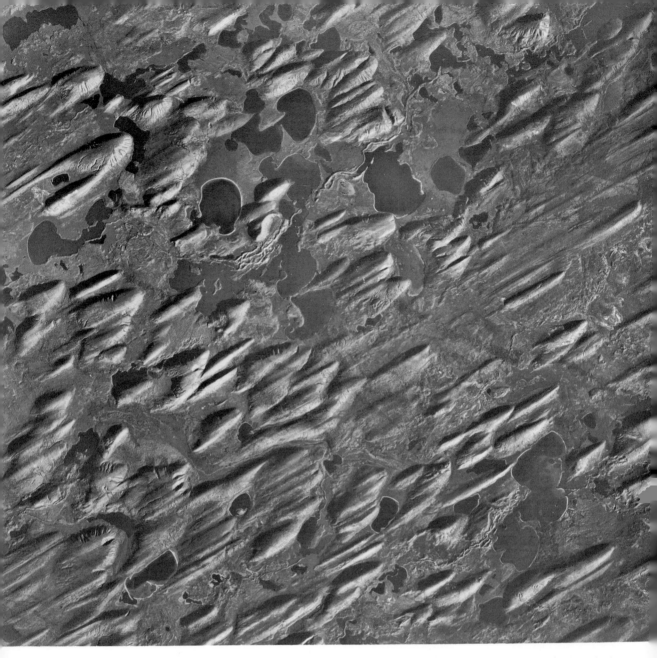

FIG. 12-33 Swarm of drumlins south of Lake Athabaska. Ice sheet moved from northeast to southwest. Note esker from center to upper right corner of left photo. Use lens stereoscope

port it to the glacier terminus. Soils, sand and gravel deposits, previously deposited glacial material, and bedrock fragments are frozen into the ice and carried or dragged to the melting front of the glacier. Some of the Greenland glaciers are heavily charged with rock debris, and it appears that they could only have procured it from the surface over which they flow. The angular and fresh fragments, at least in part, were obtained by plucking.

The grinding of rock flour and its transportation by melt waters have already been mentioned. The streams that discharge from the front of glaciers also carry much sand and gravel and deposit the material in lakes

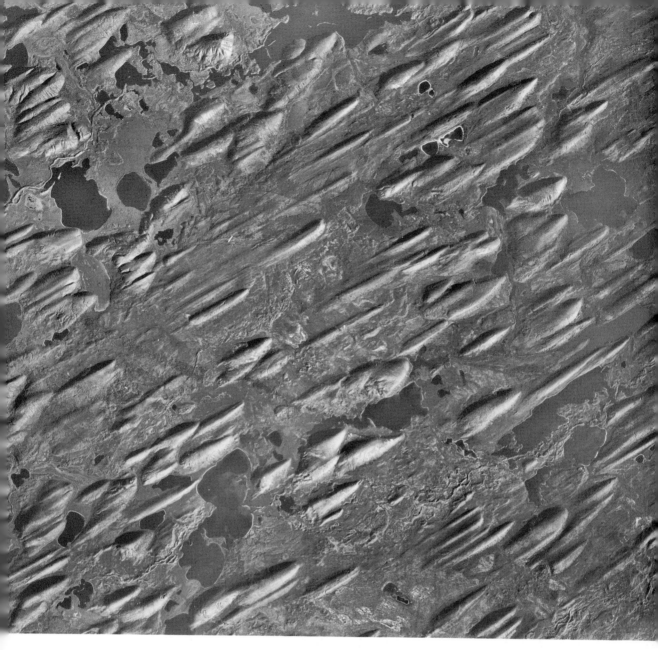

for viewing. *(Courtesy of Geological Survey of Canada and Ed Schiller.)*

and depressions at the ice front and down the valley beyond the glacier (Fig. 12-27). The pebbles and cobbles are commonly rounded, in contrast to the angular fragments transported directly by the ice. The ice may pick up already rounded cobbles and boulders, and in certain deposits these are more abundant than angular fragments.

GLACIAL DEPOSITS

Types of Material Deposited

Glacial deposits may be classified on the basis of the type of material contained in them, on their outward size and form, and on their position relative to the ice front. The types of material are of two general kinds. One kind is deposited directly by the ice and is a heterogeneous mixture of silt, sand, and large fragments, either rounded or angular or both. It is unsorted and unstratified (Fig. 12-28) and is called *till*. The other kind of glacial deposit is formed by melt-water streams and is sorted and stratified into layers of silt, sand, and gravel. It is said to be of glacio-fluvial origin (fluvial pertains to streams) and is sometimes referred to as *stratified drift*. All

on the ice are also included in the definition of moraine.

Both continental and valley glaciers leave considerable deposits of terminal moraine. The longer the ice front remains steady, and neither advances nor recedes appreciably, the larger the terminal moraine. The terminal moraine marks the position, then, of a stationary ice front at some time in the past. The hilly and lake country of the Great Lakes states is due to the ter-

FIG. 12-34 Esker near Fort Ripley, Minnesota. *(Courtesy of Duncan Stewart.)*

kinds and forms of glacial deposits are called collectively *drift* or *glacial drift*.

Moraines and Glacial Lakes

The term *moraine* is used to denote the deposits by the ice, particularly till, at the terminus. Glacio-fluvial material may be included in the terminal moraine, and the lateral and medial moraines in transport

minal moraines of the continental glaciers that formed in northern Canada and spread in large lobes southward into the Missouri, Mississippi, and Ohio River drainages. It was Louis Agassiz in the period of 1845–1873 who first recognized the deposits as those of glaciers and laid the foundation for the working out of the history of the ice age in North America. This subject is taken up in Chap. 21.

The relief of the deposits in a terminal moraine of a continental glacier is generally about 100 ft, but some hills may be 300 ft high. There are many undrained depressions in the terminal moraine that harbor small lakes and bogs. Minnesota's "ten thousand lakes" are glacial. The streams in the morainal complex seem to have a confused and aimless pattern, and only after considerable geologic time do they establish a system of trunk streams and tributaries by erosion and deposition that drain the area effectively.

The terminal moraines of valley glaciers are generally crescent-shaped and extend

dent in some places and is referred to as *recessional moraine*. A scattering of till, as the front withdraws rather rapidly, is called *ground moraine,* and the volume of such material in the Great Lakes region is undoubtedly very great.

In places the fronts of the great continental ice cap lobes have advanced and ridden over their terminal, recessional, and ground moraines. In doing so, these hummocky deposits have been dragged out and streamlined into elongate hills, with the long axis in the direction of ice movement. As such they are called *drumlins.* They vary considerably in size and have been char-

FIG. 12-35   Part of esker in Labrador. (Courtesy of Ed Schiller.)

across the valley in hummocky form (Figs. 12-29 and 12-30). As the ice front recedes from a terminal moraine, a lake is commonly impounded between the moraine and ice (Fig. 12-31). It rises to overflowing, and then the overflow stream cuts a gorge through the moraine (Fig. 12-32). As the gorge or outlet is cut down, the lake is drained. It is, therefore, evident that these "morainal dam" lakes are ephemeral. Generally those which exist today in our glaciated mountain valleys were once higher and larger but now are in the process of being drained and also being filled with sediment.

The process of withdrawal of glaciers is usually marked by periods of still-stand of the front, when small terminal moraines are built. A succession of these moraines is evi-

acterized as tens of feet high, hundreds of feet wide, and thousands of feet long. They commonly occur in swarms (Fig. 12-33) and are numerous in the Great Lakes region of Canada and the United States. Drumlins consist for the most part of till.

Glacio-fluvial Deposits

The streams discharging from glaciers breach the terminal moraines and spread stratified silt, sand, gravel out in front. Spread out beyond the moraines of continental and piedmont glaciers are deposits similar to broad alluvial fans, called *outwash plains.* Outwash plains are also built inside a previously deposited terminal moraine between the ice and the moraine, but only where the melt water can drain

FIG. 12-36 Glaciers of Ellesmere Island, Canada, showing development of surface streams and their erosional features on the ice such as meanders. The glacier of upper left part of left photograph is probably stagnating. The rocks are probably

away and is not impounded into a lake. In this situation, blocks of the retreating ice front become isolated and surrounded or even buried by stratified deposits. These blocks of ice later melt and leave depressions in the plain called *kettles*.

The swollen streams from valley glaciers are almost always overloaded with silt and sand, and although their rate of flow is fairly rapid they cannot carry all their load

and proceed to drop the coarsest fragments. Alluviated valleys result, with picturesque braided streams the rule. See Fig. 12-27.

A surprising deposit of sand and gravel is found in some areas covered by continental glaciers. It is a long, winding ridge, usually about 25 to 50 ft high and 50 to 200 ft wide. Some have such an even crest that they look like an artificial railroad

below freezing under the glacier, and no subglacial streams exist. Use lens stereoscope for viewing. (Courtesy of Geological Survey of Canada and Ed Schiller.)

grade winding across the country side. (See Figs. 12-34 and 12-35.) They are called *eskers*. They occur back of the main terminal moraine in the area of the ground moraine and seem to require a special condition for their formation. If the ice were in active flow, such deposits would have been smeared out at the base of the advancing glacier, so that it is postulated that at times and places sections of an ice lobe become dead or stagnant. During this time aggrading streams that flow in tunnels at the base of the glacier fill or nearly fill their ice-walled passage ways with sand and gravel. Then, with the complete melting of the stagnant ice, the winding eskers were left standing above the general ground moraine. Study Fig. 12-36.

Glacial lakes that are fed directly by melt water often receive a thin dark layer of silt in winter and a thick light gray layer in summer. They constitute a year's deposit. Such a pair of layers is called a *varve*. Lake deposits containing hundreds and even thousands of varves have been dissected by later stream erosion and, thus exposed, have been counted and used in the same manner as the annual growth rings of trees in deciphering the history of certain glaciers. By an intricate system of correlation of several varved deposits the time that has elapsed since the glacier made its last stand has been approximated (see Chap. 21).

Suggested Aids

Readings

Field, William O.: "Glaciers," *Scientific American,* September, 1955.

Flint, Richard F.: *Glacial and Pleistocene Geology,* John Wiley & Sons, Inc., New York, 1957.

"The Ice of the Antarctic," *Scientific American,* September, 1962, 132-146.

Péwé, T. L., and E. Church: *Glacial Regimen in Antarctica,* etc., University of Alaska, Department of Geology, Reprint Series, no. 15, 1962.

Maps

Glacial Map of North America, Geological Society of America, Special Paper 61, 1945.

Glacial Map of the United States East of the Rocky Mountains, R. F. Flint, chairman, special colored map of the Geological Society of America, 1959.

Chapter 13

WHAT IS AN EARTHQUAKE?

From the layman's point of view an earthquake is the rumbling, shaking, rolling, and jolting of the earth under and around him. From the scientist's point of view it is the vibration of the earth due to trains of waves that travel through it. The waves originate at a point where much energy is sharply released. The newspapers are most interested in the damage done, lives lost, and the peculiar and humorous situations in which people found themselves or the crazy things that happened to them during the quake. In areas where universities operate earthquake laboratories the public, however, is generally most anxious to learn what the scientist has to say about the earthquake, where it centered, how strong it was, and if there will be any aftershocks.

The science of earthquakes is called *seismology*, the person who specializes in seismology is a *seismologist*, the instruments designed to record the vibrations are

Earthquakes and the Depths of the Earth

seismographs, and the records they write are *seismograms.* Seismology is a division of the larger field of geophysics.

It is estimated by seismologists that about 220 truly great shocks and 1,200 strong shocks occur around the earth each century. Thousands of small shocks occur every day.

Many large earthquakes have been marked at the surface by a fresh escarpment a few inches to 40 ft high or by open fissures. At the site of others there has been

FIG. 13-1 Fault scarp formed at the time of the Hebgen Lake earthquake, near West Yellowstone, Montana.

horizontal slipping of the rock masses on either side of a master fracture. Such examples led geologists many years ago to believe that earthquakes are caused by sudden movements or displacements along faults. Examine Figs. 13-1 and 13-2. However, many small and even some major earthquakes have occurred without the development of a scarp at the surface, and for these it is somewhat difficult to prove that displacement along a fault caused the earthquake. There can be no doubt that the source of the trains of waves is very localized, because the seismograms indicate the source as a fairly definite point. If no fresh fault scarp forms, we can generally relate

the earthquake focus logically to a fault by assuming that the motion was considerably below the surface. See Fig. 13-3 for such a situation. The rocks are sufficiently elastic or plastic to absorb the motion above the focal point without displacement at the surface. In the same way that movement may be localized along a fault in the horizonal direction, so it may be limited in the vertical also.

The localized place of slipping on the fault and the source of the earth waves is called the *focus,* and the vertical projection to the land surface of the focus is called the *epicenter.* See Fig. 13-3.

EXAMPLES OF EARTHQUAKES

Hebgen Lake Earthquake

At 11:37 P.M. on the night of August 17, 1959, a displacement occurred along two faults in the Hebgen Lake and Madison Canyon area of southwestern Montana, just north and northwest of the west entrance of Yellowstone National Park. There are numerous summer cabins and dude ranches around Hebgen Lake as well as several U.S. Forest Service camp sites in the canyon. Although the height of the tourist season was at hand, it was fortunate that the area was sparsely inhabited because the earthquake was of frightful proportions. The first intense shaking lasted for several minutes, and then, at one minute intervals approximately, the ground continued to heave and writhe throughout the rest of the night. Aftershocks that were easily recognizable occurred for two weeks.

The earthquake was recorded on seismographs as far away as New Zealand. Fresh scarps up to 20 ft high were formed. It set up giant waves on 7-mile-long Hebgen Lake, which rolled from one end to the other and back several times, like water in a bathtub would do if one end were lifted a few inches and then set down again. Each time the wave, or *seich,* hit the concrete dam the waters sloshed over the top like a

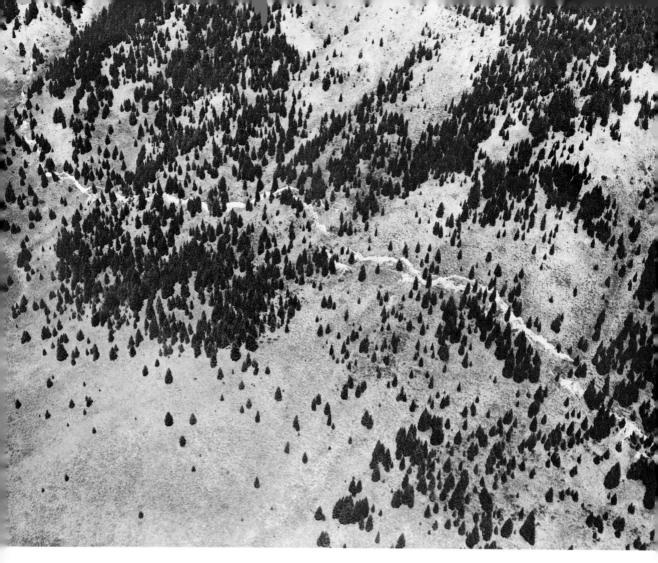

FIG. 13-2 Faulting in Red Canyon, tributary to the Madison River, as seen from the air, incident to the Hebgen Lake earthquake. *(Courtesy of U.S. Geological Survey.)*

giant breaker, 4 ft high and 721 ft wide, the length of the dam. This caused floods down the canyon, but the dam miracuously held, although it was badly cracked, and the spill-way shattered. Some bench marks near the dam settled between 18 and 19 ft. After the quakes subsided, it was evident that the water on the north side of the lake had encroached about 8 ft on boat piers and cabins, whereas on the south side docks and boats were 8 ft out of water.

Many new springs burst forth, old springs increased in flow, and all streams in the area discharged more water than formerly for several weeks. This was due to the com-

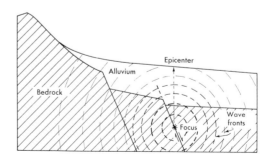

FIG. 13-3 Relation of focus to epicenter. This is an example of a fault displacement not reaching to surface.

FIG. 13-4 Sixteen-foot-high scarp through the Cabin Creek camp site on the Madison River, which formed suddenly on the night of August 17, 1959.

FIG. 13-5 Landslide at lower end of Madison Canyon, caused by Hebgen Lake earthquake. The rock mass broke away from the crest of the ridge and steep canyon wall. *(Courtesy of U.S. Geological Survey.)*

FIG. 13-6 Madison Canyon landslide viewed from downstream looking upstream. The slide came from the right side (south) and flowed across the valley and up the left side about 300 ft. Note the buried highway and dry river bed. A 4-mile-long lake formed back of the slide dam. (*Courtesy of U.S. Geological Survey.*)

paction incident to the shaking of the sand and gravel water-bearing beds that fill the basin. The compaction excluded some of the water.

Several landslides carried parts of the black-topped highway into the lake. A number of tourists were thus trapped between the slides. Huge rock fragments were dislodged from the steep canyon walls and came crashing down to the highways and canyon bottom. Possibly a hundred tourists were bedded down for the night in the Cabin Creek camp site when a 16-ft-high fault scarp formed directly through the place, (Fig. 13-4), and some giant boulders crushed the life out of two of the campers.

The vibrations tipped off a tremendous land slide at the lower end of Madison Canyon (Figs. 13-5 and 13-6), and an estimated 80 million tons of rock rushed at almost falling velocity down the south canyon wall to the bottom, across the canyon bottom, and about 300 ft up the opposite wall. It split in the process and spilled both up and down the canyon. Many campers were injured, a few of whom died, and 19 more are believed buried beneath the slide. The slide formed a dam back of which a new 4-mile-long lake has formed, covering the highway and several favorite camp sites of the canyon bottom.

Earthquakes in Densely Populated Regions

Earthquakes in densely populated regions often take a great toll of lives, primarily because buildings collapse on the inhabitants and secondarily because of fires and giant ocean waves. The earthquake in Iran near Tehran in September, 1962, claimed over 4,000 lives, mostly in village houses made of mud and straw bricks. The Chilean earthquake of May, 1960, claimed many lives from falling roofs and walls and from landslides down steep mountain slopes that overran parts of several villages. In addition the sea withdrew from one of the embayments and then rushed back in a wall of water up to 35 ft high and drowned hundreds of people. In one village alone, 500 people were drowned.

The terrible Lisbon, Portugal, earthquake of 1755 was much the same. Many people were in church at the time on All Saint's Day when the ground began to shake and writhe with jarring shocks that lasted six minutes. At the end, most of the buildings in the city had crumbled and crashed in rubble, killing a large segment of the population. Here, as in Chile, the water withdrew from the harbor, then rushed back in a wall 50 ft high and drowned thousands more. Fires broke out to complete the destruction. By nightfall 60,000 people had perished.

The San Francisco earthquake of April, 1906, was noted for its cause and the resultant fires. A slip of about 20 ft on the well-known San Andreas fault in a horizontal direction was the cause of the earth tremors. Fires started in numerous places. The earth waves broke the water mains, and firemen and citizens alike were helpless to fight the many blazes, which went uncontrolled. The losses in property and personal belongings exceeded $400,000,000, which would be several billion dollars in terms of the 1963 dollar value. This earthquake and many others since in California have made the people there very conscious of proper building regulations to safeguard against destruction by earthquakes and of precautionary engineering measures, as far as possible, in the construction of dams and bridges, and the results have been very successful so far.

METHODS OF RECORDING EARTHQUAKES

Pictures and chandeliers swing and trees sway during an earthquake. Utilizing this phenomenon, which is the pendulum mechanism, an instrument can be devised that records the earth waves. If a pendulum is hung from a frame that is anchored to the rocks of the earth's crust, then, as the waves pass by, the frame moves back and forth, but the pendulum tends to stand still (Fig. 13-7, top). It appears, however, as if the pendulum swings and the frame stands still. Now, the swinging of the pendulum can be recorded on a rotating drum either mechanically by a series of amplifying levers or, better, by a light beam. It is evident that a free-swinging pendulum would be difficult to manage. It must be controlled to swing in one direction so as to record its oscillations. See Fig. 13-7, middle. But since the earth tremors may come from any direction, we must set up two seismographs, one with the pendulum swinging in an east-west direction and one in a north-south direction (Fig. 13-7, bottom). With these two pendulums in operation, the approximate direction from which the earth waves come can be determined. Study Fig. 13-8.

The mechanical principle of the seismographs just described pertains to the recording of the horizontal component of motion of the trains of waves that radiate from quakes. Automobiles, trucks, trains, and operating heavy machinery contribute to this background, so that seismographs constructed to record the very small waves cannot be used. With a very low background noise, amplification of 400,000 can be obtained. This means that the oscillations written on the seismogram are 400,000 times as large as the actual earth waves. At such amplification a nearby earthquake, although very small, might throw the oscillations off the record sheet.

READING THE SEISMOGRAMS

In order to read a seismogram, it is necessary to understand the kinds of waves propagated through the earth. There are two basic kinds of waves namely, the pressure type (P) and the shear type (S). By pressure type is implied the transfer of energy by compression and expansion, as exemplified by striking a long rod of steel on one end with a sledge hammer and

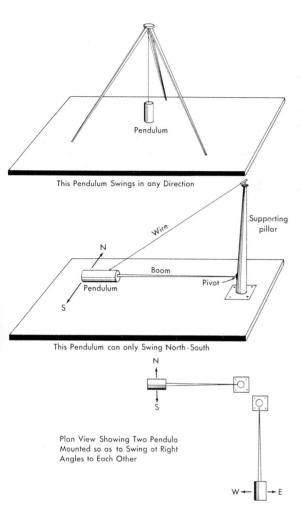

FIG. 13-7 The mechanical principle of the horizontal seismograph.

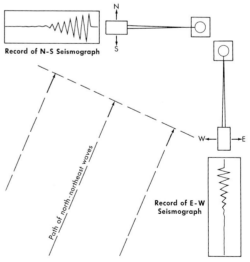

FIG. 13-8 Simplified version of seismograms recorded by two horizontal seismographs for a certain wave train. The N-S seismograph records greater amplitudes than the E-W seismograph for the waves traveling to the north-northeast.

earthquake foci. Special instruments, called vertical seismographs, must be constructed to record the vertical component of motion, and modern seismograph stations are equipped with both horizontal and vertical seismographs. See Fig. 13-9.

Actually, there are several kinds of earth waves with several frequencies. There are long-period and short-period waves, and different instruments must be constructed to record each. Like radio, there is more or less background noise that at some stations obscures the incoming waves of earth-

FIG. 13-9 Seismographs for detecting earthquakes in the seismograph laboratory, Geophysics Department, University of Utah.

noting the bounce that is imparted to an object in contact with the other end. A compressional wave travels down the bar. Compressional waves travel about 5.5 km per sec through granite, 6.5 through basalt, and about half as fast through unconsolidated sediments.

In shear waves the rock particles vibrate transverse to the direction of travel. If a rope is tied to a post at one end and you hold it taut by the other, then give it a sharp shake, a wave proceeds from your hand down the rope to the post. It is reflected back up the rope to your hand, then back and forth until it dies out, owing to the internal friction in the rope.

Now, if an earthquake occurs at a point as shown in Fig. 13-10, waves will radiate in all directions. Both pressure and shear waves will travel into the earth and will pursue a curved path to the seismograph station, owing to the increase of wave velocity with depth. But other trains of waves will follow the surface, and these are the ones that are recorded with greatest amplitude on the seismograms. They are labeled L waves on seismograms, and their motion is complex. Thus for simple purposes we have to deal with P waves and S waves through the earth and L waves along the surface.

The P waves travel 1.73 times as fast as the S waves and reach the seismograph station first. The S waves arrive next, and the L waves last. The L waves are the large waves on the seismogram. A seismogram for a somewhat distant earthquake will then look like the one shown in Fig. 13-11.

The difference in time between the arrival of the P waves and the S waves is a

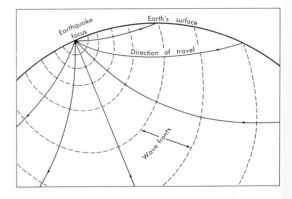

FIG. 13-10 Nature of wave propagation from an earthquake focus in the earth.

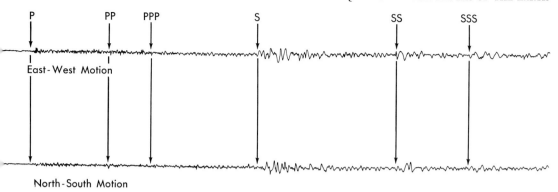

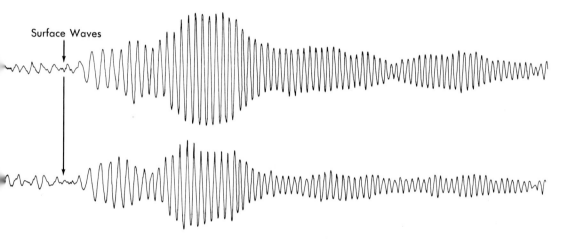

FIG. 13-11 Kermadec Islands earthquake of February 27, 1955, as recorded on horizontal seismographs at the University of Utah. The lower two records are a continuation on the right of the upper two. *(Courtesy of S. T. Algermissen, with wave arrivals determined by him.)*

measure of distance between the earthquake and the seismograph station. Tables have been worked out that can be referred to in order to note the distance away of the quake. The basic travel-time curves of the three waves are given in Fig. 13-12.

In the case of the Kermadec earthquake, whose seismograms, as recorded in Salt Lake City, are shown in Fig. 13-11, we note that, in addition to the arrivals of the P and S waves, PP and PPP, and SS and SSS are designated. These letters represent reflected P and S waves. In Fig. 13-13 it will be seen that from the Kermadec focus one path

leads directly although in a curved line to the seismograph station. The first arrivals of these waves are indicated by P and S on the record. Another path reaches the seismograph after having been reflected once from the surface. Waves along this path arrive after those of the direct path and are labeled PP and SS. Still another path is one of two reflections, and waves pursuing it reach the station still later. They are labeled PPP and SSS. These several waves give you some idea of the complexity of wave trains that are recorded, and in reality it is still more complex. Seismologists

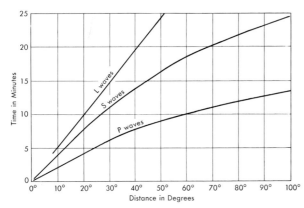

FIG. 13-12   Velocities of P, S, and L waves.

are not just very skillful in deciphering the complex seismograms but have developed the theory of elastic waves through rocks and through the earth to a high degree of understanding.

LOCATING THE EARTHQUAKE

Method of Intersecting Arcs

With two horizontal seismographs at right angles to each other, the approximate direction of the earthquake may be recognized, but it generally cannot be told, for instance, whether it comes from the northwest or southeast. If, in addition, a vertical seismograph is present, then in theory, the single direction can be told. It takes at least three stations to make an accurate fix on the epicenter. One way to do this is to take a map and draw an arc from each station the distance away the earthquake was determined to be. The arcs should intersect in a point on the surface that is the only place that satisfies the data of all three stations. This is the epicenter. See Fig. 13-14.

Depth of Focus

The foci of some earthquakes are far below the surface, but the determination of the depth is generally an intricate job. If

possible, it is best to fix the epicenter and then to hope that a seismograph station is nearby whose record may reveal the depth. Earthquake foci are classed as shallow, intermediate, and deep-seated, and they will be discussed later.

SCALES OF INTENSITY

The intensity of an earthquake may be measured roughly by the degree of damage or the extent to which it was felt at the epicenter and at varying distances away from the center. Twelve degrees of intensity were set up by the Italian seismologist Mercalli and in somewhat modified form these are now used as a simple guide. Lines drawn through the points of equal intensity

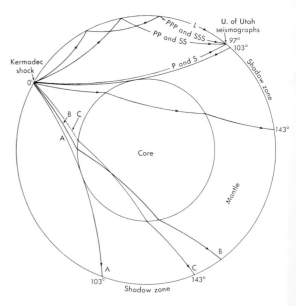

FIG. 13-13   Paths of the Kermadec Islands earthquake waves to the University of Utah seismograph station, and the effect of the core of the earth on the wave paths, producing the shadow zone for P and S waves. The Kermadec epicenter is about 97° away from the University of Utah station, and the shadow zone extends from 103° to 143° away from an epicenter. The P and S wave paths to the University of Utah station, therefore, just missed the core.

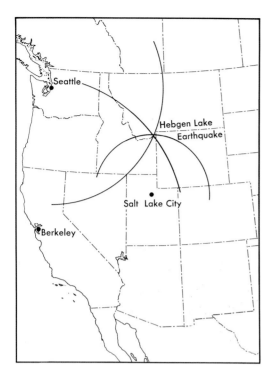

FIG. 13-14 Intersection method of locating earthquake. Arcs were described from Berkeley, Seattle, and Salt Lake City seismograph stations with radii equal to the distance the shock was from each.

generally surround the epicenter and, in fact, locate the epicenter. Figure 13-15 is an example. When an earthquake rocks a certain city, you go to the local newspaper office and note all communications regarding the earthquake. Plot these on a map according to Mercalli's scale, or a more simplified one of your own design, and soon you will perceive where the center of greatest destruction or disturbance is. It is this simple.

However, the Mercalli method is subjective and approximate. It would be better to measure the *energy* released, if possible, and compare earthquakes on this basis. Professor C. F. Richter, of the California Institute of Technology, has proposed a scale of this sort. Several seismograph stations must participate and be equipped with a specified seismograph, so that records are

uniform. Then the largest horizontal trace (amplitude) is measured at each station. From these it can be computed what the maximum trace would have been for a station located 100 km (about 60 miles) from the station. This is the standard of comparison. A scale of these measures is used (the Richter scale) in which the magnitude is based on the logarithm of the amplitude. This means that an earthquake of magnitude 4 records with an amplitude of about ten times greater than one of magnitude 3, and one of 5 about ten times more than one of 4.

THE EARTH'S INTERIOR

The Core and Mantle

Of all geophysical methods of determining the nature of the earth below the observable skin or crust, seismology is the most useful. Of course, all avenues of research must be integrated for maximum results, but the study of waves that have penetrated deeply in the earth is the best and most informative guide.

Perhaps the most positive information that earth waves have given us is that the

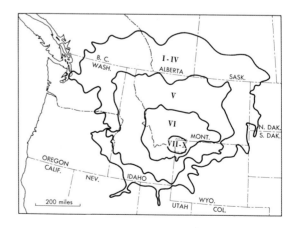

FIG. 13-15 Isoseismals of Hebgen Lake earthquake of August 17, 1959. This is according to the modified Mercalli scale. *(From U.S. Earthquakes, 1959, U.S. Coast and Geodetic Survey.)*

earth has a core that is decidedly different in physical properties from the shell around it. Waves that pass through the core are slowed down or damped out. From Fig. 13-16 it can be seen that the P waves increase in velocity to a depth of about 2,900 km and then suddenly fall off to about their near-surface velocity. The S waves are absorbed or damped out completely at this depth. They have reached the outer boundary of the core. The paths of travel of the waves through the earth are made com-

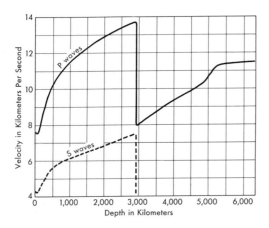

FIG. 13-16 Velocities of waves within the earth. The sudden drop in velocity of the P waves and the damping out entirely of the S waves mark the outer boundary of the core. The leveling out of the P wave velocity curve near the center of the earth is due to an inner core, probably liquid.

plicated by the presence of the core, but they will be understood by the study of Fig. 13-13, which is a cross section of the earth. It will be seen that path A, just tangent to the core, is not deflected but that paths B and C penetrate the core and, in doing so, are *refracted* like light rays passing from the air into water. The interesting aspect of the refractions is that no waves can pass through the earth and reach the surface between A and C. This zone around the earth begins at 103° away from the focus and extends to 143° from it. It is known as the *shadow zone* and in itself is further evi-

dence of the core at 2,900 km below the surface.

The damping out of the S waves and the refraction of the P waves by the core indicate that it has the properties of a liquid. The core, furthermore, is now thought to have an inner solid division, again because seismograms indicate an increase in velocity of the P waves that have passed through this inner core.

As to the composition of the core, three main lines of evidence converge on a single conclusion, namely, that it is composed chiefly of nickel and iron. The first comes from a calculation of Von Jolly of Munich in 1878, in which he showed that the earth has a specific gravity of 5.7 (now reckoned to be 5.5). Since the density of rocks at the surface averages about 2.7, the core must be unusually dense to compensate. The second line of evidence comes from the infalling meteorites (Chap. 23), which are of two general kinds. The metallic ones, principally of nickel and iron, are believed to indicate the composition of the core, and the stoney ones, of iron-magnesian silicates, suggest the composition of the mantle. The third line of evidence comes from consideration of the rotational inertia of the earth. Since seismology fixes the limits in depth between the crust and mantle and the mantle and core, the shells of the earth must have certain densities in order to yield a rotational inertia equal to that determined astronomically. The core is thus believed to be composed of iron and nickel but compressed from their surface densities of 7.9 and 8.6, respectively, to about 9.5. The outer and greater part of the core is probably molten and the inner and smaller part is solid.

Walter Elsasser, of the United States, and E. C. Bullard and H. Gellman, of Great Britain, have shown mathematically that the earth's magnetic field is maintained by circulation in the earth's fluid, electrically conducting core. It is similar to a self-excited dynamo in which the electric current generated by induction in the rotor provides the necessary magnetic field.

Low-velocity Zone in Upper Mantle

The great thick shell from the base of the crust (5 to 70 km below the surface) to the core is called the *mantle*. By volume it makes up the greater part of the earth.

Near the top of the mantle a low-velocity zone has recently been detected. If the mantle were one of uniform increase in velocity with depth, then the wave paths from an earthquake focus would be as shown in the upper drawing of Fig. 13-17. Professor Gutenberg, of the California Institute of Technology, thought he recognized a low-velocity zone at about 100 to 200 km below the surface because the waves did not follow the theoretical paths. In a study of the seismograms of underground nuclear blasts in Nevada and New Mexico Dr. Anderson, also of the California Institute of Technology, has clearly defined the low-velocity zone, as indicated by the travel paths in the lower diagram of Fig. 13-17. The shadow zone is one in which the amplitude of P waves reaching the surface is decreased. The shadow zone extends horizontally from about 100 km from the

focus to a distance of about 1,000 km away. Beyond 1,000 km the amplitude picks up again.

The low-velocity zone is also verified by other types of analysis of seismological data and is of world-wide occurrence, both under the oceans and under the continents. It is probably of utmost significance to crustal deformation and volcanic activity because it represents a layer where the rocks are about to change from the crystalline to liquid condition if, indeed, they have not already done so in pockets in places. The melting curve of rocks from the surface down, as deduced by Anderson, is reproduced in Fig. 13-18, and it will be seen that in the low-velocity zone the rocks are at the incipient melting point. Here, then, is a source of the primary magmas. Here also is a very weak, layer where not only isostatic adjustments can take place readily, such as in response to the melting of ice caps or the building of great deltas, but possibly along which the entire outer 100-km shell can slide on the inner earth. The much discussed postulate of polar migration might thereby be reasonably explained.

Deep-seated Earthquakes

Until thirty-five years ago the mantle below the crust was supposed to be too weak to break and cause earthquakes, but since then many earthquake foci have been fixed at considerable depth in the mantle. The deepest yet recorded occurred at 690 km below the surface. The number per year down to 500 km is shown in Fig. 13-18 (right-hand graph). They are known best in the Kermadec Island arc, the Japanese and Kurile Island arcs, and in the Andes of Peru. In each of these places a deep trench on the ocean floor lies in front of the island arc, or in case of the Andes in front of the continental margin. The earthquakes, especially those below 70 km, lie fairly close to an inclined plane which projects upward to the trench at the surface and which dips

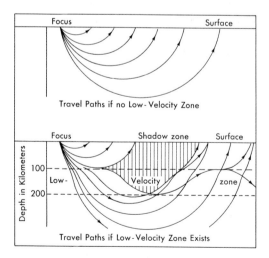

FIG. 13-17   The shadow zone, or zone of decreased amplitude of L waves, which is due to the low-velocity zone 100 to 200 km below the surface. (*After Don L. Anderson, Scientific American, July, 1962.*)

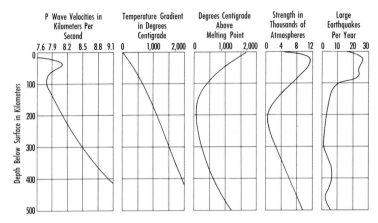

FIG. 13-18 Physical properties of the outer 500 km of the earth, showing the zone of low velocities and low strength. Temperature and strength curves are largely theoretical. *(After Anderson, 1962.)*

under the island arc or continental margin. See Fig. 13-19.

The foci are classed as shallow-surface down to about 70 km, intermediate from 70 to 250 or 300 km, and deep-seated from 300 to 690 km.

Since the foci define a surface of great magnitude that dips to 45° to 60° under the island arc and since the seismograms indicate upward movement of the overriding block, Benioff, of the California Institute of Technology, has postulated that the great plane is in effect a reverse fault along which

horizontal strain in the upper mantle is being relieved. The upper mantle shell, he suggests, is under world-wide compressive stress.

Moho Discontinuity and Layering of the Crust

Any abrupt change in the physical properties of the rocks below the surface causes the earth waves to be reflected and refracted, and such a boundary, when detected, is called a *discontinuity*. Other than the mantle-core discontinuity the most discussed one is the Moho. The word Moho is a short version of Mohorovičić, the name of a Yugoslav seismologist, who discovered the discontinuity.

It lies at an average depth of about 35 km under the continents and 5 to 10 km under the ocean floors and is arbitrarily regarded as the boundary between the crust and the mantle. See Fig. 13-20. By various studies of earth waves, both refracted and reflected, a sharp increase in velocity is noted below the discontinuity. Immediately above, the P waves have velocities of 6.5 to 7.0 km per sec but just below they travel at 8.0 to 8.2 km per sec. These velocities are those of basalt and peridotite or eclogite when measured in the laboratories,

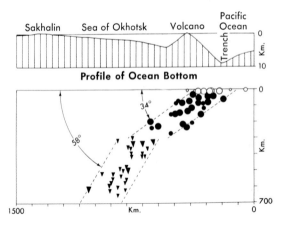

FIG. 13-19 Shallow, intermediate, and deep-seated earthquakes in the region of the Kurile volcanic arc. *(After Benioff, 1955.)*

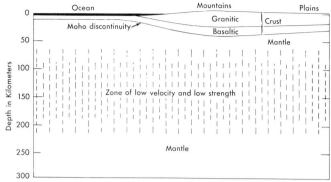

FIG. 13-20 The Moho discontinuity, the crust, and the zone of low velocity in the upper mantle. Note difference in crust of continents and oceans. *(Somewhat after Anderson, 1962.)*

and this with other evidence has led geologists and geophysicists to postulate that the layer of rocks above is made up of basalt or its more coarsely equivalent gabbro, and the upper part of the mantle of peridotite or eclogite. Eclogite has the composition of basalt but is constituted of high-density minerals. Basalt has a density of 3 and peridotite and eclogite of 3.3.

In fact, numerous seismological analyses have led to the recognition of several layers in the crust. Basically there are three layers, the upper consisting of unconsolidated and consolidated sedimentary rocks (low-velocity layer), an intermediate one of igneous and metamorphic rocks, generally referred to as the granitic layer (intermediate-velocity layer), and the lower basalt layer (higher-velocity layer). More recently under parts of the intermountain region of western United States a still higher layer has been discovered by several investigators. The layers with their respective velocities are compared in Table 13-1.

The Moho discontinuity has attracted much attention because answers to im-

Table 13-1 VELOCITY LAYERS OF THE EARTH'S CRUST

Depth, Km	Oceanic crust	Normal continental crust	Continental crust with 7.5 layer
10	6.5–7.0 km/sec Basaltic	1.8–5.5 km/sec Sedimentary rocks	5.73 km/sec Stratified rocks?
20	8.0–8.2 km/sec Mantle	5.8–6.1 km/sec "Granitic" layer	6.33 km/sec Crystalline rocks?
30		6.5–7.0 km/sec Basaltic layer	7.59 km/sec Transition layer, Basalt to peridotite
40			
50			
60		8.0–8.2 km/sec Mantle	
70			
			7.97 km/sec Mantle

SOURCE: Berg, J. W. *et al.*, 1960, Seismic investigations of crustal structure in the eastern part of the Great Basin, *Bull. Seis. Soc. Am.*, vol. 50, pp. 511-536.

portant questions can only come when we know more about the nature of the rocks above and below. Answers would help explain igneous activity and mountain building in the broad sense. Perhaps the recognition of the low-velocity zone in the upper mantle has taken some of the luster from the Moho, but earth scientists still believe it is very important to know for sure what conditions prevail at the discontinuity. The value of such information is appraised sufficiently high by the National Science Foundation to convince it to finance preliminary efforts in the design of drilling equipment. It will be necessary to core in 10,000 to 12,000 ft of water through about 5 miles of oceanic crust to reach the Moho, and the project, known as the Mohole, has attracted much attention. An experimental effort was successful in drilling through about 2,000 ft of sediment on the ocean floor into hard basalt and the recovery of a basalt core.

It appears that geophysicists are closing in on momentous discoveries as the upper-mantle low-velocity zone, the Moho discontinuity, and the 7.5-velocity zone in the lower crust are becoming known and the secrets wrung from them.

DO YOU LIVE IN A POTENTIAL EARTHQUAKE ZONE?

Circum-Pacific Belt

The island arcs and continental margins of the great Pacific Ocean make up the earth's dominant earthquake belt. Tens of thousands of respectable earthquakes have been recorded in this long zone. Figure 13-21 shows only the largest of the shallow earthquakes that occurred between 1904 and 1943. The large dots represent earthquakes of 8½ to 7¾ intensity on the Richter scale, and the small dots those of 7.7 to 7.0

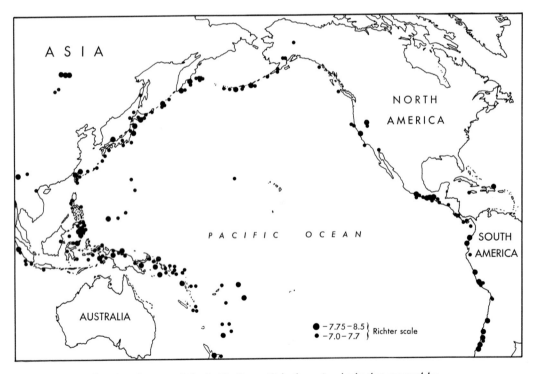

FIG. 13-21   Zone of earthquakes around the Pacific Ocean. Only the major shocks that occurred between 1904 and 1943 are plotted. *(From Gutenberg and Richter, 1945.)*

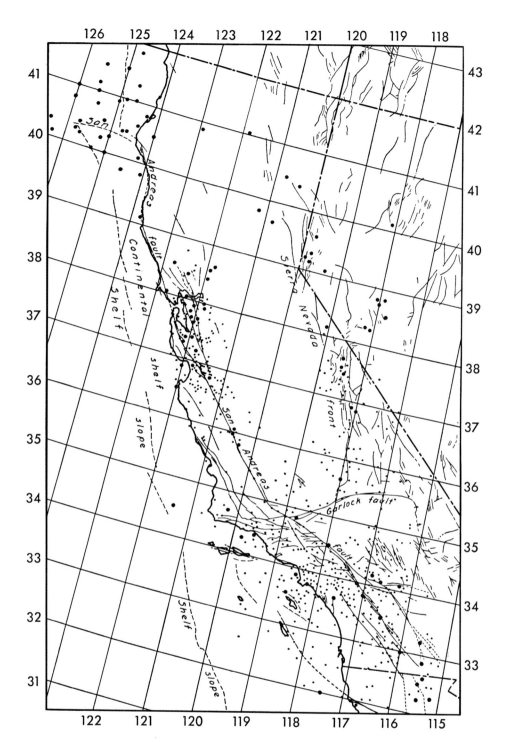

FIG. 13-22 Earthquake shocks and faults of California and western Nevada. The faults are those generally considered to have suffered late Pleistocene or Recent activity. Earthquakes above the magnitude of 5 are shown by large dots, those below by small. In the compilations some earthquakes may have been shown twice because of overlapping and discrepancies in location assignments. *(Earthquakes compiled from Byerly, 1940; Gutenberg, 1941; Byerly and Wilson, 1936, 1937; and tables supplied by C. F. Richter.)*

intensity. These great earthquakes define the zone very well, but if all the smaller shocks were recorded, it would be fairly solid with dots.

Coincident with the circum-Pacific earthquake belt is a volcanic belt. Most of the world's volcanic fields of late geological time, including the volcanoes that are now active, are in this belt. It goes as a necessary corollary of major earthquake and volcanic activity that this is a belt of most active crustal deformation. We are confident that mountains are being built in parts of this belt as energetically and rapidly today as any time and at any place in the geologic past. If we would understand the growth of ancient mountain systems, this is the place to study the phenomenon. The earth's crust is creaking and groaning constantly here in the throes of deformation, whereas other major continental and oceanic regions seem fairly or quite stable.

Earthquakes in North America

Baja California and the Imperial Valley and Coast Ranges of California are part of the circum-Pacific belt of earthquake activity and display the greatest seismicity in North America. Movements on the San Andreas fault, or on its several branches and related subparallel faults, can generally be defined as the cause of the shocks. See Fig. 13-22. The San Francisco Bay area has displayed the greatest activity in historical times, according to Richter,[1] with the Coast Ranges of northwesternmost California second, and the Los Angeles and Imperial Valley areas third.

Another active zone of earthquakes runs through central Utah, southeastern Idaho, western Wyoming, and western Montana into the Rocky Mountain Trench of British Columbia. See Fig. 13-23. The Hebgen Lake earthquake of 1959 is in this zone. Two shocks of intermediate intensity oc-

[1] Charles F. Richter, *Elementary Seismology*, W. H. Freeman and Company, San Francisco, 1958.

curred in Utah during the writing of the manuscript for this chapter (1962). Whereas in California the slippings on the faults are mostly horizontal, here in the Rocky Mountains the motion is vertical, and a dozen or more very fresh scarps of 10- to 90-ft displacement are very striking, such as seen in Figs. 13-23 and 13-24. Some of these scarps have formed in historic times, but some predate the arrival of white man but are so fresh, still, that they must be only a few hundred years old.

The western part of the Great Basin just east of the Sierra Nevada is a very active one, in the same manner as the belt through western Montana, Wyoming, and Utah.

Seismicity is rather inconsequential in the Great Plains, Mississippi Valley, Appalachian Mountains, and Atlantic seaboard and

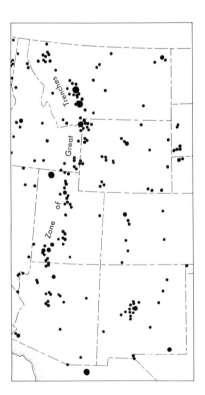

FIG. 13-23 Earthquake epicenters of the Rocky Mountain region showing coincidence of zone of concentrated seismic activity and the belt of trenches. (Taken from a map compiled by G. P. Woolard from U.S. C.&G.S. reports.)

FIG. 13-24 Fresh fault scarp at base of Mount Nebo, central Utah. Two stages of slipping are evident, the combined displacement being about 90 ft.

in all Canada east of the Rockies. However, three major earthquakes have beset parts of this vast continental region and may suggest the possibility of more major shocks near the same centers. Short notes about an intense earthquake in Quebec in 1663 were written by the Jesuits. The area of the St. Maurice River, a tributary of the St. Lawrence, was the center of the activity. Landslides were particularly described.

The New Madrid earthquakes of southern Missouri in 1811 and 1812 shook the region for a year. In Louisville, 200 miles away, 8 shocks were severe, and 1,874 were felt over the year's time. An area in the river lowlands 140 miles long and 35 miles wide sank 3 to 10 ft, water rushed in, and new lakes, swamps, and bayous were formed. See Byerly[2] for details.

Charleston, South Carolina, was the site of another bad earthquake in 1886. A few minor vibrations preceded the major shock, which lasted for 70 sec. Then aftershocks were felt for two years. The size of the area affected was very large and a large amount of energy was released. However, not so much damage, although considerable, occurred there as might be expected.[3]

PREDICTING EARTHQUAKES

The U.S. Coast and Geodetic Survey has published bulletins that itemize almost all earthquakes year by year. When one peruses these accounts, he wonders if there might be a certain frequency or periodicity in place and time to the shocks, and actually a number of efforts have been made to find the formula or law that defines the rhythm and would lead to the prediction of the next quake. Certainly, this is a worthy endeavor, but unfortunately little system has been noted in mother nature's conduct in regard to earthquakes. Davidson's *Studies on the Periodicities of Earthquakes,* of 1938, shows that they occur in greatest proportion in the summer, particularly in July. The tendency, however, is not strong enough to warrant using it to predict, according to Byerly.

We have hopes that modern stations and the recording, plotting, and study of micro-

[2] Perry Byerly, *Seismology,* Prentice-Hall, Inc. Englewood Cliffs, N.J., 1942.

[3] *Ibid.*

seisms will lead us to recognize spots of build-up of strain and that this plus an experience with the earthquake activity in the region will allow us to make some short-range predictions. Also, by establishing a network of benchmarks on either side of certain "active" faults and by reoccupying them at regular intervals to determine shift of the ground, if any, that we can gain some understanding of the limits of strain before a sharp movement will occur. Tilt meters may help in this work also.

Suggested Aids

Readings
Byerly, Perry: *Seismology*, Prentice-Hall, Inc., Englewood Cliffs, N.J., 1942.

Richter, Charles F.: *Elementary Seismology*, W. H. Freeman and Company, San Francisco, 1958.

Movies
What's inside the Earth, Planet Earth Series, WSC-161.

Project Mohole, Planet Earth Series, PSC-193.

Chapter 14

DEFINITION OF FOSSIL

A *fossil* is any evidence of former life. It may be, for instance, a footprint, a mold of a shell, a carbonaceous film of a former leaf, an insect preserved in amber, a chemical replacement of some part of an animal or plant, or a part or whole of the original skeleton or shell. The term "fossil" generally refers to evidence of life that preceded the historical period of the particular place in question. *Paleontology* is the study of ancient life by means of fossils. Since fossils with rare exceptions occur only in sedimentary rocks, they provide significant information about the conditions of deposition of the sediments. They reveal the climate and the life of the habitat at the time. Fortunately fossils are abundant in many sedimentary layers, and all major divisions of plant and animal life are represented by them. Because of this, the paleontologists have been able to construct an absorbing panorama of life through the ages. Later chapters in this book will deal

Fossils
in Sedimentary Rocks

with the evolution of life through geologic time, but at the present we will be concerned with the ways in which fossils are formed and the principal kinds of animals and plants in fossil form. It is hoped that you can take a field trip at this stage to some fossil-bearing strata and collect specimens. These should be compared with the illustrations on following pages, where representatives of many common forms are shown.

HOW FOSSILS ARE FORMED

Preservation by Burial

Fossil remains of shelled forms that lived in shallow marine waters are most abundant. There, clay and silt particles or tiny crystals of calcium carbonate were accumulating rapidly and buried the shells. It is commonly said that there are two prerequisites for the preservation of life forms, namely, that the life forms possess hard parts and that these become buried soon by fine or fairly fine clastic sediments or chemically precipitated carbonate muds. These prerequisites do not always hold, as we shall see, but they stress the common conditions for fossilization. If water does

not percolate through the enclosing sediments, then the original shells may remain for us to see millions of years later when we split apart the layers of sedimentary rock (Fig. 14-1). If water moves through the sediments, the shells may be dissolved away, leaving a mold of the shell. The molds commonly retain the details of the shell's features and serve very well for identification. Sometimes we find only casts of the shells, sometimes molds of the exterior, and sometimes molds of the interior of the shells. The soft parts of an animal that dies on the shallow sea floor readily decay, and only the hard parts are left entombed in the sediments.

Animals without hard parts, such as the worms and jelly fishes, leave impressions only under the rarest of circumstances. Upon death they must be buried immediately by the gentle fall of fine particles. Waves or currents cannot agitate the bottom before or during burial, else the organic parts will be disturbed and destroyed. See Figs. 16-17 and 18-2. Worms leave trails and burrows in the bottom sediments, but these are seldom diagnostic of individual species. Some snails and clams burrow in the bottom muds, and such burrows are generally hard to distinguish from worm tubes.

FIG. 14-1   Marine snails in a Jurassic rock of southern England. *(Courtesy of Dr. Ansel Gooding.)*

In some formations the calcium carbonate of the shells has been dissolved away, and then the void neatly filled with another material. Silica is usually the replacement compound. If shells have been replaced by silica, and the enclosing material is limestone or dolomite, the enclosing material (matrix) may be dissolved away with hydrochloric acid and some remarkable specimens freed from the rock. See Fig. 18-29.

The normal procedure is to crack and split the rock layers with a hammer or chisel and hope that the split will circumvent the fossil rather than cross it. The acid treatment is a very gentle one and is used principally where silica replacement of fossils in a carbonate matrix has occurred.

Anyone who has traveled the semiarid plains or the deserts will have noted that cattle or horses that die there putrify for a season or so, and soon only their skeletons are left. In the open air, exposed to the variable weather, even the bones disintegrate and turn to powder, rendering a small amount of soluble calcium phosphate to the soil underneath. But here and there, especially in old river flood-plain silts and in sand bars of rivers, we find bones in a good state of preservation (Fig. 14-2). Occasionally we find an entire skeleton with the bones assembled as in the living animal. This would be called an *articulate* skeleton. We believe that in such specimens the carcass had not decayed to the point that the bones came apart from each other before it was safely buried by the river silts or sands. In the event that articulate skeletons are found in sand deposits that are manifestly fills of river channels, then we presume that the animal died near the river edge, that the carcass, perhaps bloated by partial decay, was caught up by the river and carried downstream some distance until it stranded on a bar. For preservation it must have been buried soon, before much further decay set in.

In the case of the "dinosaur quarries" in the Morrison formation of the Rocky Moun-

FIG. 14-2 Mass of bones in a sandstone bed of the Harrison formation in Nebraska. Three genera are represented: a clawed ungulate, a giant pig, and a small rhinoceros. See Chap. 20. This may have been a quicksand water hole. (*Courtesy of the Smithsonian Institution.*)

tain states the bones are found all mixed up. Not only are the bones of one individual disarticulate and mixed up in a sand and silt matrix, but those of many individuals of several species are found in a mixture without order. In the dinosaur "dig" of the University of Utah near Price, Utah, under the direction of Professor William Lee Stokes and James Madsen, about 12,000 bones have been taken out during the past three summer field seasons (Fig. 14-3). These, upon fitting together, belong to at least 40 individuals of 7 quite unlike species. Professor Stokes interprets the deposit to have been a quicksand marsh into which the dinosaurs wandered for food or water and foundered. Decay of the flesh and tendons followed to such an extent that the

FIG. 14-3 Top, main part of the "dig" of the University of Utah dinosaur excavation; middle and bottom, bones in place as they are being uncovered. Matrix of sand and silt, fortunately, is fairly soft and easily removed.

bones parted from each other, and then in movements of the quicksand, they became mixed up. The confusion of bones is truly remarkable, and admittedly not clearly understood, even in the quicksand situation.

Organisms such as live in reefs cause the precipitation of base structures or scaffolds of calcium carbonate to house or support their soft parts. Various corals, bryozoans, and algae are the chief builders (Fig. 14-4). The hard deposits in part are intricately detailed and serve nicely for the identification of individual species. See Fig. 14-14 and the photographs in Chap. 18. Reefs are both large and small and in the course of time become buried in carbonate and clay sediments. Old reefs are common in certain sedimentary rocks and, of course, are made up almost entirely of the deposits of the organisms that lived there. Reefs are generally fairly porous and in places contain large amounts of oil and gas. In the last twenty-five years these reefs have been a focus of prospecting by petroleum geologists, and the search has been very rewarding.

Fossils of organisms so small that they must be studied under the microscope to perceive the details are called microfossils. Many of these organisms live in the plankton of the seas and, when they die, settle to the bottom to become part of the sediment. If they contain hard parts, and some of them do, like the foraminifers, diatoms, and ostracodes, the hard parts may become preserved very well. Some strata contain myriads of microfossils. Simple crushing of the rock often frees the tiny fossils in suitable form for study. Other treatments are needed for certain rocks. The chips of rock that come from wells drilled for oil contain microfossils in good shape, whereas the larger fossils that might occur are ground to pieces by the bit. The microfossils have proved very useful in the search for oil and will be mentioned again in later chapters.

It has been stressed that the hard parts of organisms are those which are generally fossilized. The hard parts of all the shelled animals are made up of finely crystalline calcium carbonate, either as the mineral aragonite or as calcite. Bones are a complex of calcium carbonate and calcium phosphate. Another form of matter that resists decay and fossilizes well is *chitin*. Chitin is the horny substance of which your fingernails are made. The protective leg covers and carapaces of insects, shrimps, and crabs are formed of chitin. Since relatives of the shrimps were abundant on ancient sea floors, there are many fossils of such forms. The *trilobites* are the best example (Fig. 14-8).

Seed and pollen coverings are very resistant to bacterial or chemical decay and last under various conditions for a long time. Hardened pitch, called resin and amber, is also extremely resistant to decay, and specimens of the original substance millions of years old are found embedded in coal beds and other sediments (Fig. 14-5).

Petrification

Petrified wood is commonplace to all mineral and rock collectors. There are large amounts of it in various formations of the Colorado Plateau and in certain volcanic ash beds of Yellowstone Park (Fig. 14-6). It is presumed there are collecting localities in every state of the Union. When we think of petrification, or petrifaction, we think particularly of petrified wood, although the process has affected parts of other organisms. It is the replacement of parts of plants or animals by mineral matter, and in the case of wood, it is generally a substitution by silica of the cellulose material. Commonly the substitution is on a microscopic scale, even molecular scale, so that the small details of the original organic material are reproduced or retained by the substituted mineral. The wood cells and growth rings of trees are commonly visible in petrified wood. **Lapidaries** like to slice petrified tree trunks with their diamond saws and then polish the surfaces. On these polished sur-

FIG. 14-4 Algal heads (Stromatolites) in Gateway Formation (Beltian), Cranbrook, British Columbia. *(Courtesy of Geological Survey of Canada and G. B. Leech.)*

faces we can see that holes must have developed through decay in the wood and that these were filled by masses of homogeneous silica. We can see a ghost structure of the annual growth rings in other places, but not the cell detail, so that it is evident that the replacement and filling were irregular and diverse in nature.

In the Colorado Plateau much of the petrified wood was originally drift logs, buried in shore-line and river sands and silts. We postulate first that the waters percolating through the sand carried silica in solution and, in order to do this, were basic (alkaline) in their reaction. Now, in coming into contact with the buried logs, the decay of which releases carbon dioxide gas, the basic condition of the water is neutralized by the acid-forming gas, and

FIG. 14-5 Caddis fly in amber. This comes from the Baltic Sea coast of East Germany. (*Courtesy of the Smithsonian Institution.*)

the silica is precipitated. This can be an intimate reaction-replacement affair, and when so, the cellular structure of the wood is reproduced by the silica. The wood that is particularly prized by the collectors not only shows the growth rings well (Fig. 19-2) but also has rich colors of red and brown. The conifers are most commonly petrified, and the botanist can usually identify the particular variety from the cellular structure.

Tracks and Trails

The tidal flats of the present and the past are and were an ideal place for the making of impressions in the wet mud and their subsequent preservation. Imagine the modern tidal flat, perhaps a mile wide. Any organism that moves on the soft mud will leave a track or a trail of some kind. The slithering worm, the crawling crab, the birds that land, walk around, and take off, or the small reptiles and mammals that search the tidal flats for food—all leave their tracks and trails.

With the incoming tides, if gentle, a new layer of mud will be spread over the impressions and thus preserve them. Any geologic setting in which wet sediment is exposed and then soon covered with a new layer is favorable for the formation of fossil tracks.

The burrows of worms are among the

FIG. 14-6 Petrified logs standing where they grew and where buried by volcanic ejecta. They are now being exhumed by erosion. (*Courtesy of Erling Dorf.*)

oldest of fossils, and the footprints of man in buried and hardened volcanic ash are among the youngest. Some tracks and trails are very puzzling and perhaps were made by animals that have left no other record of their existence. They may have been species, now extinct, of which we have no further evidence, and attest to the incompleteness of the organic record through geologic time.

When a layer of fine-grained sedimentary rock is split apart, and we find prints of various kinds, there will be the actual imprint in the lower layer and the mold in the upper layer. In the case of a footprint the mold will be in effect a cast of the lower part of the foot.

Carbonaceous Residues

Imprints of leaves are very abundant in many fine-grained sedimentary rocks. The soft foliage of ferns, palms, conifers, and the modern flowering plants are all represented in profusion in fossil form, from which the species may be identified. Leaf fossils are usually simply films of carbonaceous material. The hydrogen and oxygen of the leaf compounds are gone, but fortunately a small amount of carbon is left as a residue. There may be very little relief to the fossil, but the carbon film usually shows the veins and outline of the leaf in minute detail. The durable surface cuticle of the leaves probably contributes mostly to the carbonaceous films on sedimentary layers. Insects are fossilized in the same way (Fig. 14-7).

Lignite, bituminous coal, and anthracite coal are residues of plants that lived and died in profusion in swamps of the past. In swamps like these, bacterial decay terminates before the plant matter is completely dissipated, because the by-products of the decay prove toxic to the bacteria. A residue results that is made up largely of carbohydrates of various kinds, but contained in the peat and coal in places are cellular fragments that may prove sufficient to identify the plant or plants that lived in the ancient swamps.

VARIETIES AND NUMBERS OF FOSSILS

As you have already surmised, the number of fossils already collected of all varities is so vast that no one has any idea of the magnitude. Museums, universities, institutes, and private collections the world over contain millions of them. And countless more remain buried in the strata, awaiting exposure by the processes of erosion.

Even so, the fossil record is incomplete. Paleontologists and biologists are most interested in obtaining unbroken racial histories (phylogenies), because such records would clarify many of the problems of evolution. But, unfortunately, there are gaps in the fossil record, and unbroken lines of descent through time are for the most part wanting. The fossil record tends to be weakest in those forms which would

FIG. 14-7 Fossil imprint in volcanic tuff of a crane fly (family Tipulidae) from southwestern Montana. *(Courtesy of Henry Zuidema.)*

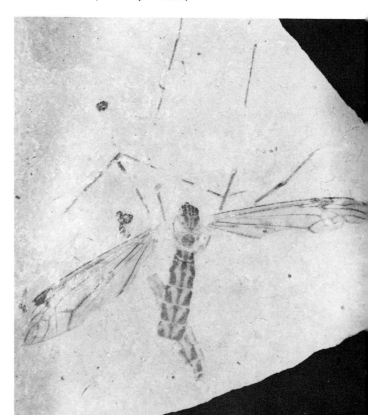

shed light on the origin and the early stages of development of the major groups. As we shall see, fossils do not appear in abundance and variety until well along in earth history and represent complex animals, fairly advanced in any evolutionary scheme. There are fossils older than this, but they are few, fragmentary, and poorly preserved, so that the long evolutionary beginnings of almost all major invertebrate groups are unknown. Not only our inquisitiveness into the origin of many species is thwarted by the paucity of the fossil record, but our inquiries into the appearance of life on the earth are pretty much stifled.

The record is incomplete particularly because organisms without hard parts do not fossilize well. Small and delicate forms decay quickly and except under very special conditions leave no evidence of their existence. Such forms may have made up major parts of the early lineage of certain groups. Gaps in the record result from interruptions in sedimentation or from shifting environments, causing the transfer of populations from place to place. A complete record would only be written where a group originates, evolves, and dies out in one place, while sediments were accumulating continuously and representative individuals were becoming fossilized in fair numbers. These conditions rarely existed.

On the brighter side of the ledger, however, are some remarkable phylogenies in fossil form. The horse, for instance, is first recognized in ancient river silts of the Middle West as a small creature the size of a fox, and in the course of about 40 million years his history is followed, with few interruptions, to the large wild horse of yesterday, geologically speaking, which is the parent of our domesticated and selectively bred types. The evolution of many branches from the central trunk is also known.

Other classical evolutionary groups of animals, both invertebrates and vertebrates, will be mentioned in later chapters.

CLASSIFICATION OF PLANTS AND ANIMALS

Need to Understand Classification

We cannot proceed intelligently without an introductory understanding of the classification of living organisms, and the following outline is presented for your perusal and for reference when later chapters are being read. All organisms are divided into three *kingdoms*: the simple and primitive forms, the *Protista*; the multicellular forms that make their own food, the *Plantae*; and the multicellular forms that cannot make their own food, the *Animalia*. The main divisions of the kingdoms are called phyla (phylum in singular).

Table of Classification

The following table was taken from Stokes (1960) with minor changes; it in turn is similar to classifications of Schrock (1955), Easton (1958), and others:

Kingdom *Protista* (simple and primitive organisms)

Subkingdom *Monera*
Phylum *Schizomycetes*
The bacteria, 1,300 species, Precambrian-Recent
Phylum *Cyanophyceae*
The blue-green algae, 1,500 species, Precambrian-Recent

Subkingdom *Protoctista*
Phylum *Chlorophyceae*
The green algae, 5,500 species, Ordovician-Recent
Phylum *Chrysophyta*
The diatoms, 5,000 species, ?Jurassic-Recent
Phylum *Phaeophyceae*
The brown algae, 1,100 species, ?Jurassic-Recent
Phylum *Rhodophyceae*

The red algae, 2,500 species, ?Ordovician-Recent

Phylum *Eumycophyta*
The fungi, 53,150 species, Devonian-Recent

Phylum *Protozoa*
The amoeba and kin, 30,000 species, ?Cambrian-Recent

Kingdom *Plantae* (multicellular organisms that can make their own food)

Phylum *Bryophyta*
The mosses and liverworts, 23,000 species, Devonian-Recent

Phylum *Tracheophyta*
Plants with vascular tissues, 261,000 species, Cambrian-Recent

Subphylum *Lycopsida*
The clubmosses and kin, 1,000 species, Silurian-Recent

Subphylum *Sphenopsids*
The horsetails, 25 species, ?Silurian-Recent

Subphylum *Pteropsida*
Ferns and seed-bearing plants, 260,000 species, Devonian-Recent
Class *Filicinae*
The ferns, 9,280 species, Devonian-Recent
Class *Gymnospermae*
The cone-bearing plants and kin, 630 species, Permian-Recent
Class *Angiospermae*
Flowering plants, 250,000 species, Jurassic-Recent

Kingdom *Animalia* (multicellular organisms that cannot make their own food)

Phylum *Porifera*
The sponges, 4,000 species, Precambrian-Recent

Phylum *Coelenterata*
The corals, jellyfish, and kin, 9,000 species, ?Precambrian-Recent

Phylum *Bryozoa*
The "moss animals," 12,000 species, ?Cambrian-Recent

Phylum *Brachiopoda*
The "lamp shells," 20,000 species, Cambrian-Recent

Phylum *Mollusca*
The "shellfish" (gastropods, pelecypods, cephalopods, and others), 73,000 species, Cambrian-Recent

Phylum *Annelida*
The segmented worms, 6,000 species, ?Precambrian-Recent

Phylum *Arthropoda*
The joint-legged invertebrates (trilobites, crustaceans, centipedes, insects, spiders, etc.) Cambrian-Recent

Phylum *Echinodermata*
The starfish and kin, 5,000 species, Cambrian-Recent

Phylum *Chordata*
Vertebrates and kin, 58,000 species, Ordovician-Recent

The phyla are divided into classes, the classes into orders, the orders into families, the families into genera (genus in singular), and the genera into species. The sequence of subdivisions for man is:

Phylum *Chordata*
Class *Mammalia*
Order *Primates* (lemurs, monkeys, apes, and men)
Family *Hominidae* (all men)
Genus *Homo* (more advanced primitive man and modern man)
Species *Homo sapiens* (modern races of man)

Species are composed of individuals so similar in functions and habits that they breed freely together. Genera are composed of related species which rarely interbreed or which, when they do, usually produce sterile offspring. You will notice on many of the fossil illustrations that the names are given in two italicized words: the first indicates the genus and the second the species. Your scientific name is thus *Homo sapiens.*

DESCRIPTION
OF MAIN FOSSIL GROUPS

Objectives

On succeeding pages are illustrations of the most common types of invertebrates. Undoubtedly, if you go on a collecting trip you will bring back specimens that can be matched fairly closely with one or more of the forms depicted. The illustrations and accompanying descriptions are planned to give you an impression of the many common varieties of fossils, the great variation within the individual phyla, and a reference compendium for use when you study future chapters and take up fossils in the laboratory.

Trilobites

Trilobites are jointed appendaged invertebrates belonging to the phylum Arthropoda and the class Trilobita. They are related to the class Crustacea, which includes lobsters, crayfishes, shrimps, crabs, barnacles, and ostracodes and may be the direct or indirect ancestors of all joint-legged invertebrates. See Fig. 14-8.

Trilobites themselves consist of a head (cephalon), thorax, and tail (pygidium), all of which have three lateral divisions. These are called lobes, and hence the name "trilobite." The fossils depicted in Fig. 14-8 are very different from each other, but all have the three longitudinal and three lateral divisions. What we see in. fossil form is generally the impression of the chitinous dorsal cover (carapace). The appendages were underneath and are only occasionally fossilized. They served for crawling, swimming, and breathing. The animals molted their carapaces from time to time as they grew, and these form almost all the fossils. Stages in the development of the individual have been determined by means of comparing the successive castoffs. During the larval stage only head and tail shields were present, and

during this stage of growth several molts occurred. During the adolescent stage molts occurred each time a new thoracic segment was added, and during adult life additional molts occurred, which permitted increase in size but did not indicate further addition of segments. The characters exhibited during these growth stages serve to define the evolutionary branches of the trilobites and the main divisions of their classifications.

The central lobe of the head is generally well defined and shows traces of at least five original segments, and these correspond to pairs of appendages on the ventral side. The side portions of the head usually are divided by a line, the facial suture, into an inner part and an outer part. The outer part carries the eyes, if present. Many species had a pair of raised, outward-facing, compound eyes provided with numerous facets. As many as 15,000 facets may occur on one of the compound eyes. Some trilobites carried only a simple eye, and some were blind.

The pygidium, like the cephalon, was formed by fusion of several segments, with paired appendages underneath for each ancestral segment. Some of the more advanced and later trilobites had the ability to roll up and thus protect their softer ventral parts. See Fig. 18-9.

In Fig. 14-8 the genus and species names are given as well as the period of geologic time during which the particular form lived. The periods of time are taken up in later chapters.

All trilobites are extinct; yet they lived in great profusion for a long time in earth history.

Brachiopods

Brachiopods are marine invertebrates that have two unequal shells or valves, the larger generally being the pedicle valve and the smaller the brachial. They are bilaterally symmetrical when viewed normal to the hinge line, as may be seen in all the

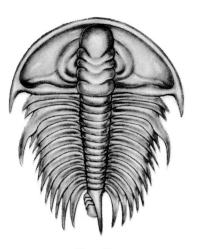

Olenellus
Lower Cambrian x½

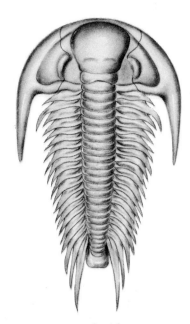

Paradoxides
Middle Cambrian x½

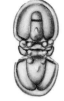

Peronopsis
Middle Cambrian x3

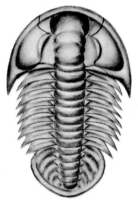

Bathyuriscus
Middle Cambrian x1

Olenus
Upper Cambrian x2

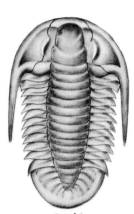

Saukia
Upper Cambrian x1

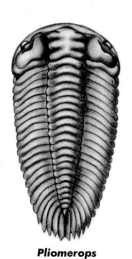

Pliomerops
Ordovician x1

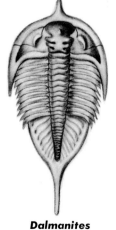

Dalmanites
Silurian to Devonian x½

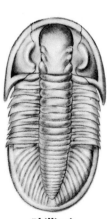

Phillipsia
Mississippian x2

FIG. 14-8 Representative trilobites.

forms shown in Fig. 14-9. The shells of almost all species consisted of calcium carbonate, but some had chitinous shells impregnated with calcium carbonate and phosphate. During all or part of the existence of the brachiopod after the free-swimming larval stage, the animal is attached to the sea bottom by a fleshy stalk, called the pedicle, that sometimes projects posteriously between the valves or more commonly through an opening in one of the valves, which thus is called the pedicle valve. The other is called the brachial valve. Some brachiopods are anchored by projecting spines (Fig. 18-29) or even by the pedicle valve that may have become cemented to foreign objects.

Both valves are generally convex, but one may be flat or even concave. One may be cone-shaped, with the other fitting like a lid upon it. In simple, nonhinged varieties (inarticulates) the two shells may be nearly flat or disc-shaped. More advanced types (articulates) have hinge teeth on the pedicle valve that fit into sockets on the brachial valve. Some varieties have considerably extended hinge lines. In all advanced types of brachiopods, the delicate fleshy arms that serve to propel food particles toward the mouth (brachia) are supported by calcified projections attached near the beak of the brachial valve. The spirally coiled ribbons of Fig. 18-15 are silicified brachial supports.

Some brachiopod shells are smooth except for the concentric growth markings. Almost all, however, have radiating striae, plications, or ribs that strengthen the shell materially. From some of the small inarticulates to the large articulates they range in longest dimension from ⅛ to over 6 in. The shape, size, and markings in many varieties and combinations have enabled the paleontologist to name some 20,000 species.

The organs of the creatures between the two valves relate the brachiopods to the bryozoans. From the shells alone you would think that they were a division of the mollusks.

Pelecypods

The pelecypods (clams and oysters) are bivalved aquatic mollusks with a bilaterally symmetrical body and generally equal sized and symmetrical valves. The brachiopod shell is bilaterally symmetrical when viewed normal to the hinge line with one large valve and one small valve, whereas the one pelecypod valve is the mirror image of the other. The pelecypods have well-developed digestive, circulatory, and nervous systems, but no head, and in this respect differ from the gastropods and cephalopods and may thus be considered morphologically more primitive. They have a muscular foot that extends anteriorly beyond the shell and may be used for locomotion. Most pelecypods have a membranous mantle that encloses the body and secretes the shell. From it are developed posteriorly two tubes or siphons: one conducts inflowing water with microscopic food and oxygen, and the other outflowing water to remove the waste products. The beak of each valve points forward, and the two valves of most species are held together by two large muscles. The oysters are a notable exception, having only one muscle and unequal-sized valves. The places of attachment to the shells leave easily recognizable muscle scars. At the hinge is an elastic ligament that, when the muscles relax, opens the valves. See Fig. 14-10.

External markings on the valves comprise concentric growth lines, projecting laminae, ridges, ribs, folds, nodes, and spines. The structures of the hinge region, musculature, and form of the shell are the chief features used in the classification of the pelecypods.

The pearly interior of the valves is the mineral aragonite, but it is more soluble than calcite (both of which are calcium carbonate), and hence pelecypod fossils are more apt to be found as molds and casts than the brachiopods, which are all calcite.

Some marine pelecypods living today are over 2 ft long, and their shells may weigh

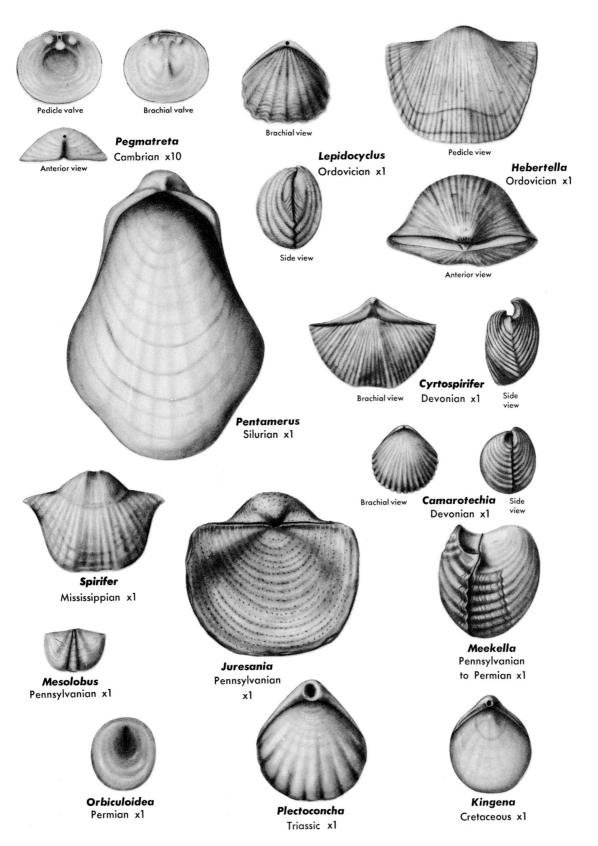

Pedicle valve   Brachial valve

Anterior view

Pegmatreta
Cambrian x10

Brachial view

Lepidocyclus
Ordovician x1

Side view

Pedicle view

Hebertella
Ordovician x1

Anterior view

Pentamerus
Silurian x1

Brachial view   **Cyrtospirifer**   Side
Devonian x1   view

Brachial view   **Camarotechia**   Side
Devonian x1   view

Spirifer
Mississippian x1

Mesolobus
Pennsylvanian x1

Juresania
Pennsylvanian
x1

Meekella
Pennsylvanian
to Permian x1

Orbiculoidea
Permian x1

Plectoconcha
Triassic x1

Kingena
Cretaceous x1

FIG. 14-9 Representative brachiopods.

100 lb. Certain forms of the past, like *Inoceramus*, attained lengths of 3 ft or more. Many pelecypods live in fresh-water streams and lakes.

Gastropods

Gastropods or snails are mollusks with a distinct head and broad foot on which they may slowly crawl. The head is equipped with a mouth armed with horny plates and a rasping process, eyes, and tentacles. Most gastropods have a single spirally coiled or cap-shaped shell, and because of it are called univalves. Some varieties have no shell at all. The shells lack chambers, and this sets them apart from the shelled cephalopods, which are univalves also but which have chambers. See Fig. 14-11.

Gastropods are most abundant in the shallow seas but live also in fresh water. Many live on land and are air breathers (pulmonates). They feed mostly on plants, but some, including the drills, bore small round holes through other shells and feed on the substance of the host. These are thus carnivores. A few are scavengers.

The body of the gastropod is united to the shell by muscular attachment, and generally the animal can draw itself into the shell. An accessory plate on some, secreted by the foot, then closes the aperture.

The shell is secreted by the mantle on its dorsal side. Like the pelecypods the inside is pearly and composed of aragonite. It is thus subject to solution after burial, and therefore in fossil form casts and molds of snails are the rule.

Generally the coiled shell is strongly elevated or screwlike and is carried on the back of the animal with the apex pointed upward and backward. Some shells are coiled in a plane rather than like a bed spring. Each complete coil is called a *whorl,* and in one group the whorls are tightly wrapped about a solid axis called the *columella.* In another group the whorls

wind about an open space called the *umbilicus.*

External ornamentation is highly varied and consists of revolving and transverse lines, grooves, ribs, frills, and spines. In addition the tropical forms have a diversity of brilliant hues and patterns.

Cephalopods

Cephalopods are the most highly organized class of mollusks. The pearly nautilus, bearing a coiled and chambered shell, is probably the best known of the living cephalopods. Other living varieties are the octopuses and the cuttlefishes. There were many varieties in the past, and they make up one of the most important fossil groups. See Fig. 14-12.

The head is provided with large eyes and a mouth with jaws and a powerful horny beak surrounded by fleshy tentacles. The tentacles of the cuttlefishes and octopuses bear sucker discs for grasping objects. Cephalopods breath by gills and are exclusively marine.

The cephalopods are in two main classes: (1) the *tetrabranchiates,* which have four gills and an external shell, and (2) the *dibranchiates,* which have two gills and an internal shell or none at all. The first is represented by thousands of fossil species but only one living species, the nautilus. The second flourished in the Mesozoic and Cenozoic eras and includes the cuttlefishes, squids, and octopuses.

The shell of the cephalopods is coiled in a plane and is bilaterally symmetrical. The body of the animal occupies only the end portion of the outer whorl beyond the last partition (*septum*), which is one of many formed in successive growth stages. These septa and chambers readily distinguish the cephalopod shell from the gastropod.

In Fig. 18-26 a large coiled cephalopod with contained animal is shown in living position. The shell is tightly coiled like some in Fig. 14-12, but in others, like the

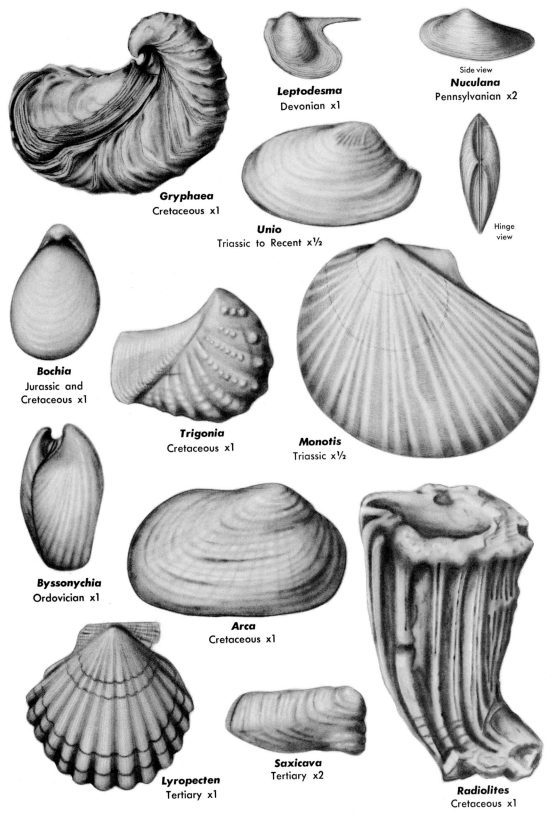

Leptodesma
Devonian x1

Nuculana
Pennsylvanian x2

Side view

Hinge view

Gryphaea
Cretaceous x1

Unio
Triassic to Recent x½

Bochia
Jurassic and
Cretaceous x1

Trigonia
Cretaceous x1

Monotis
Triassic x½

Byssonychia
Ordovician x1

Arca
Cretaceous x1

Lyropecten
Tertiary x1

Saxicava
Tertiary x2

Radiolites
Cretaceous x1

FIG. 14-10   Representative pelecypods.

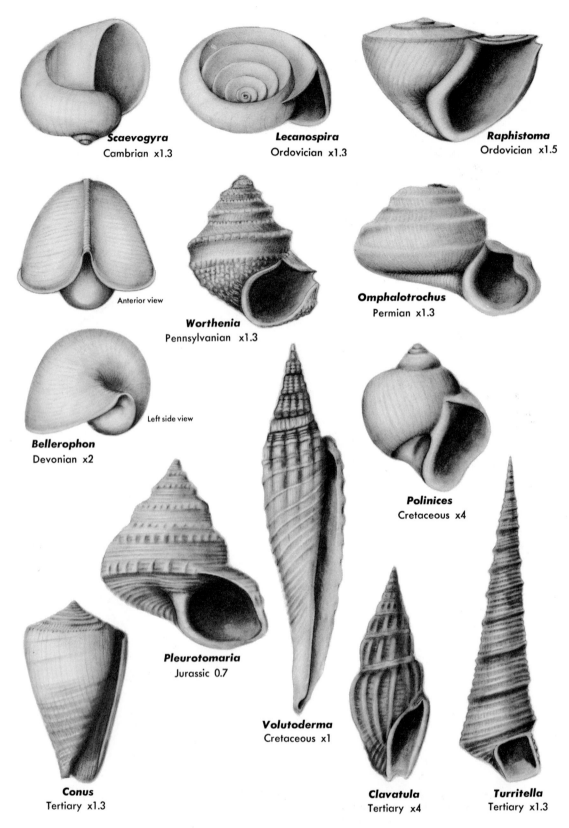

Scaevogyra
Cambrian x1.3

Lecanospira
Ordovician x1.3

Raphistoma
Ordovician x1.5

Anterior view

Worthenia
Pennsylvanian x1.3

Omphalotrochus
Permian x1.3

Left side view

Bellerophon
Devonian x2

Polinices
Cretaceous x4

Pleurotomaria
Jurassic 0.7

Volutoderma
Cretaceous x1

Conus
Tertiary x1.3

Clavatula
Tertiary x4

Turritella
Tertiary x1.3

FIG. 14-11 Representative gastropods.

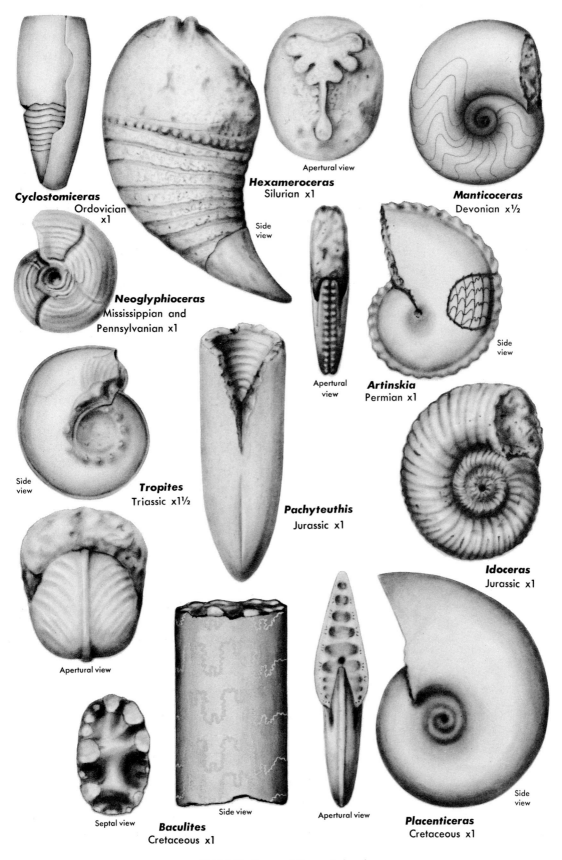

Cyclostomiceras
Ordovician
x1

Hexameroceras
Silurian x1

Apertural view

Side view

Manticoceras
Devonian x½

Neoglyphioceras
Mississippian and
Pennsylvanian x1

Apertural view

Artinskia
Permian x1

Side view

Tropites
Triassic x1½

Side view

Pachyteuthis
Jurassic x1

Idoceras
Jurassic x1

Apertural view

Side view

Septal view

Baculites
Cretaceous x1

Apertural view

Placenticeras
Cretaceous x1

Side view

FIG. 14-12 Representative cephalopods.

living nautilus, each enlarging whorl enveloped and concealed the inner ones. This condition is nearly attained by the lower-right specimen. Other species exhibited openly coiled forms, such as shown in Fig. 18-16, and still others, were long, straight horn-shaped forms (Figs. 18-6 and 18-16).

The junctions of the septa with the outer wall of the shell are termed sutures. They cannot be seen from the exterior unless the outer shell is broken away. The sutures of early Paleozoic cephalopods are straight or gently curved, but as time went on they became angulated and complexly fluted, as may be seen in specimens in Figs. 14-12 and 19-5. The suture diagrams serve nicely for purposes of classification. Some species were thin and disc-shaped, whereas others were broad and rounded. External ornamentation consists of color bands and faint growth lines on the smooth-shelled forms, but others have strong ribs and spines. The lower-middle specimen is a section of a straight form but with complex sutures.

Squidlike cephalopods known as the belemnoids had a solid internal cigar-shaped structure of concentrically laminated and radially fibrous calcite, which are very common fossils of the Mesozoic era (middle specimen of Fig. 14-12).

Echinoderms

The echinoderms are the starfishes, sea urchins, sea lilies, and a host of other less well-known but related forms. They are exclusively marine, and all are characterized by combined bilateral and radial symmetry and by the presence of a skeleton consisting of crystalline calcareous plates embedded in the skin. The mouth is located on the ventral side, which, in free-moving forms, is normally downward but, in forms attached by a stalk, is upward. The echinoderms have a true digestive canal, a distinct body cavity, a vascular and water circulatory system, and an exclusively sexual mode of reproduction. See Fig. 14-13.

The starfishes and brittle stars are bottom-dwelling echinoderms characterized by prominent radial extensions of the central body. The mouth is on the underside, and movement of the starfishes is accomplished by means of slender tubular structures that occur in rows along the underside of the rays. Each "tube foot" terminates in a small sucker disc capable of clinging to objects.

The sea urchins are semiglobular, heart-shaped, or discoid in form. The firm skeleton has innumerable spines on the exterior, with socketlike hollows at the base for articulation with rounded tubercles on the plates of the shell. The spines are thus movable by muscle fibers, and their function is to support the animal, to aid in locomotion, and to defend against prey. There are also delicate tube feet that may be extended through perforations in the plates. These serve for locomotion also, and for respiration.

The sea lilies are the most abundant among the echinoderms in fossil form and are known as *crinoids*. Almost all crinoids are attached by long stems, but some are anchored only during adolescence, becoming free in adulthood. Almost all fossil stems are about 2 ft long, but some are known that are 50 ft long. It is rare that a complete specimen is found in fossil form; usually only sections of the stems and plates of the calyx (head or bud) are preserved. Complete forms are shown in Fig. 18-22. The stem supports the calyx, composed of regularly arranged plates that enclose most of the soft parts of the animal. Emerging from the calyx are well-developed movable arms that gather in food particles. Although there are various numbers of arms, there is a five-fold symmetry in all.

A second group of stemmed echinoderms is the blastoids. These have a symmetrical budlike calyx about ½ in. in diameter and composed of 13 or 14 plates. See specimens in upper-right corner of Fig. 14-13. Five food-groove ambulacral areas extend downward from the summit along the sides.

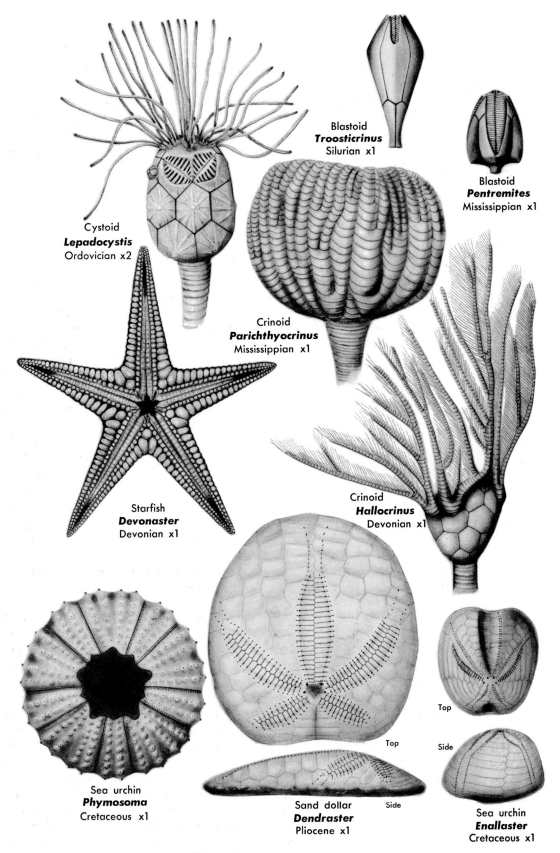

Cystoid
Lepadocystis
Ordovician x2

Blastoid
Troosticrinus
Silurian x1

Blastoid
Pentremites
Mississippian x1

Crinoid
Parichthyocrinus
Mississippian x1

Starfish
Devonaster
Devonian x1

Crinoid
Hallocrinus
Devonian x1

Sea urchin
Phymosoma
Cretaceous x1

Top

Side

Sand dollar
Dendraster
Pliocene x1

Top

Side

Sea urchin
Enallaster
Cretaceous x1

FIG. 14-13 Representative echinoderms.

The cystoids (upper left) had a more or less egg-shaped calyx enclosed in calcareous plates usually pierced by a peculiar system of pores. They were short-stemmed or stemless.

Sponges, Corals, and Bryozoans

Pictured in the upper-left corner of Fig. 14-14 is an example of an extinct group known as the Archaeocyathans. They lived only in Early and Middle Cambrian time, and although once thought to be a strange sort of sponge or even coral, they are now classed as a distinct phylum. Maximum size was about 2½ in. in diameter and 4 in. high. A double-walled, porous, calcareous skeleton was characteristic. They lived singly or in colonies to build reefs. They were world-wide in distribution.

Another spongelike form was *Receptaculites*, which resembled the large center of a sunflower. It is a valuable index fossil of the Ordovician.

The sponges (Porifera) are characterized by a hollow globular or cylindrical structure with a fairly large opening at the top. They grow attached to the bottom as single individuals or joined in colonies and range in size from pinheads to over 3 ft in height. They are mostly marine, but a few species live in fresh water. They lack internal organs, have no nervous system, and are void of circulatory or digestive systems. The majority of sponges have either siliceous or calcareous spicules that are loosely embedded among soft cells or knit together so as to form a strong framework. The spicules are abundant in fossil form.

The coelenterates, to which the corals belong, are more specialized than the sponges but still the most simple organized animals having well-developed body tissues. They are all aquatic and highly varied. The corals are bottom-dwelling marine forms, varied in color, and with their outstretched tentacles are distinctly flower-like. Some are solitary, and some grow in colonies. Most species build a solid calcium carbonate base or skeleton, which is the common fossil. The skeleton is normally secreted by the outer portion of the body wall, which thus either encases the lower part of the coral in a cylindrical or conical tube or forms a fairly flat basal expansion. Radial calcareous walls (*septa*) are built by infolded parts of the body covering. The outer wall is the *theca*, and the central depression the *calyx*.

Bryozoans superficially resemble the coelenterates but differ radically in having a distinct body cavity, an alimentary canal, a highly developed nervous system, and delicate respiratory tentacles surrounding the mouth. With a single exception bryozoans are colonial and secrete a calcareous, horny, or membraneous covering. The calcareous bodies are those generally fossilized and are present in a great variety of forms. The simplest bryzoans build a simple, chainlike series of tubes, one budding from the other. Some grow in slender tuffs, and some spread over shells in a delicate network of interwoven threads. Still others form thin, leaflike expansions, rounded branches, or lacy fronds. The drawings in Fig. 14-14 are all much enlarged, a hand lens being necessary to see the small openings in which the individual animals lived.

Graptolites, Conodonts, Ostracodes, and Foraminifers

The only thing these assorted forms have in common is small size. They all need to be studied under low-powered microscopes and are common groups of the so-called microfossils. See Fig. 14-15.

Most fossil graptolites appear as flattened carbonaceous films on the bedding surfaces of black shale. They look like someone had marked a small saw-toothed pattern with a lead pencil on the shale. They are all extinct, so that we have no living forms to examine for an understanding of their anatomy. The saw teeth are rows of tiny cups each of which housed an individual, and the structure is composed of chitin. In

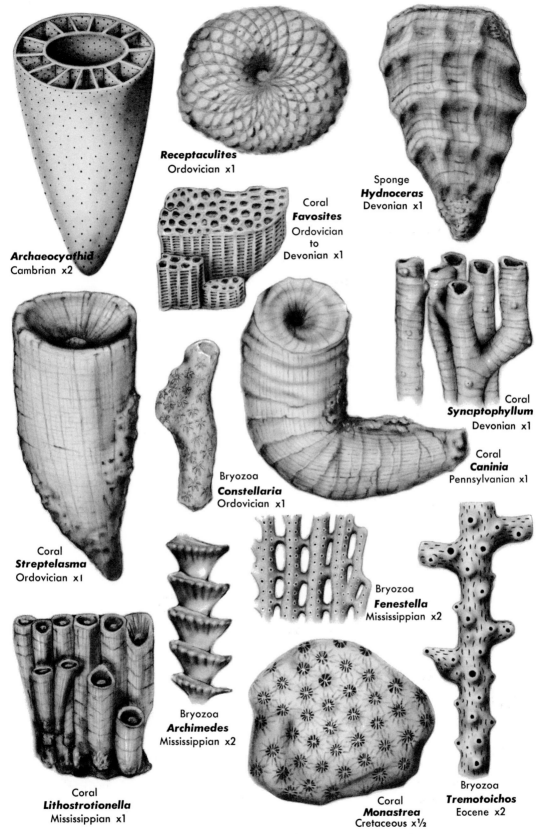

Receptaculites
Ordovician x1

Sponge
Hydnoceras
Devonian x1

Coral
Favosites
Ordovician
to
Devonian x1

Archaeocyathid
Cambrian x2

Coral
Synaptophyllum
Devonian x1

Coral
Caninia
Pennsylvanian x1

Bryozoa
Constellaria
Ordovician x1

Coral
Streptelasma
Ordovician x1

Bryozoa
Fenestella
Mississippian x2

Bryozoa
Archimedes
Mississippian x2

Coral
Lithostrotionella
Mississippian x1

Coral
Monastrea
Cretaceous x½

Bryozoa
Tremotoichos
Eocene x2

FIG. 14-14 Representative sponges, corals, and bryozoans.

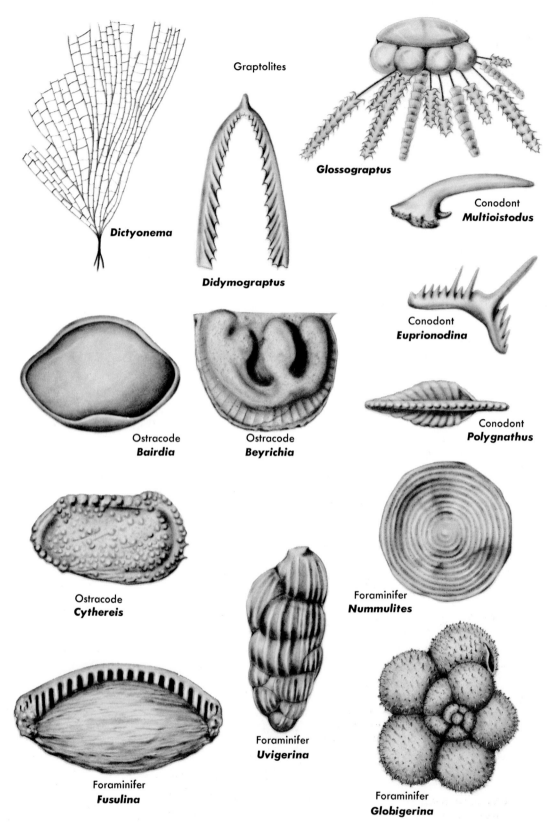

Graptolites

Glossograptus

Dictyonema

Didymograptus

Conodont
Multioistodus

Conodont
Euprionodina

Ostracode
Bairdia

Ostracode
Beyrichia

Conodont
Polygnathus

Ostracode
Cythereis

Foraminifer
Nummulites

Foraminifer
Uvigerina

Foraminifer
Fusulina

Foraminifer
Globigerina

FIG. 14-15 Representative graptolites, conodonts, ostracodes, and foraminifers.

recent years graptolites have been found in limestone, which can be dissolved away, leaving structures much more revealing of the anatomy of the animals. They are now believed to have had a close affinity to the pterobranchs and are included as primitive forms of the phylum Chordata. All were marine.

Most colonies of graptolites are straight or branching stems with the cups on one side or both. Some colonies have a leaf-like shape, and a few were spirally coiled. Some colonies were fixed like plants to the bottom, but others floated freely and spread widely. They diversified greatly during the Ordovician and Silurian periods and are thus good guide fossils.

The conodonts are minute toothlike phosphatic bodies of platy or spiny form that occur in strata of Cambrian to Triassic age. Their considerable variety makes them valuable for correlation. Some authorities have supposed that they are teeth of worms or other invertebrates, and others postulate that they are teeth of unknown fishes. What they are is still a mystery.

The ostracodes are pinhead-sized, bean-shaped, crustaceans housed between two valves. They are profuse today in both marine and fresh water and have been so since Early Ordovician time. Although the fresh-water ostracodes are numerous they are limited to two families, but many varieties occur in the oceans. They exhibit a diversity of surface markings, such as raised lobes, pits or groves, flangelike frills, and projecting spines. Unharmed specimens are common in oil-well cuttings and thus are useful in correlation by the petroleum geologist.

The foraminifers are the most important group of protozoans represented by fossils. They are mostly microscopic in size, but some, the nummulites, attain the size of a half dollar. The shells of most "forams" are composed of calcium carbonate, but a few secrete silica tests, and some have a covering of sand grains, mica flakes, and sponge spicules cemented by either calcium carbonate, iron oxide, or chitin. The structure of the shells ranges from a simple globular or cylindrical chamber to extremely complex, multiple-chambered arrangements. Like the ostracodes they have proved very helpful in correlation by petroleum geologists. The *fusulines* are good guide fossils in the Pennsylvanian and Permian periods.

Suggested Aids

Readings

C. A. Arnold: *An Introduction to Paleontology*, McGraw-Hill Book Co., Inc., New York, 1947.

C. L. Fenton and M. A. Fenton: *The Fossil Book*, Doubleday & Co., Garden City, 1958.

D. L. Jones: *Introduction to Microfossils*, Harper & Row, Publishers, Incorporated, New York, 1956.

A. S. Romer: *Vertebrate Paleontology*, 2nd ed., University of Chicago Press, Chicago, 1945.

H. W. Shimer and R. R. Shrock: *Index Fossils of North America*, John Wiley and Sons, New York, 1944.

Stokes, Wm. Lee: *Essentials of Earth History*, Prentice-Hall, Inc., Englewood, N.J., 1960.

Chapter **15**

ESTABLISHING A SEQUENCE OF GEOLOGIC EVENTS

Earth History and How It Is Discerned

Of basic concern to scientists over the past 100 years has been the history of the earth. How old is it? When were the Alps, Appalachians, and Rocky Mountains built, and which first? What has been the nature of climatic changes, and if the climate changed, how many times and when? How long ago did the dinosaurs live, and what was the earth like in those days? Have the oceans and continents always had the same shape and arrangement? Have the continents been invaded by the seas? In fact, can we define the evolution of the continents from early beginnings? And most absorbing is the procession of life on the earth from remote times to the present. Do we have sufficient fossil evidence to establish the main events in the adaptation of life to changing climates and geog-

Building
the Geologic Record

280

raphies? Do the changes in the plant and animal forms that we recognize in the fossils occur systematically through geologic time and support the theory of organic evolution? What has all this to do with the search for oil and gas, for ground water, and the thousand and one other mineral substances? To answer these questions we must start in a basic and simple way by

events and stack these on top of one another to arrive at a coherent summary of earth history.

Superposition

Considering a series of sedimentary rock layers, the one at the bottom was deposited first, and the one at the top last. The bed

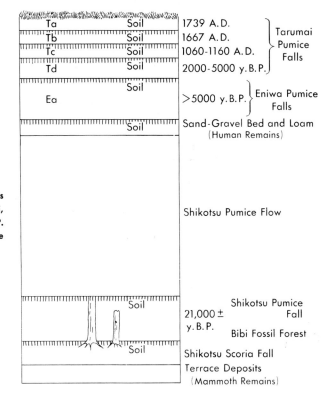

FIG. 15-1 Ash beds of three volcanoes and nine eruptions at Bibi, Hokkaido, Japan. B. P. means years before the present.

building sequences of geological events. You recognize for example that the glaciers eroded the U-shaped valleys after the streams had carved the V-shaped valleys. Soils develop on moraines after the moraines are deposited. The rocks that are cut and offset by faults are older than the faults. Fossils contained in sedimentary rocks represent life forms that lived while the sediments were accumulating. With this brief introduction let us review the simple ways in which we build series of geologic

on top is younger than the bed underneath. This observation is so obvious that it hardly needs to be mentioned; yet it is the most basic guide in establishing a series of events. It is indisputable and regarded as a law in geology. It is called the *law of superposition*.

In the study of volcanoes in Chap. 5 the ash falls from certain volcanoes in Japan were described. For convenience the illustration of these several ash falls, one on top of the other, is repeated here (Fig.

15-1). Let us start at the bottom (oldest) layer and list the series of events that can be discerned from the strata.

The oldest deposits here exposed are river terrace gravels containing fossil remains of the mammoth, now extinct. The mammoth was drawn on the cave walls of France and Spain by men of the Stone Age, and therefore, the great beasts lived contemporaneous with prehistoric man but are now extinct.

of sand, gravel, and loam (silty sediments) in which shell heaps and other evidence of early man's existence have been noted. This layer was probably spread by the shallow sea invading the land and then withdrawing. The sea and shelled animals were evidently nearby at the time of this habitation. Enough time elapsed after the sea withdrew to form a fourth soil.

Now, from another volcanic center some more pumice falls blanketed the area, and

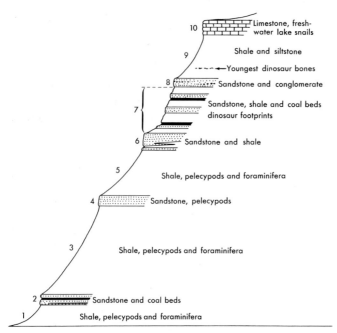

FIG. 15-2 Succession of formations exposed on an escarpment in the Colorado Plateau, near Price, Utah.

On the old terrace gravels was a coarse ash fall (scoria), and on this layer a forest grew and a soil developed. Then came another volcanic ash fall (pumice, this time), which burned and charred the forest in the process of burying it. The charred stumps yield an age of 21,000 ± years by the C^{14} method, which is described in a later chapter. It is evident, therefore, that the mammoths of the river terrace lived some time before this pumice fall. Finally a soil developed on the pumice layer.

Then another thick pumice flow spread over the area. On this was deposited a layer

from C^{14} analysis this occurred about 5,000 years ago. Time lapsed and still another soil formed. Then, a succession of pumice falls from a third volcanic center occurred. An interim of soil formation occurred between each, and the last soil has been developing since A.D. 1739, which is a date recorded in writing by the Japanese.

Now let us look at a series of sedimentary strata in the Colorado Plateau. The sequence is portrayed diagrammatically in Fig. 15-2.

The formations are analyzed as follows, beginning with the lowest:

✦ Dark gray mud, now shale, deposited on a shallow sea floor fairly remote from the shore line. Marine fossil types indicate shallow marine water. An arm of the ocean thus spread over this part of western North America at the time the dark gray muds were accumulating.

✦ The sea retreated bringing the shore line with its sands and river deposits across the former mud bottom, thus spreading layers of sand over the mud. The coast was low and swampy in places, and peat beds formed, later changing to coal.

✦ The sea advanced, and the area again became one of shallow marine deposition of muds. The shore line was fairly distant.

✦ The sea again withdrew, and the shore-line sands were spread across the bottom.

✦ In still another oscillation the sea advanced, and the area again became one of shallow marine mud deposition. The three advances of the sea and the two withdrawals, thus far described, may be due to elevations and subsidences of the land or to rises and falls of sea level.

✦ Advancing and retreating shore line.

✦ The sea withdrew, and the low-lying region became one of river flood-plain and swamp deposition. The swamps were extensive, lasted for a long time, and thick beds of peat accumulated in them. Gigantic dinosaur footprints are common in tops of the coal beds, which were once the swamp peats.

✦ River deposits of sand and conglomerate. Evidently mountains were being uplifted nearby, and floods of sand and gravel were spread over the swamps and broad flood plains.

✦ Extensive river flood plains, on which, red, purple, chocolate, green, and gray muds were spread, succeeded the floods of sand and gravel. The colors are due to the erosion of tropical or subtropical soils in which iron oxides of several kinds produce the various colors.

A few dinosaur skeletal remnants occur in the lower part of this formation, but nowhere has anyone found dinosaur fossils in higher and younger beds. This, then, is apparently the time of extinction of the dinosaurs and is taken arbitrarily to mark the termination of a great era of geologic time, the Mesozoic, and the beginning of another, the Cenozoic. The formal divisions of geologic time will be discussed presently.

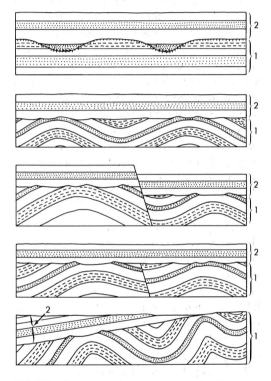

FIG. 15-3 Sequences of events connected with unconformities.

✦ Somewhere nearby an uplift occurred, and a body of fresh water was impounded in which lime mud or marl was the chief deposit. Fresh-water snails and clams are found in the lime muds, now limestone.

Two examples have been described of stratigraphic sequences illustrating the law of superposition and the series of events that we can interpret from them. Other principles for the establishment of a sequence of geologic events must be reviewed before we attempt to say whether the Japanese story is later or earlier than the Colorado Plateau story, and how much.

Deformational and Erosional Events

In many stratigraphic sequences we have to deal with unconformities. Several situations involving unconformities are illustrated in Fig. 15-3.

At the top, the lower series of beds (1) was eroded and then covered by the beds of series 2. If the fossils in series 1 indicate that the beds were deposited in shallow ocean water, then uplift of the beds above sea level must have occurred, whereupon they were dissected by streams. The erosion surface was subsequently buried by series 2. Now if series 2 is the flood-plain deposit of rivers, then we need only postulate a change in the regimen of the streams from one in which they eroded to one in which they deposited. Lowering of gradient by the tilting of the land, change in climate, or an uplift in the headward reaches of the river system might have caused the streams to change from erosion to deposition. If, however, the upper series of beds contains marine fossils, then we must postulate subsidence below sea level after the uplift. So, you can see, a simple unconformity situation, like that shown at the top, contains a significant story.

Referring to the unconformity in the second drawing, we can see that, first, series 1 was deposited, then folded, then eroded, and then covered by series 2. In the third drawing the same sequence of events occurred, but in addition and lastly, the beds were faulted. In the fourth drawing we note that the lower series was folded, then faulted, then eroded, before being covered by series 2.

In the fifth drawing we would read as follows: first, deposition of series 1; second, folding of series 1; third erosion of the folded beds; fourth, deposition of the upper series (2); fifth, tilting of the upper

series and all rocks underneath; and sixth, erosion of the tilted beds.

Figure 15-4 is a photo of an angular unconformity between two sets of beds. See also Figs. 3-42 and 3-43.

Intrusive and Extrusive Rock Relations

Magmas that penetrate or intrude are younger than the rocks so intruded. Dikes, sills, laccoliths, stocks, and batholiths are all younger than the rocks in which they are emplaced. Lavas and all pyroclastic rocks extruded on the surface are younger than the rocks that they cover. If the lavas and pyroclastic rocks are cut by dikes, then the dikes are younger than the extrusive rocks. Turn back to the chapters on igneous rocks and volcanoes, and observe some of these relations in the diagrams there.

Included or Derived Fragments

The pebbles and boulders of a conglomerate, such as those shown in Figs. 2-1 and 2-2, were derived from preexisting rocks. The conglomerate is now suffering erosion, and its pebbles are being loosened and freed. They slide down to the base of the cliff to form a talus cone. The cone is younger than the conglomerate. Some of these boulders may roll downhill into a river bed and be transported downstream and built into bars or flood deposits, which are also younger than the conglomerate. Such relations seem too evident to dwell upon; yet they are important in building fragments of the geologic history of a region. Now, we must put the fragments in proper order.

Sedimentary Basins and the Problem of Correlation

By correlation is meant the relating or tying together of fragments of the geologic record. By the simple concepts already presented we can generally establish the

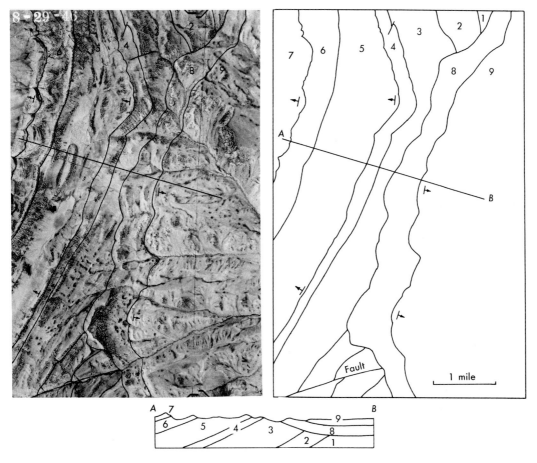

FIG. 15-4 Left, vertical aerial photograph with contacts inked in; right, corresponding geologic map; bottom, cross section AB. Oldest formation is labeled 1, youngest 9. Near Evanston, Wyoming.

correlation by physical relations if the two fragments of history are derived from two places close together, but to compare in point of time a sequence of events as we read it in Pennsylvania with another in Tennessee or still another in Nova Scotia is another matter. Before considering the problem of distant correlation, we should first look beyond the set of beds exposed in the hillside before us and visualize the entire region of sedimentary layers. Sediments accumulated in places in the past, as at present, because there was a reason for it. There were flood plains, continental shelves, and basins of various sizes. Oil-exploration geologists especially visualize *sedimentary basins* because this is the

setting of almost all oil occurrence. Now, basins are filled sometimes from one side and sometimes from both. Sediments accumulate along shores, in shallow water, and in deep water, and each environment leaves its impress on the sediments. Figure 15-5 shows three types of basins and different types of sediments deposited in them. You can see that silts and clays accumulated in one place while sands formed in another, and lime muds in still another. These are called *sedimentary facies* and sometime make correlation difficult.

In basins 200 or 300 miles across, for instance, we recognize sedimentary sequences perhaps 2 or 3 miles thick, with most of the beds having the character of

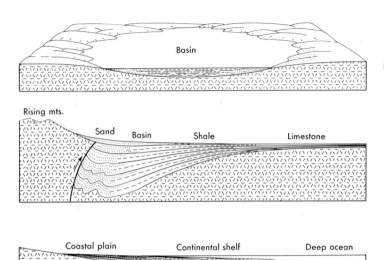

FIG. 15-5 Various kinds of basins of sedimentation. Top, somewhat circular or oval-shaped basin due to gentle subsidence. Sediments contributed by rivers at several places; sandy around margins and shaly and limy in central part. Middle, rising mountains adjacent to subsiding basin. Coarse, clastic sediments near mountains. Bottom, continental-margin type of basin, such as Mississippi delta. All three types should be visualized as 50 to 500 miles wide.

shallow-water deposits. They have mud cracks and shallow-water fossils. Some may be flood-plain deposits. This can only mean that the basin was subsiding as it was being filled with sediments. The rate of sedimentation seemed to be in balance or controlled by the rate of subsidence. Now, a sequence 2 or 3 miles thick, as in the Michigan Basin, took a long time to accumulate. It may contain several unconformities, which in effect are time gaps in the record, and these extend the span of time represented by the sequence. When well known, these thick sequences serve as major scaffolds for the building of the geologic record. The many small fragments can usually be tied to the large, and add significant detail to it.

Continuity

Certain beds or sedimentary formations are fairly uniform in lithology and thickness over a large part of a basin. They may be followed in outcrop for several hundred miles and thus may be recognized in outcrop at many different places. The resistant Clinch quartzite of the Appalachian Mountains and the varicolored Morrison shales of the Rocky Mountains are examples. If sequences of strata containing such beds are measured and described in separate places,

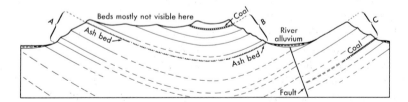

FIG. 15-6 Building a stratigraphic sequence by recognizing certain unique beds in different places. The ash bed crops out at the top of section A and at the bottom of section B. The coal bed crops out at the top of section B and at the bottom of section C. The complete sequence then consists of A plus B plus C. Which way was the displacement on the fault? Where should the ash bed be on the right side of the fault?

they may be related or tied together by these beds. For instance, examine the three sedimentary sequences of Fig. 15-6. They are made up mostly of shales and sandstones that may not be distinctive. But sections A and B both have a characteristic volcanic ash bed and may be tied together by it. Sections B and C are related by the unique coal bed. It is evident now that three separate sequences of strata, and hence three series of events, can be related, and a history compiled that is much longer than that revealed in any one section.

Most formations change in character from place to place; solid sandstones at one place contain shale beds in another, and in still another the sequence is all shale. Without some characteristic unit, such as a volcanic ash bed, running through the sandstones and shales, it might be difficult to correlate them from one locality to another.

FOSSILS AS TIME MARKERS

Do Fossils Occur Systematically?

Fossils have been our major medium of correlation, especially for sedimentary sections long distances apart in which there are no common recognizable beds.

You have seen in Chap. 14 that a great many different kinds of fossils have been found and classified. All the major plant and animal groups are represented in fossil form. Perhaps you have been on fossil-collecting trips and have discovered that specimens are abundant in some formations, scattered in others, and probably absent in still others. Now, the important question arises, Is there a system, a recognizable order in the occurrence of fossils, or do we find them in haphazard and unpredictable occurrences and associations? The answer is, Yes, there is a meticulous order and system in the occurrence of fossils. If we will only search for all the forms and details, and study and classify the specimens carefully, this order will

become clear. The principle was recognized by William Smith of England 150 years ago. It is absorbing to read how he came about the discovery.

Discoveries of William (Strata) Smith

Born in 1769, William Smith's father died before he was eight, whereupon his uncle, a crotchety farmer, unmarried and with little interest in anything but manual labor, agreed to raise the lad. William's early collecting of "pundibs," or fossil clams, and poundstones, or fossil sea urchins, as well as his interest in geometry in school, was nonsense to his uncle. At eighteen he became a surveyor's assistant, and from then on his eager interests were allowed expression:

For three years he held the rod and dragged the chain, but he also observed different kinds of soil, noted "agricultural and commercial appropriations" of the land, and studied borings for coal. . . . At twenty two he began independent work which led to a detailed subterranean survey of some important coal mines. It showed that certain rocks always lay in a definite order, a fact that the tradition bound miners stubbornly refused to accept.[1]

At twenty-five William Smith became surveyor and engineer of the Somerset Coal Canal, and for six years, while surveying its course, he examined the strata through which it was being excavated. He noticed the dip of the beds, and by knowing the succession, he was able to predict the formations across which the canal would be extended. He was always fascinated with the fossils that almost everyone dismissed as curios. He made the very basic discovery that each formation or lithologic unit had its own peculiar fossils and that he could rely on this occurrence. As far as he traced a certain group of shale beds, for instance, they had the same fossils; no irregular mixtures of fossils of other beds appeared. This was of great help to him, because in a succession of interlayered sandstone and shale formations the several shales were much alike, and the standstones

[1] Carroll L. Fenton, *Giants of Geology*, Doubleday & Co., Garden City, 1952, p. 71.

were also alike, but not the fossils. By the fossils he could tell whether or not he was in the bottom of the sequence or near the top. He identified one formation by its thick poundstones, another by its thin poundstones, another by its pundibs, and still another by its petrified nuts. He was able to use the fossils intelligently even without scientific classification and name.

Years later he became a respected member of the British scientific community, and in connection with the printing of his geologic map of England in 1815, which was a remarkable and pioneering achievement, and the first of its kind, he wrote:[2]

I have devoted the whole period of my life . . . to prove that there is a great degree of regularity in the position and thickness of all these strata; and although considerable dislocations are found in collieries and mines, and some vacancies in the superficial courses of them, yet . . . the general order is preserved; and . . . each stratum is also possessed of properties peculiar to itself, has the same exterior characters and chemical qualities, and the same . . . fossils throughout its course. I have, with immense labour and expense, collected specimens of each stratum, and of the peculiar fossils, organic remains and vegetable impressions, and compared them with others from very distant parts of the island, with reference to the exact habitation of each, and have arranged them in the same order as they lay in the earth; which arrangement must convince every scientific or discerning person, that the earth is formed as well as governed, like the other works of its great Creator, according to regular and immutable laws, and which form a legitimate and most important object of science.

Fossils of the Paris Basin and Their Significance

"Strata" Smith, as he became affectionately known, pointed up the significance of fossils so clearly that a number of able scientists soon began systematic collecting and made new discoveries. The beds of the Paris Basin in France yielded many fossils, especially those which had come to be known as the Tertiary. Three main groups

of formations were recognized in France and Germany in these early days of the science of geology, the Primary (oldest), the Secondary (intermediate), and the Tertiary (youngest). In 1883 Sir Charles Lyell's book *Principles of Geology* appeared, and one of the notable contributions in it was the discussion of the Tertiary strata of the Paris Basin and the fossils in them. He recognized four divisions.

In the uppermost and youngest division, containing several hundred different species of shells, 90 to 95 per cent of them are species still living and found today especially around the Mediterranean, whereas 5 to 10 per cent are not found and evidently are no longer living. In the next older division of strata (those next lower in the sequence) 35 to 50 per cent are represented by living forms, and 50 to 65 per cent are extinct. In the next older division only 17 per cent are still living, and in the lowest and oldest division only 3½ per cent are represented by living forms. Besides the marine mollusks there were vertebrate fossils, and these were recognized as species not now living.

From the geologic facts gained in good measure from the Paris Basin, Lyell published several conceptions that are now regarded as truisms:

✦ Changes in plants and animals occur gradually. The older theory of sudden and profound changes in the organic world, lacking in phylogenetic order and due to mysterious or cataclysmic causes is "calculated to foster indolence and to blunt the keen edge of curiosity."

✦ Certain species have greater longevity than others. Some are quite susceptible to changes in climate, particularly temperature changes, and vanish under the new conditions. Other species survive the changes and live through the time consumed in the deposition of hundreds or even thousands of feet of strata.

✦ Some species are able to migrate freely and follow the course of climatic change, becoming extinct in the original area but surviving in another. One species, *Melania inquinata,* fossil in the lower beds of the Paris Basin, and extinct in the European locale, still lives in the Philippine Islands.

✦ By comparing fossil assemblages with modern assemblages and by noting the environmental conditions under which the present species live, the climates of the past can be deciphered. It is clear that the climate of the Paris Basin was tropical at times during the Tertiary, whereas now it is temperate.

✦ Lyell affirmed the conclusion of Strata Smith that fossils could be used for correlation. The "blue clay" of London and the "coarse white limestone" of Paris are marked by a considerable variety of similar, peculiar, extinct species of testacea and by a paucity of living forms. He concluded that the two formations are of the same age, and this has been amply verified since. The conception enabled him and other geologists to relate sedimentary successions across the English Channel, and by the same reasoning fossil-bearing sequences have been related across the oceans.

Guide Fossils and Correlation

Great collections of fossils have been made from strata the world over since the time of Smith and Lyell, and much is known about the types of plants and animals that lived through long spans of earth history and about those which had a very short life span. The time ranges of thousands of species are now well known, and the procession of life forms as they appeared on the earth, changed, and died off is fairly well documented. It is an absorbing story and will form parts of following chapters.

Those fossil species which can be used best for correlation must have two chief characteristics. They must be short-lived and must have had a widespread distribution. It helps little if an animal or plant evolved and became extinct in a certain

basin of sedimentation but did not spread to other areas of sedimentation. Likewise, if a certain species spread along shore lines to many places around the world but changed little over long spans of time, it cannot be used for correlation purposes. For practical purposes it helps considerably if the individuals of the species were very abundant and fossilized well. This means that if the fossils are easy to find they are readily useful. It is discouraging to have to search for rare specimens to solve practical problems of correlation.

Now, the most abundant and useful forms for correlation are trilobites, the shelled animals (the brachiopods, cephalopods, clams, and snails), and the microscopic forms, the foraminifera. In fresh-water lake and river flood-plain deposits plant and vertebrate fossils are important. Sedimentary rocks originally deposited in marine waters are very abundant in almost all mountain ranges, and plateaus where we can examine them in outcrop, and under plains where they are penetrated by wells drilled for oil and gas. It is by means of guide fossils in such marine strata that we tie the geologic history of one continent with another across the oceans.

How did the shelled forms and the trilobites migrate from one continent to another? Since almost all of similar species are forms confined to shallow water today, we conclude that related forms in the past were also limited to shallow water, and thus shallow waterways along banks and continental shelves must have existed from one continent to another at times in the geologic past. These were the migration routes for brachiopods, clams, snails, corals, bryozoans, and many others. Species that lived in the upper layer of the oceans, and composed the plankton, were free-swimmers or drifters in the oceanic currents and spread from one continent to another without being restricted to shallow-water migration routes. The cephalopods, graptolites, and foraminifera were of this group. When short-lived, they are excellent guide fossils. Another Smith, James P. Smith, professor at Stanford University about fifty years ago, had been working on the many species of elaborate cephalopod shells, and among the thousands of described species he recognized that a singular assemblage of species from the Himalaya Mountains was almost precisely the same as an assemblage from the Wasatch Mountains in Utah. From what we now know this was a time in earth history that we might call medieval in the evolution of life, and we conclude that at this time the ocean currents transported the floating cephalopods so as to distribute the same species in Asia and western North America. Earlier studies had brought out the striking similarities of trilobites in New England and the Maritime Provinces with those of the British Isles. These forms migrated along shallow-water connections, possibly by way of the North Atlantic, or as some believe,

the shallow sedimentary basins were continuous at a time when Europe and North America were in close proximity.

GEOLOGIC MAPS AND THE RECORD

Principles and Importance

A geologic map is one that shows the areas of outcrop of the recognizable rock units. With it you can tell what formation is at or immediately beneath the surface in any place. Figure 15-7 is an example. Since the land surface is one of variable relief, we must understand that the map, in geometric terms, is a vertical projection to a horizontal surface. Just the horizontal extent of the formations is shown. The block diagram at the bottom represents an area of three formations: a lower and older shale, a middle sandstone, and an upper

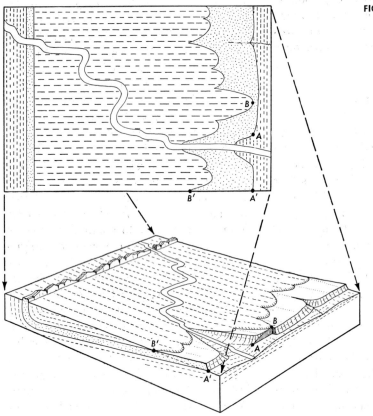

FIG. 15-7   Principle of the geologic map.

and younger shale, folded into an asymmetrical syncline. Where the sandstone appears at the surface in vertical position it shows as a narrow band on the geologic map. Where it appears as a gently inclined layer, the upper shale has been stripped back by erosion, and the width of its belt of outcrop is wide but variable.

Strata Smith's concern was not only with the systematic occurence of fossils in the numerous formations of England but with the possibility of charting the outcrops of the formations on a map. He came to realize that almost all the formations there were fairly uniform in character and thickness over considerable distance and that they could be traced by simply learning their characteristics and "walking them out." He had noted futile efforts to farm certain areas, which, when he examined them, always turned out to be on a certain formation. Now, if a geologic map were available, the lands on this formation could be easily avoided:

By a classification of soils according to the substrata good practical farmers may choose such as are best suited to their accustomed mode of management, and they may thus be tempted to transfer useful and well-established practices in husbandry to many parts of the same stratum as are still highly susceptible to improvement.[1]

Smith noted also that "immense sums of money were imprudently expended in searching for coal and other minerals" in formations other than those that contain these substances. He noted that the shipping canals, so vital to transportation of bulk materials, could be built easier and the water supply and water surplus problems more readily solved if the formations were considered. By means of his geologic map not only the formation at the surface at any one place could be told, but those in succession that underlie the surface could be confidently predicted. This should help in the drilling of water wells and in the search for limestone, brick and pottery

clay, fertilizer rock, as well as coal and oil and gas. The fossils helped him identify the formations as he drove in his carriage over the roads of England. Nothing has been more basic than the geologic map to the mineral and industrial economy of the prosperous nations of the world. As he wrote: "The wealth of a country primarily consists in the industry of its inhabitants, and in its vegetable and mineral productions; the application of the latter of which to the purposes of manufacture, within memory, has principally enabled our happy island to attain her present pre-eminence among the nations of the earth."

The basic purpose of the U.S. Geological Survey is to prepare a detailed geologic map of the country and to have it printed for all to use. The progress has been appreciable but slow, and many states have helped attain the goal by supporting mapping projects of their own. Although the geologic map is a basic tool in exploration and development, it has still another highly important use and purpose, namely, the assistance it gives in working out the geologic history of a region. This is the main point of the present discussion of geologic maps.

Methods of Survey

Geologic maps were originally made by the standard surveying practices, and almost all geologists until twenty years ago had to be trained in surveying. They spent almost all their time in the field making maps and precious little time on the rocks themselves. About thirty years ago vertical aerial photography made a dramatic impact on the field geologist, and nowadays, base maps of all kinds are made principally in the laboratory from photographs. This new science is called *photogrammetry*. The geologist now takes the photographs into the field, notes the contacts of the different formations directly on the photographs, and then these are compiled by the photogrammetrist on the base maps. The photographs commonly reveal the trend of the strata better than they can be seen in the

_____
[1] *Op. Cit.*, p. 3.

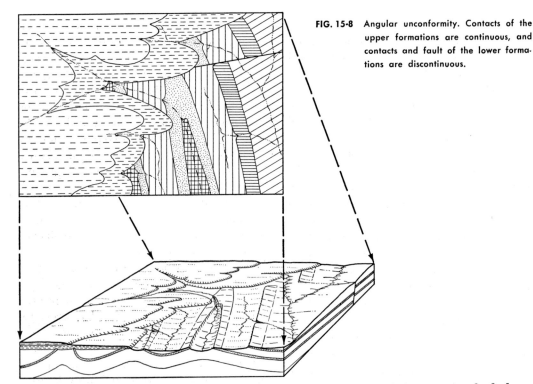

FIG. 15-8 Angular unconformity. Contacts of the upper formations are continuous, and contacts and fault of the lower formations are discontinuous.

field, and an elaborate detail is also usually perceptible. They save the geologist endless tramping and climbing and lead him to the most critical places for observation.

Figure 15-4 is an example of a vertical aerial photograph (left) with contact lines between the recognizable formations drawn on it. It becomes, then, a geologic map, which would be printed as shown on the right.

Interpretation

The succession of formations can be recognized on a geologic map. Folding and faulting of the beds is evident, and intrusive and extrusive relations can be made out. Often obscure from field observations are unconformities, but these will be detected if a map is made by tracing out the formations. Study Fig. 15-4 again and its accompanying cross section. Figure 15-8 is a block diagram and geologic map of an angular unconformity. An early series of beds was folded, eroded, and then covered by a later series. During the modern ero-

sion cycle some of the younger beds have been removed, leaving an irregular escarpment. The geologic map pattern may be analyzed by noting that the contacts of the upper series of formations are continuous but that those of the lower series terminate, or are discontinuous, against the basal beds of the upper series. Now this is the relation that will emerge if an angular unconformity exists between two sequences of beds when their contacts are traced out in the field. From casual inspection, without mapping, the relation may not be realized.

The geologic relations of Fig. 15-8 are much the same as those in west-central England, where Strata Smith first worked. The older folded and faulted series contained the valuable coal beds, which with the advent of the steam engine were becoming basic to England's rising industrial economy, and Smith knew this. No wonder he was indignant that miners would waste money seeking coal in the upper series. He never quite realized, however, that the folding of the beds of the lower series attested to a major episode of mountain building in England and continental Europe. The mountain building is now known to have occurred in an extensive belt through southern England and Ireland, France, Germany, and other adjacent countries, and it occurred after the lower series was deposited and before the upper series was laid down.

In conclusion it may be said that the working out of stratigraphic sequences, the collecting of fossils, and the recognition of structural and igneous-rock relations goes hand in hand with the geologic mapping of a region. All activities must be integrated carefully to obtain a satisfactory notion of the history of the region.

DIVISIONS OF GEOLOGIC TIME

The Time Scale

It was not many years before geologists in Europe and North America had gained real insight into earth history and were proposing names for the major and minor divisions. Certain intervals were first studied and better known in England, others in Germany, others in France, and somewhat later, still others in North America. There was the need for a standard geological time scale that geologists all over the world would recognize and could use as a scaffold on which to build and relate their local histories. For purposes of study of world-wide climatic changes, intercontinental plant and animal migrations, and wide-spread mountain building, we must be sure that we are dealing with events that occurred at the same time; hence a standard time scale and strenuous efforts to secure our correlations.

The rest of this book will be devoted to earth history, and the time scale will be part of almost every paragraph. Although some of the names are new and perhaps forbidding, they will soon become your second ABCs and no problem at all.

It should be noted that the major divisions are called *eras*, the subdivisions *periods*,

and the divisions of periods *epochs*. This is a standard practice by geologists everywhere.

Origin of the Names of the Periods

In England between 1830 and 1850 several sequences of strata were clearly recognized to be bounded above and below by unconformities. The area where the relations were visible was taken as a name for the sequence. For instance, the word Cambrian comes from *Cambria*, the Latin name for Wales. It is there that the strata occur that were originally studied and named by Adam Sedgwick, a British geologist, in 1835. In the years since, however, these strata have been assigned partly to the Precambrian and partly to the Ordovician. The name has been retained, but the fossils characteristic of the period have been defined in Scandinavia and North America.

Ordovician comes from the name of an ancient tribe in Wales, the *Ordovices*. Another early people, the *Silures*, inhabited an area now along the border of Wales and England, and it was there that a third sequence of strata was recognized and named the Silurian.

The Devonian was named for Devonshire, England, in 1839. The Mississippian and Pennsylvanian were named by American geologists in 1869 and 1891 respectively. The British use the term Carboniferous to include both the Mississippian and Pennsylvanian.

The British geologist R. I. Murchison studied the widespread outcrops of rocks in the province of Perm, in Russia, and recognized the strata to be younger than the Carboniferous in England. He named the period that they represent the Permian.

Triassic comes from Germany and refers to a striking three-fold division of rocks there. Jurassic comes from the Jura Mountains that lie between France and Switzerland. The Cretaceous comes from the chalk cliffs along the English Channel, the Latin word for chalk being *creta*.

Tertiary was proposed in 1760 by an Italian, Giovanni Ardnina, who, from consideration of available information at his time, thought there were three great divisions of geologic time, the last being the Tertiary. The Tertiary is preeminently the age of mammals and is now divided into five epochs. The great British geologist Sir Charles Lyell named the Eocene, Miocene, and Pliocene from the Paris Basin. The Paleocene and Oligocene have since been inserted, principally from fossil evidence.

Quaternary stands for the four classical glacial stages that have occurred since the Pliocene. Pleistocene includes all the Quaternary except the last 11,000 years and means "most recent."

Absolute Ages

The standard time scale that has become established is a relative one. By this is meant that one phase of history occurred before or after another one, and geologists are accustomed to think about geologic time in this way. The layman is apt to ask, however, how many years ago did the dinosaurs live, or how old are the oldest rocks of the earth's crust? Although the relative time scale has served amazingly well as an outline of earth history, geologists themselves have always had a secret urge to find out in years how long ago certain events occurred, and now in the past twenty years this goal has been partially achieved in a major scientific advance. The key was found in unstable isotopes whose half-lives and constant rates of decay are known. Ages stated in years are called *absolute*, and now the relative geological time scale is becoming decked out with absolute ages. See Fig. 15-9. It is seen that we have to deal with tens of thousands, millions, and billions of years. The figures stagger the human mind, like astronomic distances. It is not necessary to memorize them, but in round figures they become second nature to a geologist like the names of the periods of the time scale themselves when he works with them a while. The common methods of absolute age determination are as follows.

Lead Methods. If you will refer back to

Era	Period	Epoch	Millions of Years Ago	Mountain Building Episodes (Orogenies)
Cenozoic	Quaternary	Recent	0.001*	Coast Range (W)
		Pleistocene	1	
	Tertiary	Pliocene	11	
		Miocene	25	Basin and Range (W)
		Oligocene	40	
		Eocene	60	
		Paleocene	70	Laramian (W)
Mesozoic	Cretaceous		135	Nevadian (W)
	Jurassic		180	Palisadian (E)
	Triassic		225	
Paleozoic	Permian		270	Appalachian (E)
	Pennsylvanian			
	Mississippian		350	Antlerian (W) / Acadian (E)
	Devonian		400	
	Silurian		440	Taconian (E)
	Ordovician		500	
	Cambrian		600±	Purcellian (W)
Proterozoic	Late		800± / 1,000±	Beltian (W) / Grenvillian (E)
	Middle		1,300±	Mazatzalian
	Early		1,700±	Hudsonian
			2,500±	Kenoran
Archean				

*10,000 years   (W) Indicates the orogeny occurred in western part of continent; (E) In eastern part

FIG. 15-9 Geological time scale.

the first chapter and refresh your mind on isotopes, and then read the paragraphs on radioactivity, you will be in good shape to proceed.

Table 1-4 shows that U^{238} disintegrates radioactively in a series of 14 steps to the lead isotope 206 and that half of a given amount of U^{238} will disintegrate in 4.5 billion years. In other words, the half life is 4.5 billion years. The percentage amounts of U^{238} and Pb^{206} in a sample of a uranium mineral, such as uraninite, may be determined by means of a spectroscope, and on the assumption that all Pb^{206} has been formed by radioactive disintegration since the original uraninite mineral was formed, the ratio $\dfrac{Pb^{206}}{U^{238}}$ related to the half-life of U^{238} is a measure of this time.

However, the uranium ore minerals contain a second uranium isotope, U^{235}, which is six times more radioactive than U^{238} and which has a half-life of 890 million years. It produces the lead isotope 207 nearly six times faster than U^{238} produces Pb^{206}. Furthermore, thorium isotope 232 is also present in some uranium ores and minerals and disintegrates into the lead isotope 208. It is therefore evident that a sample of uranium mineral may yield three lead isotopes from three different sources. All three ratios are separate measures of the time that has elapsed since the mineral was formed. Also the ratio of $\dfrac{Pb^{206}}{Pb^{207}}$ is a measure of age and has the advantage of not requiring an analysis of U^{238} or U^{235}. The relative abundances of U^{238}, U^{235}, Th^{232}, and the lead isotopes can be determined spectroscopically. If all three ratios yield tolerably close age figures, then the determination is felt to be fairly secure; but if the figures are different, as has happened, then the causes of the discrepancies must be considered, and this is beyond the scope of the present volume. A complication, but really a refinement in the lead method of age determination, is the discovery of still a fourth lead isotope, Pb^{204}. This isotope is believed to

be original lead built into the mineral at the time it was formed.

We owe much to the pioneering work of Arthur Holmes, of Great Britain, whose work on the age of the earth and in setting dates to the geological time scale is reviewed in his paper of 1956. "How old is the earth?" To this question his answer is 4.5 billion years, and it comes from the uranium-lead isotope ratio. The meaning of the statement will be discussed in the chapter on astrogeology.

The main trouble with the uranium-lead method is the scarcity of appropriate uranium minerals on which to make the analyses. They come principally from pegmatite dikes, and these do not serve well in defining the boundaries of the Periods of the geological time scale. We need radioactive materials that occur in igneous and sedimentary rocks in abundance and on a widespread basis. Such have been recognized, and dating methods to match have been developed. They are described below.

Zircon Lead-alpha Method. The mineral zircon ($ZrSiO_4$) is used in the lead-alpha method because, it is reasoned, the atoms of zirconium are too small (0.82 A) to have permitted the much larger lead atoms (1.32 A) to occupy any of their positions in the crystal lattice during the original cooling of the magma and the crystallization of the zircon grains. Any lead that is detected by spectroscopic analysis has formed by disintegration of U^{238}, U^{235}, or Th^{232}. Alpha-ray counters are used to determine the amount of helium given off per milligram of zircon per hour. The approximate age is then found by the equation $t = \dfrac{CPb}{\alpha}$, where $C = 2,480$, Pb equals lead in parts per million, and α equals number of alpha particles (helium atoms) per milligram of zircon per hour. The amounts of each lead isotope are found spectroscopically, and then ages determined for each isotope. These commonly vary appreciably. However, much useful information has been obtained, even though the

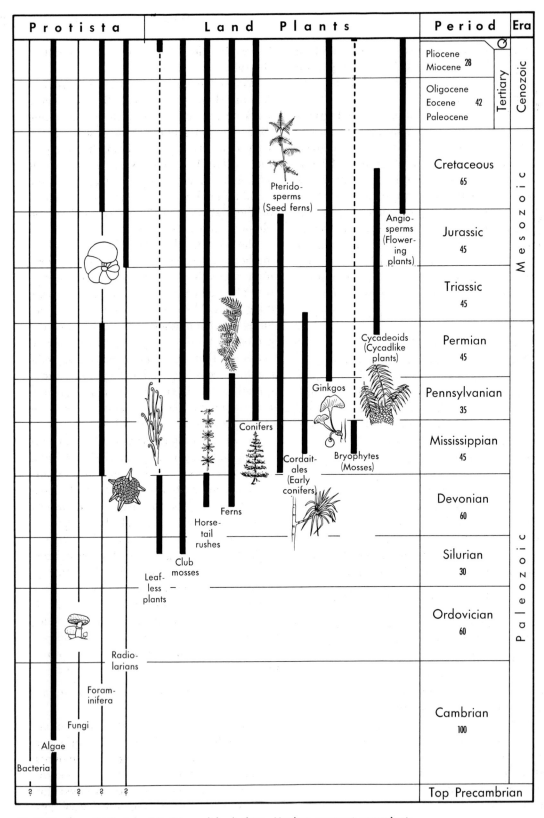

FIG. 15-10 Time distribution of Protista and land plants. Numbers represent approximate duration of periods in millions of years.

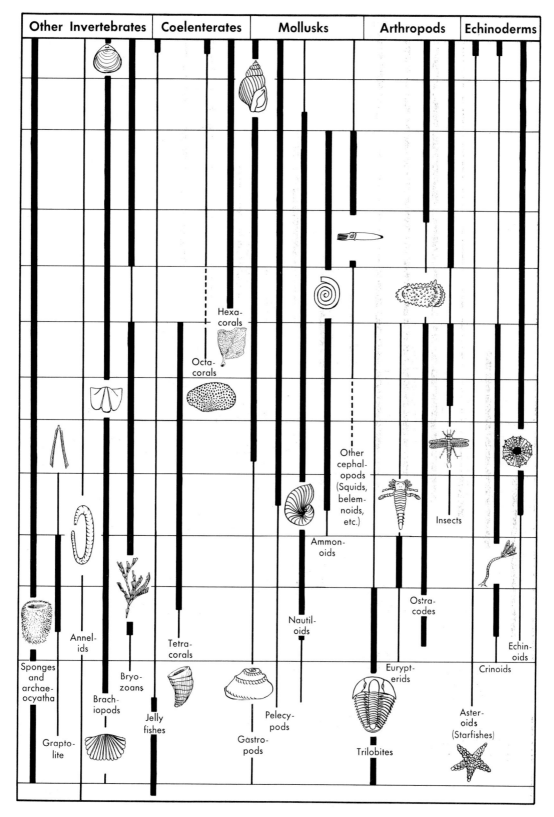

FIG. 15-11 Time distribution of principal fossil groups of invertebrates.

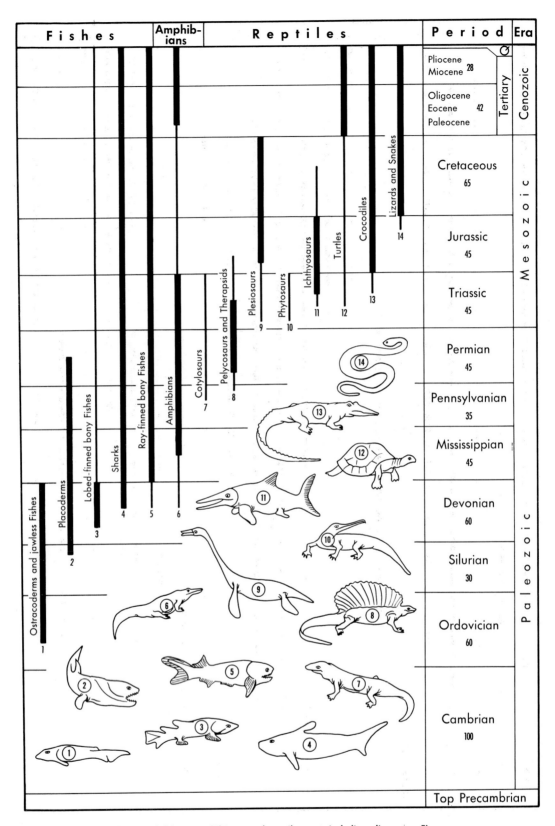

FIG. 15-12 Time distribution of fishes, amphibians, and reptiles, not including dinosaurs. Figures under each column refer to drawings, and figures under periods indicate duration in millions of years.

FIG. 15-13 Time distribution of dinosaurs, birds, and mammals. *(Data and idea of presentation taken from Moore, 1958 and 1952.)*

age determined may be in error by as much as 25 per cent. Zircon grains can be extracted and concentrated from almost all igneous rocks and from many sandstones, arkoses, and graywackes, and hence, the method is applicable to many rocks that can be dated relatively by fossils.

It has been found, for one thing, that zircons may yield an older age than other methods, and this probably indicates that the zircon grains, say in a sandstone, came from a much older igneous or metamorphic rock than the sandstone in which they occur. Also this may mean that zircons from a schist are part of the original volcanic material and have not been changed in a later metamorphism, which produced mica grains and from which the age of metamorphism is told by the potassium-argon or rubidium-strontium method.

Potassium-Argon Method. The isotope K^{40} is the only radioactive part of common potassium and constitutes only $1/8,400$ part of it. K^{40} undergoes a dual transformation: one part to Ca^{40} and one part to A^{40}. The ratio of Ca^{40} to A^{40} is about 0.1235. The half-life of K^{40} is 1,310 million years. It is now known that biotite mica retains the A^{40} that is developed in it by the disintegration of K^{40} better than the potash feldspars and hence is now used in the determination. Biotite mica is present in many rocks, and hence the potassium-argon method has proved very important.

Rubidium-Strontium Method. Rubidium-87 disintegrates to strontium-87 with the emission of beta rays, and its half-life is 4.9 to 5.0 $\times$ 10^{10} years. Rubidium-bearing minerals are the feldspars and micas, and hence many igneous-rock bodies can be dated by determining the proportions of Rb^{87} and Sr^{87} that exist in these minerals. The method has undergone refinement and testing and is now widely used, especially for the very old rocks of the crust.

The ages determined by both the potassium-argon and strontium-rubidium methods are said to be minimum dates. This means that the ages assigned to the minerals are the youngest that they could possibly bear; the true ages are probably somewhat older.

A common mineral in marine sediments, namely, glauconite, forms at the time the sediments accumulate and contains both potassium and rubidium. It is thus amenable to both potassium-argon and rubidium-strontium methods of age analysis.

Carbon-14 Method. Neutrons produced by cosmic rays convert atmospheric nitrogen to radioactive carbon, C^{14}, which then combines with oxygen to form carbon dioxide. This radioactive carbon dioxide, along with normal carbon dioxide, is taken up by plants and hence by all living matter. The C^{14} gives off beta particles constantly and reverts to nitrogen. Dr. W. F. Libby in 1947 achieved a successful analysis of carbonaceous items of archeological antiquity by counting the beta radiations and computing the amount of C^{14} remaining. He thus opened the door to the determination of many important dates in the past 30,000 years. The half-life of C^{14} is only 5,570 years, and hence the method at the very best is only good to a maximum age of about 50,000 years. Organic matter is necessary, but analyses on carbonate carbon ($CaCO_3$), for instance, have been made. These have proved rather divergent and capricious, however.

The ratio of radioactive carbon dioxide in the atmosphere to normal carbon dioxide may not be an equilibrium condition, and possibly also the rate of cosmic ray bombardment has varied in the past 50,000 years. These conditions may affect the age calculated. Nevertheless, thousands of C^{14} age analyses have proved a remarkable boon to archeological and late Pleistocene geological research and are pretty well trusted.

A gap still exists in our ability to determine absolute ages. It extends from the limits of C^{14} dates, 30,000 to 50,000 years, to the upper limit of the potassium-argon method, which is possibly 1.5 million years ago. Dates this young by the K-A method

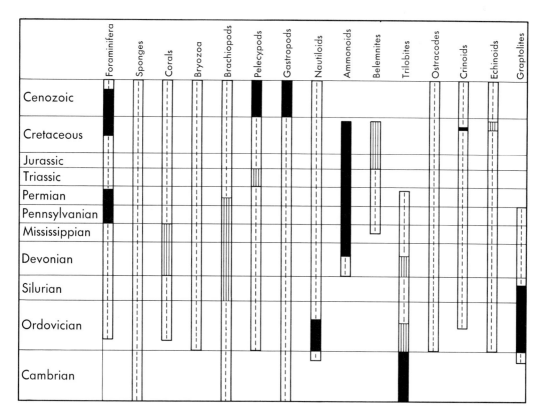

FIG. 15-14 Chronological significance of major groups of marine invertebrates: solid black, important for world-wide correlation; vertically lined, used in correlation of formations of restricted regions; dashed, used only occasionally or not at all in correlation. *(From Teichert, G.S.A., v. 69, 1958.)*

are still very few and possibly a bit questionable. Another method is badly needed to bridge the gap.

DISTRIBUTION OF LIFE FORMS THROUGH GEOLOGIC TIME

Time Span of Major Classes and Orders

The time of origin and the length of time during which the important classes and orders of vertebrates, invertebrates, and plants lived are shown in Figs. 15-10 to 15-13. The charts are reproduced here with the hope that they will summarize effectively a great body of paleontologic information and convey to the student the impression that the known record of life is

varied, tidily systematized, and in part bizzare, extravagant, and wonderful. As the parade of life is reviewed in the next four chapters on the Precambrian, Paleozoic, Mesozoic, and Cenozoic, you will have numerous occassions to refer back to the charts. They should be helpful for review purposes prior to examinations.

Index or Guide Fossils

The trilobites are known only from the Paleozoic; the dinosaurs only from the Mesozoic; and the horses, camels, and elephants only from the Cenozoic. We generally need to know the age in smaller divisions of time than denoted by the eras, and certain fossils permit such determination. An animal or plant that lived in abundance and left appreciable numbers of fossils, that evolved and disappeared in a rather short time, and that had wide distribution over one or more continents is ideal as an index of geologic time. Such fossils are called *index* or *guide fossils*.

Chronological Significance of Major Fossil Groups

Although the major groups of animals and plants lived through long periods of time, we find that they are most significant in numbers and as guide fossils in more restricted time ranges. It is well to observe these larger relations, because the numerous genera and species, when individually considered, may prove bewildering. For this purpose Fig. 15-14 has been prepared, and after a preliminary examination at this juncture, it should be referred to from time to time as the chapters on the Paleozoic, Mesozoic, and Cenozoic eras are studied. It concerns the invertebrates solely.

Suggested Aids

Readings
Knopf, Adolf: "Measuring Geologic Time" in *Study of the Earth,* J. F. White (ed.), Prentice-Hall, Inc., Englewood Cliffs, N.J., 1962, pp. 41-62.

Chapter 16

WHERE DO WE START IN GEOLOGIC HISTORY?

In human history a convenient starting point for discussion is at the beginning of written descriptions and accounts. The period from this time on is called historical, and the period before is the prehistorical. Historical time is fairly detailed and precise in comparison with the prehistorical, which must be constructed from artifacts, hearths, buildings, carvings, skeletons— all commonly fragmentary. The prehistorical record may be considerable for certain places, but it is at best spotty. Historical time began 6,000 or 7,000 years ago in the Mediterranean Sea region, whereas it began 400 years ago in eastern North America and only 200 years ago in parts of western North America.

Geologic time has certain parallels. Fossils appear in abundance, and in some considerable variety rather suddenly, and mark an important division point in the geologic record. Time from this point on can be considered

Precambrian History

FIG. 16-1 Horizontal Cambrian strata resting unconformably on Precambrian metamorphic rocks (lower left quadrant of photograph). Aerial view of Devon Island, Northwest Territories. *(Courtesy of Geological Survey of Canada and Ed Schiller.)*

similar to historical time in the human record, because we know so much about it and so little about preceding events. Geologic history, represented by an abundance of fossils of many forms, starts with the Paleozoic era, and extends through the Mesozoic and Cenozoic eras. Paleozoic time for the animal and plant world is like ancient human history, Mesozoic time is like medieval history, and Cenozoic time is like modern history.

This chapter will deal with the geologic record before life became very complex and with rocks that contain few or no fossils. This very ancient era is called the Precambrian because it predates the Cambrian period, which is the oldest or first division of the Paleozoic era.

The fossil record everywhere does not start with the Cambrian, so that the great and natural break between the historic and prehistoric does not everywhere represent the same time. However, in the building of the geologic record on a world-wide basis and in the establishment of the master concepts of continental and organic evolution, the boundary between the Paleozoic and the Precambrian is strikingly clear and significant. See Fig. 16-1.

KINDS OF PRECAMBRIAN ROCKS

Precambrian rocks are predominantly metamorphic and igneous. The metamorphism was commonly intense, to produce various gneisses and schists (Figs. 16-2 to 16-4). Large granitic intrusions have penetrated older rocks, have contributed to their metamorphism, and in turn some of these early intrusive masses have been metamorphosed. Banded marbles, phyllites, slates, and quartzites are widespread and occur in great thicknesses.

The Precambrian is noted for its iron ore formations near Lake Superior (Fig. 16-5), in Labrador (Fig. 16-6), in Wyoming, and in Missouri. The native copper deposits of the Keweenawan Peninsula of Michigan are late Precambrian in age. Various important deposits of nickel, gold, and uranium are being mined in the Precambrian rocks of Canada.

Angular unconformities separating sequences of the ancient metamorphic and igneous rocks together with the intrusions attest to several times of crustal deformation within the Precambrian era.

Deposits of till, now lithified and called tillite, have been noted in several places in North America and in Australia. If correctly interpreted, they indicate times of extensive glaciation in the Precambrian.

DISTRIBUTION

The greatest expanse of Precambrian rock is in Canada, in the provinces of Manitoba, Ontario, Quebec, and the Northwest Territories. See Fig. 16-7. This is called the Canadian Shield. Almost all of Greenland is believed underlain by Precambrian rock. There are outcrops of Precambrian rock in the Appalachian Mountains system from Newfoundland to Alabama. It appears in local areas at the surface in Missouri, Oklahoma, Texas; and in dozens of mountain ranges in the western Cordillera of North America. Further, a thousand wells drilled in the search for oil and gas in the Missouri, Mississippi, Ohio, and Red River drainage regions have penetrated a blanket of Paleozoic sedimentary rock and bottomed in the Precambrian. We know a great deal about it. The Precambrian is variously referred to as the basement, the basement complex, or the crystalline basement of the continent. A cross section from the Canadian Shield to the Canadian Rockies of Alberta and British Columbia is generalized in Fig. 16-8. Another cross section is given in the same figure from the shield to Texas. It is quite evident that the Precambrian rocks truly represent the basement or foundation rocks of the continent and that the overlying sedimentary rocks of Paleozoic, Mesozoic, and Cenozoic age, although thousands of feet thick in places, are superficial.

The seismologists refer to the Precambrian crystalline basement as the "granitic" layer. It is only in part granite but it has wave velocities approximately those of granite. The layer extends to depths of 10 to 25 km under almost all of the continent, but under certain mountain ranges it is perhaps thicker. Important to note is the fact that the granitic layer does not exist under most parts of the great ocean basins.

DIVISIONS OF PRECAMBRIAN TIME

Progress of Study

Noted scientists for the past 100 years have been studying the rock relations and history of the Canadian Shield. The immensely valuable iron ore deposits have focused much attention around Lake Superior. Nickel, copper, gold, cobalt, and silver mines have led to extensive study in the region northeast of Lake Huron. Gold and uranium discoveries in the Lake Athabaska, Great Slave Lake, and Great Bear Lake led to considerable geologic knowledge of that region. Transportation in the Canadian Shield was formerly a slow pro-

FIG. 16-2 A banded gneiss occurring in northern Manitoba. *(Courtesy of Geological Survey of Canada and Ed Schiller.)*

FIG. 16-3 A gneiss made up of stretched pebbles. It was formerly a conglomerate. Cross Lake, Manitoba. *(Courtesy of Geological Survey of Canada and Ed Schiller.)*

FIG. 16-4 Crenulate gneiss of Precambrian age. *(Courtesy of Geological Survey of Canada and Ed Schiller.)*

FIG. 16-5 View of Hull Rust pit in 1946, an iron ore mining operation of the Oliver Iron Mining Company, near Hibbing, Minnesota. The iron ore is being mined from banks, loaded into freight cars, and shipped to blast furnaces. The iron formation is nearly flat-lying and is called the Biwabik. The light gray bank under the water tower is unconsolidated sand and gravel of the Pleistocene (Chap. 21). *(Courtesy of R. W. Marsden.)*

FIG. 16-6 Pillow lavas resting on banded iron ore formation, Belcher Islands. *(Courtesy of Geological Survey of Canada and Ed Schiller.)*

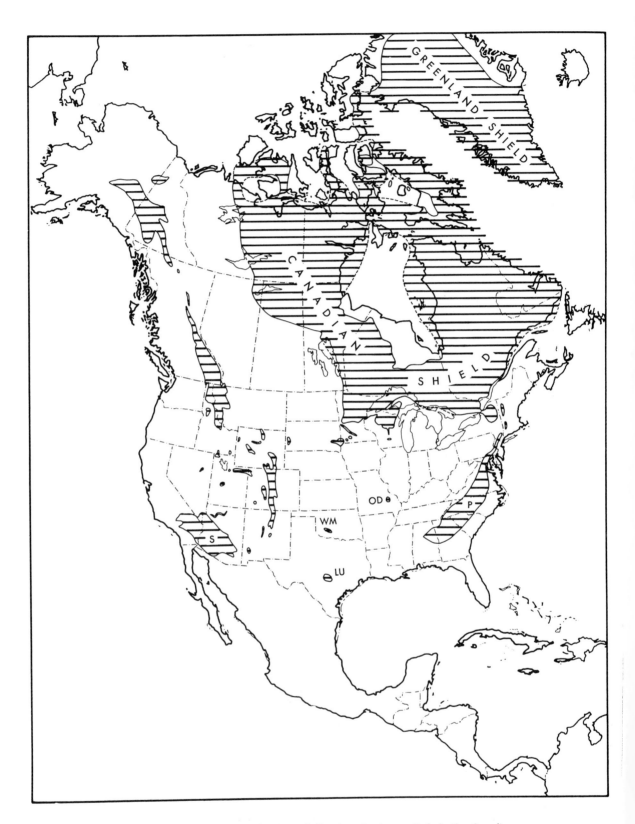

FIG. 16-7 Exposures of Precambrian rocks in North America, showing particularly the Canadian Shield. S means area of scattered outcrops, and P means partly Precambrian and partly Paleozoic. OD, Ozark Dome; WM, Wichita Mountains; LU, Llano Uplift.

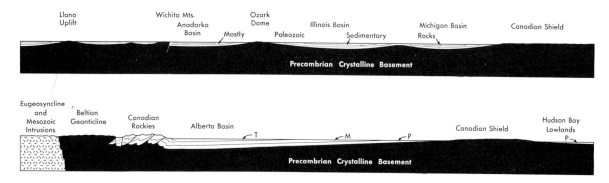

FIG. 16-8 Cross sections showing the Precambrian basement of North America and the sedimentary veneer. Lower section, from the Hudson Bay Lowlands westward across the Shield, the Alberta Basin, the Canadian Rockies, and the Beltian uplift or geanticline. No attempt is made to show the different divisions of Precambrian rocks. Top section, from the Canadian Shield along a crooked course through the Michigan and Illinois basins to the Ozark Dome, and thence to the Wichita Mountains of Oklahoma and the Llano uplift of Texas.

cedure by canoe along the rivers and lakes, but now with aerial photographs, pontoon planes, and helicopters its study is proceeding relatively rapidly, and it is becoming somewhat understood in its entirety, whereas formerly it was known only in local areas.

The great problem has been correlation. How does a succession of events in one place relate to a succession in another? In the absence of fossils in Precambrian rocks the job has been almost impossible. A happy new guide is helping out, however, in the problem of correlation and in the understanding of the shield as a whole, and this is the dating of crystalline rocks by the radioactive isotopes in them. The methods of absolute age determination have been discussed briefly in Chap. 15. Before considering the results we should review a few classical sections of the Precambrian rocks of North America in order to appreciate the problem better.

Lake Superior Succession

The Precambrian rocks around Lake Superior have received much study and are considered classic representatives. Geologists of the ancient rocks of Minnesota, Wisconsin, and the Northern Peninsula of Michigan have not agreed entirely with the Canadian geologists, but now that isotope dates have become fairly numerous, better resolution of the problems of correlation and the geologic time scale exist, and the following discussion is patterned after the classification of the Canadians.

The Geological Survey of Canada recognizes two major divisions of Precambrian rocks: the Archean and the Proterozoic. See Fig. 16-9. The Proterozoic spans a tremendously long time and is divided into lower, middle, and upper divisions.

The Archean rocks of Lake Superior consist of clastic sediments, largely graywacke, and various volcanic rocks, conformably interbedded. In places in Minnesota these rocks, although extremely old, have been little affected by metamorphism, so that the original sedimentary structures are clearly visible. In the general Canadian Shield, however, metamorphism is more pronounced. We note particularly immense volumes of intrusive rocks, and estimates have been made that the intrusions, largely granites, constitute 80 per cent of all the rock. Needless to say, that with so much intrusive activity, adjacent metamorphism has been intense, and gneisses and schists are extensively developed.

A number of episodes of deformation

and metamorphism are listed in Fig. 16-9. The times of intrusion are probably simultaneously times of folding and metamorphism. Mountain chains were undoubtedly built but have since been eroded away. Only the stumps or cores of the ancient ranges remain. In fact, the processes of erosion and planation occurred before the succeeding group of rocks was laid down. This produces an angular unconformity, and we have already discussed the meaning of unconformities. With five or six unconformities in a sequence, attesting to as many times of mountain building and destruction, you can begin to grasp the concept of the immensity of Precambrian time.

One of the columns of Fig. 16-9 is labeled *orogeny.* An orogeny is an episode of mountain building and is generally accompanied by great intrusions and extensive metamorphism. Some of the oldest rocks have suffered two or more orogenies and may be so metamorphosed as a result that their original nature is obliterated. If primitive organisms had been fossilized in any way, it is most probable that they would have been destroyed in the process of repeated metamorphisms.

The first and oldest invasion of extensive granitic batholithis is generally related to the Kenoran orogeny. Certainly these granites occur in vast volumes throughout the Canadian Shield, and deformation and metamorphism of the older graywackes and basalts was widespread.

The newly formed minerals incident to the solidification of the magmas and the metamorphism yield dates approximately of 2,500 million years.

After a long episode of erosion, in which the core of the Kenoran ranges was exposed (Fig. 16-10), another group of strata was laid down. A quartzite is at the base, and then on this rests the valuable iron ores, which were originally sediments high in iron oxide and silica. On these is a siliceous shale (argillite). An interesting deposit of tillite is recognized northeast of Lake Huron, which possibly is younger than the iron formation and attests to the first glaciation of which we have record. Now, another orogeny occurred with still more granitic intrusions. It is called the Hudsonian and is dated as 1,700 million years approximately.

Another long episode of erosion occurred, and then various quartzites accumulated unconformably on the old erosion surface. An episode of volcanism then broke out, and the basaltic lavas and conglomerates were laid down in great thicknesses. In their cavities one of the world's largest stores of copper, and certainly the major deposit of native copper, was emplaced by mineralizing solutions percolating upward through the rock. Finally great sills of gabbro were intruded near the base of the copper-bearing series, known as the Duluth sills or complex. This was followed by widespread igneous activity and metamorphism through the southern part of the Canadian Shield, and along the Atlantic margin of the continent, and is known as the Grenvillian orogeny. The eruption of the volcanics and intrusion of the Duluth sills seemed to mark the beginning of the orogeny, which lasted a long time afterward in various places. (Fig.

Era		Type of Rock	Orogeny	Years Ago
Paleozoic (Base)		Sandstone		
		~~Unconformity~~~	?	600
Proterozoic	Upper	Sandstone		
		~~Unconformity~~~	Grenvillian	900-1100
	Middle	Volcanics (Bearing native copper) Conglomerate		
		~~Unconformity~~~	?	
	Lower	Quartzite Unconformity Tillite Argillite Iron formation Quartzite	Hudsonian	1700 ±
		~~Unconformity~~~	Kenoran	2500 ±
Archean		Schist		
		~~Unconformity~~~	?	
		Metamorphosed volcanics		
		Schist		

FIG. 16-9 Generalized representation of the Precambrian rocks of the Lake Superior region. Ages are in millions of years. Compare with Fig. 15-9.

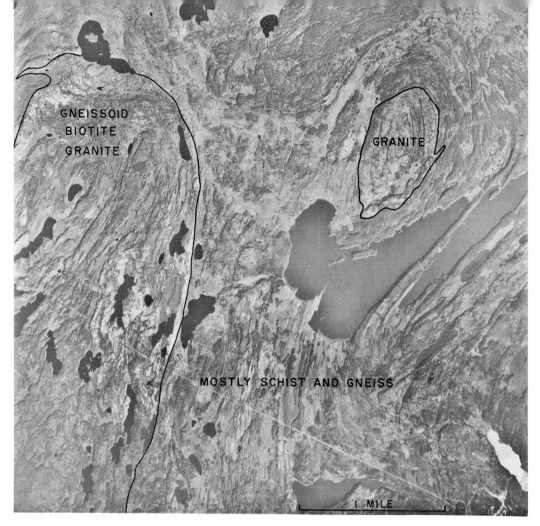

FIG. 16-10 Vertical aerial photograph of a granite, schist, and gneiss terrace in west-central Manitoba, illustrating the crystalline rock nature of large parts of the Canadian Shield. *(Courtesy of Geological Survey of Canada.)*

16-11). Isotope dates range from 1,100 to 900 million years.

A continuation of Precambrian history is better taken up in the western part of North America, so that we will next go to Arizona.

Arizona Succession

An ancient mountain range existed in central Arizona at the close of Precambrian time. It had been eroded down to a number of ridges of resistant quartzite, and when the Cambrian seas invaded the region, these ridges were nearly buried by sands, now known as the Tapeats sandstone. Further examination of the old range shows the following rocks present and events to have

occurred: an old series of volcanics overlain by shale and quartzite (the uppermost unit being the Mazatzal quartzite) was deformed and intruded by granitic magma. See lower cross section of Fig. 16-12. Erosion followed, and then a thick sequence of shales and sandstones, the Apache group, accumulated. Finally, these were tilted and eroded, leaving the ridges previously referred to as those buried when the Cambrian seas invaded the area.

Approximately the same Precambrian history is revealed in the bottom of the Grand Canyon of the Colorado. There the rock units have been given different names than those farther south in central Arizona, but the same unconformities are

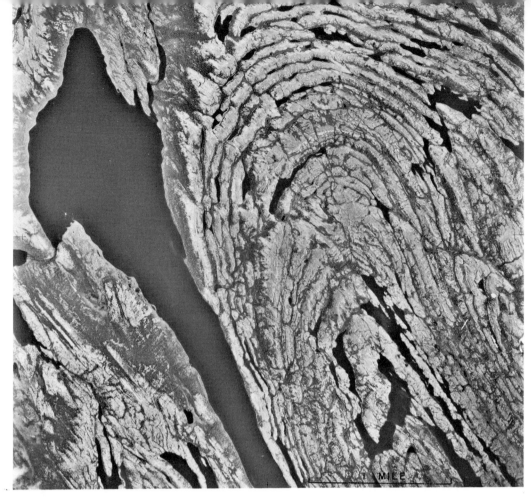

FIG. 16-11 Anticline in Proterozoic sedimentary rocks and interbedded gabbro sills, near Schefferville, Quebec. (Courtesy of Geological Survey of Canada and Ed Schiller.)

present. See upper cross section of Fig. 16-12. The Vishnu schist is equivalent to the old volcanics and Mazatzal quartzite, and the Grand Canyon of the Colorado is better known because of its spectacular nature and the succession of Paleozoic strata on top of the Precambrian, but it is now fairly well established that the orogeny represented by the unconformity between the Apache group and Mazatzal quartzite and by the granite intrusive into the Mazatzal quartzite is very widespread throughout the central and southwestern United States. It has been called the Mazatzal orogeny, and from radioactive isotope analyses its age seems to be later than the Hudsonian orogeny and earlier than the Grenvillian.

The unconformity between the Apache group and the Mazatzal quartzite and be-

tween the Grand Canyon series and the Vishnu schist is recognized at many other places in the Rocky Mountains and will be discussed more fully under the next heading.

British Columbia Succession

The Apache group and Grand Canyon series represent a thick deposit of shale and sandstone in a long basin that extended from Arizona on the south to Alaska on the north. The sediments in this basin in western Montana, Idaho, and southern British Columbia are known as the Beltian. The strata visible in the glaciated mountains of Glacier National Park, of northwestern Montana, and many places in the scenic Canadian Rockies are the Beltian (Fig. 16-13). All the sedimentary rocks

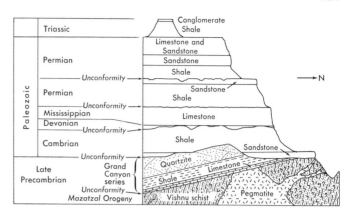

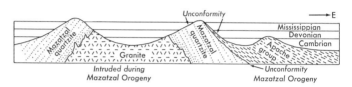

FIG. 16-12 South wall of Grand Canyon of the Colorado (upper diagram) and Mazatzal Land of northern central Arizona (lower diagram), showing Precambrian unconformities and interpreted orogenies. The unconformity between the Grand Canyon Series and the Cambrian strata and between the Apache Group and the Cambrian strata is a combination of both the Purcell and Beltian orogenies. See Fig. 16-14.

of these late Precambrian sequences are mildly metamorphosed into quartzites, slates, and phyllites.

By careful field work the many sedimentary units of northeastern Washington and southern British Columbia have been correlated and composed into a picture, as shown in Fig. 16-14. Two major unconformities are noted: one between the Lower Purcell series and the Upper Purcell and

FIG. 16-13 Beltian strata in Glacier National Park. (Photograph by H. E. Malde and courtesy of U.S. Geological Survey.)

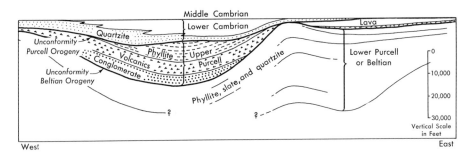

FIG. 16-14 Precambrian succession of strata and unconformities in southern British Columbia and northeastern Washington. *(After Eardley, 1962.)*

one between the Upper Purcell and the Lower Cambrian strata. The Lower Purcell strata are equivalent to the Beltian, and the age of the orogeny represented by the unconformity between the Lower and Upper Purcell, the Beltian orogeny, on the basis of a single radioactive isotope age analysis is not yet well established but is here considered younger than the Grenville. See the succession of orogenies in Fig. 15-9.

The unconformity between the Upper Purcell and Lower Cambrian represents the Purcellian orogeny, and it is now dated as about 600 million years. Referring to the Arizona succession, it would appear that both the Beltian and Purcellian orogenies are represented by the one unconformity between the Apache and Cambrian strata. By this is meant one of two things: either the erosion interval in Arizona continued from Beltian to Purcellian orogenic times, or a series of beds, like the Upper Purcell, was deposited and then eroded away, so that the later erosion cycle reduced the terrain to the old erosion surface.

In an intervening area between Arizona on the south and British Columbia on the north, in north-central Utah, a series of beds, apparently equivalent to the Upper Purcell, contains a thick tillite. This is evidence of a second episode of glaciation in the Precambrian. The first, as noted, occurred northeast of Lake Huron in Middle Proterozoic time, between the Hudsonian and Grenvillian orogenies. The tillite of Utah is Late Precambrian in age and was deposited between the Beltian and Purcellian orogenies.

BELTS OF MOUNTAIN BUILDING

Isotope Age Determinations

The isotope dates represent the time when minerals first formed by the crystallization of molten rock or when a rock was recrystallized and new minerals formed in an episode of metamorphism. Ths original age of a sedimentary rock is not determined. The isotope ages for Precambrian rocks, therefore, generally represent times of orogeny. As the dates from Precambrian rock became more numerous from various parts of the continent, belts of similar ages have appeared, and these, we believe, are ancient belts of orogeny or mountain building.

Precambrian Belts of Orogeny in North America

The Precambrian belts of orogeny on the basis of all available dates through 1961 are shown in Fig. 16-15. The oldest part of the continent is between Hudson Bay and the

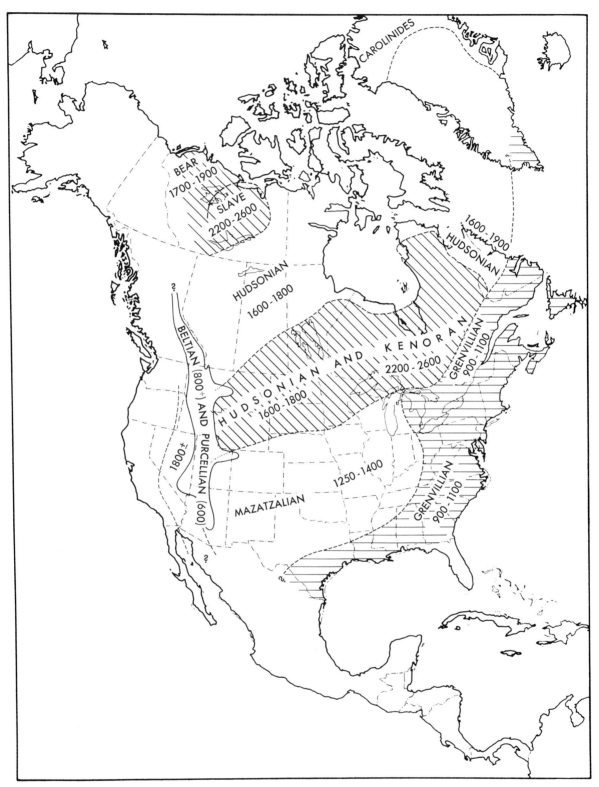

FIG. 16-15 Precambrian belts of orogeny in North America. Figures indicate ages of orogeny in millions of years.

FIG. 16-16 Algal concretions (stromatolites) in limestone of the Purcell group, Waterton National Park, Alberta. *(Courtesy of Geological Survey of Canada and Ed Schiller.)*

FIG. 16-17 Rare and unique Precambrian fossils from South Australia. Scales on side of each photograph are in centimeters. All are soft-bodied forms, and very remarkably, the impressions are in sandstone. About 600 specimens have been found to date. *(Photographs furnished by Professor M. F. Gaessner, discoverer.)*

▶

▼

Tribrachidium heraldium, a strange form not yet clearly recognized.

Dickinsonia costata, a wormlike form

Great Lakes and in a belt projected to the southwest. Some very old ages are noted in western Montana. Another very old orogenic unit is the Slave to the far northwest. These two areas supply dates of 2,200 to 2,600 million years. Liberally sprinkled in the 2,200- to 2,600-million-year dates of the Ontario-Minnesota region are dates ranging from 1,600 to 1,800 million years. It appears that the two groups of dates represent two orogenies, one superposed in part on the other. The older one is the Kenoran orogenic belt and the younger the Hudsonian orogenic belt. It has been suggested that the Hudson Bay–Great Lakes and Slave regions originally constituted the nucleus of North America and that an orogenic belt, the Hudsonian, developed through the middle of it. Subsequently and successively younger orogenic belts developed around the old nucleus. The picture to date, as may be seen from Fig. 16-15, only mildly supports such a thesis. More pronounced is a trend of the main belts to the southwest and the extension of the Beltian basin and orogenic belt discordantly across them. It would appear that a vast change occurred to the western configuration of the continent after Grenvillian time and that the Beltian marks the first shaping up of the western margin somewhat parallel with that of today. Later belts of orogeny west of the Beltian have occurred in Paleozoic, Mesozoic, and Cenozoic time and have fashioned the extensive Cordillera as it is today.

Life in the Precambrian

The principal exhibit of life in the Precambrian of North America is in the form of concentrically laminated masses or heads of limestone, presumed deposited by algae. See Fig. 16-16. These occur in the Hastings sequence of southern Ontario, possibly Middle Precambrian in age, and in the Beltian of Montana, of Late Precambrian age. Worm burrows, a jellyfish, and certain filamentous structures, presumed blue-green algae, are also known. This is indeed a thin and fragmentary story. Many men have searched diligently for Precambrian fossils, but the pickings have been slim.

Recently some remarkable fossils in Precambrian (?) rock have been found in Australia. The fossils may represent a unique and very significant find of late Precambrian organisms, but they occur in strata only 200 ft below good Cambrian fossils and may themselves be Early Cambrian in age. See Fig. 16-17.

Spriggina floundersi, presumably a worm but may be an arthropod

Beltanella gilesi, a jellyfish

Suggested Aids

Readings

Age Determinations and Geological Studies: Report 3, Geological Survey of Canada, Paper 62-17, 1963.

Eardley, A. J.: *Structural Geology of North America,* 2d ed., Harper & Row, Publishers, Incorporated, New York, 1962.

Engel, A. E. J.: "Evolution of North America," *Science,* April, 1963.

Stevenson, John S. (ed.): *Tectonics of the Canadian Shield,* University of Toronto Press, Toronto, Canada, 1962.

Chapter 17

ASPECTS OF
PHYSICAL EVOLUTION

The parade of life across the pages of geologic time, culminating in the last paragraph, so to speak, in man, is a most fascinating history. In like manner the story of the changing face of the earth holds much interest, simply because profound changes can be recognized and placed in chronological order. Animals and plants have been wafted and driven about by invading seas, rising mountains, and changing climates. They have been forced out of certain regions but have responded by adaptive change to new conditions in others, or changed as they migrated, and have thus survived. In still other places many species have been destroyed. Perhaps this constant struggle to adapt to new conditions has been the driving force toward evolutionary improvement.

Aside from the fascination of the story of change of the earth's surface a knowledge of the details of this physical evolution is basic in several ways in our endeavor to find

Physical Evolution of
North America and
Mineral Deposits

new mineral deposits and to understand their origin. Such knowledge is part of the equipment of every professional geologist.

In the physical development of the continent the following particulars will be noted and discussed:

+ The major basins of subsidence where extensive thicknesses of sediments accumulated

+ The building places of mountains of several kinds

+ The parts of the continent which remained stable or which were invaded by shallow seas

+ Times and places of extensive volcanism

+ Development of the adjacent ocean basins

NEW TERMS THAT WILL BE USED

Plates 1 through 5 show the evolution of North America. They are called *tectonic maps*, which means that each illustrates the structural features, such as basins, uplifts, faulted areas, mountain belts, and volcanic regions, that developed during a certain period of time.

During Paleozoic time particularly, the broad margins of the continent, both Atlantic and Pacific, were the sites of subsidence and sedimentation. These marginal basins are called *geosynclines* (see Chaps. 2 and 6). In places sedimentary rock 40,-000 ft thick now exists that accumulated as sediments in the geosynclines. The Appalachian Mountains and large parts of our complex western Cordillera were built by the deformation of the geosynclinal sediments.

The oceanward sides of the geosynclines were commonly characterized by volcanism and are called *eugeosynclines*. There we find volcanic rocks of many kinds interlayered with fossil-bearing marine shales and limestones. The feldspathic sedi-

mentary rocks of Chap. 6 are the particular property of the eugeosynclines.

The inner belts of the geosynclines are characterized by shales, sandstones, limestones, and dolomites and are called *miogeosynclines*. In some places the miogeosynclinal belt is absent, and the entire basin appears to be eugeosynclinal. The eugeosynclines were also the sites of repeated deformation, and we commonly find their volcanic and sedimentary layers metamorphosed. Slates, phyllites, and marbles are the rule.

Two terms commonly used in describing the tectonic divisions of the continent are *orogeny* and *orogenic belt*. An orogeny is a phase of deformation and intrusion of the rocks in a region, and an orogenic belt is a zone of disturbed rock created by the deformation. It is now or has been once a mountain system.

EARLY PALEOZOIC DEVELOPMENT

The early Paleozoic is represented by the tectonic map of the Ordovician period, Plate 1. First, it should be noted that over half of the continent was invaded by seas. The total spread of the seas was even larger than shown because the sediments deposited in the seas have been eroded away in places. From the distribution of existing sedimentary rocks of Ordovician age we are at least reasonably sure of the seaways as shown. Second, the land areas in Canada, including Greenland, are more extensive than in the United States, which was entirely covered with the exception of the Transcontinental Arch and the New Mexico-Texas Arch. We know nothing of the Ordovician history in central and southern Mexico and Central America, because younger rocks there cover any older rocks, if they exist, and no Ordovician strata are known to crop out.

Third, the western and eastern margins of the continent were geosynclinal regions, with both miogeosynclinal and eugeosynclinal divisions, as indicated on the map. The eugeosynclinal divisions were marked by much volcanism. The interior seaways were generally shallow and covered areas that subsided only slightly, so that the resulting sediments were thin. They now constitute a layer only a few hundred feet thick, whereas in the geosynclines the thicknesses in places are several thousand feet. A narrow belt of crustal deformation, a complex anticlinal uplift, separates the miogeosyncline from the eugeosyncline along the Atlantic margin. This later became essentially the Blue Ridge of the Appalachian Mountains.

A narrow basin subsided in southern Oklahoma and northern Texas and was filled with limestone and dolomite up to 9,000 ft thick in places. The subsidence took place in Late Cambrian and Early Ordovician time, and the basin is known as the Arbuckle.

MID-PALEOZOIC DEVELOPMENT

Mid-Paleozoic time in the evolution of North America is illustrated by the tectonic map of the Devonian period, Plate 2. We should note first that Canada around Hudson Bay and including Greenland now is less invaded by seas than in the Ordovician. This vast region is mostly a terrane of Precambrian rock and is known as the Canadian Shield. From Devonian time onward to the present it has remained mostly above water and has been a region of erosion.

The Williston Basin has expanded northwesterly and now merges with the Alberta Basin. An arm of the Transcontinental Arch has risen to the east and along it are the Ozark dome in Missouri, the Nashville dome in Tennessee, and the Cincinnati dome in Kentucky, Ohio, and Indiana. These were broad gentle uplifts, and in only one is the sedimentary cover stripped off by erosion to the Precambrian rocks.

This occurred on the Ozark dome probably during the Cenozoic era.

Between the Ozark and Cincinnati domes is the Illinois Basin, which has now taken definite form. The Michigan Basin also becomes distinct in the Devonian and hereafter sinks as an almost circular and symmetrical depression.

The eugeosyncline along the Atlantic margin becomes involved in intense deformation. The Precambrian basement rocks and the overlying Cambrian (?) and Ordovician sedimentary layers, including volcanic materials, were profoundly folded and intruded by numerous large batholiths. As a result almost all the rocks were metamorphosed to various degrees. This profound change along the Atlantic margin occurred in two phases: one in latest Ordovician or earliest Silurian time, which is called the *Taconian orogeny*, and one during the Late Devonian, which is called the *Acadian orogeny*. The Taconian orogeny affected particularly a belt of country up the Hudson River valley, the Lake Champlain lowlands, and northeastward through Quebec to the Gaspé Peninsula. The Acadian orogeny was profound along the entire length of the belt from Alabama to Newfoundland and was characterized by great batholithic intrusions. Considerable volcanism in New England marked the final stage of the orogeny.

As the Acadian orogeny progressed it became a belt of high mountains that suffered much erosion. Large streams discharged much sediment to the west, particularly in Pennsylvania and West Virginia, and resulted in the Late Devonian Basin shown on the map. As the sediments accumulated, their weight depressed the crust under them, and gradually a maximum of 10,000 ft of gravels, sands, and silts accumulated.

Another orogenic belt began to develop in very late Devonian time in western North America. Folding, uplift, and erosion occurred approximately between the eugeosyncline and the miogeosyncline, resulting in the Antler orogenic belt. Henceforth through the Paleozoic two separate basins of sedimentation existed: the one on the west continued as eugeosynclinal with many volcanic eruptions largely on the sea floor, and the one on the east was free of volcanism.

A third belt of orogeny spread along the northern margin of the continent, from northern Greenland through the Canadian Arctic Archipelago to northern Alaska. It was characterized chiefly by folding uplift, and erosion, and is called the *Innuitian fold belt*.

LATE PALEOZOIC DEVELOPMENT

Nearly all the northern part of the continent had become emergent by the Pennsylvanian period, shown by the tectonic map of Plate 3. The Innuitian fold belt of the Canadian arctic islands had subsided and become invaded by Pennsylvanian seas, and a blanket of sediment was spread across the eroded folds. The Pennsylvanian seas invaded a small area in northern Yukon Territory and in northeastern Alaska.

During one part or another of Pennsylvanian time nearly all the central United States was covered with seas, and in this region, especially from Kansas westward, a number of major uplifts occurred. The uplifts in New Mexico, Colorado, Utah, and Arizona are known as the Ancestral Rockies. They rose sharply from the surrounding seas and shed much clastic sediment around them like skirting fans. As the sediments accumulated, the uplifts were gradually covered. Burial became complete during the Permian for most of them, but the higher parts of the two large ones in Colorado were not covered entirely until late Mesozoic time.

Other uplifts related to the Ancestral Rockies rose in Nebraska, Kansas, Oklahoma, and Texas during Early Pennsyl-vanian time but became completely buried by Late Pennsylvanian time. These are outlined by dotted lines on the map.

The most momentous event was the development of the Appalachian Mountains and their associates, the Ouachita Mountains and Marathon Mountains. The Appalachians came into existence when the thick sediments of the miogeosyncline were folded and broken into thrust sheets. The Ouachitas and Marathons exhibit similar structures to the Appalachians. However, the folds and thrusts developed chiefly in very thick Late Mississippian and Early Pennsylvanian sediments. The older Acadian and Taconic orogenic belt lay to the east of the newer Appalachians of Pennsylvanian age, which now constitute the Valley and Ridge Province of physiographers and geographers.

Subsidence of the Acadian belt and the spread of seaways over it occurred in parts of New England, the Maritime Provinces, and Newfoundland. This resulted in the deposition of Mississippian and Pennsylvanian sediments unconformably on the older Acadian structural complex.

Crustal unrest evolved new structures in central Nevada, where the Antler orogenic belt continued active. It became mountainous in places and shed coarse clastic deposits on either side.

The geology of Mexico and Central America is shown for the first time, but not with much confidence. We know that an orogenic belt of Permian age formed in southern Mexico, Guatemala, and Nicaragua, but we are not sure of its connections with the Appalachian belt through the Marathons or with the Antler orogenic belt. The interpretation shown is not compatible with the geology of Baja California, but we theorize that the peninsula in Pennsylvanian time lay close against the mainland and about 350 miles to the south, so that no Gulf of California existed. In this position there would be no conflict with known geologic facts, but the facts are simply very few in central Mexico.

LATE MESOZOIC AND EARLY CENOZOIC DEVELOPMENT

During Jurassic and Cretaceous times a great inland seaway spread from the Gulf of Mexico to the Arctic Ocean and at times probably separated the continent into two isolated regions: the Canadian Shield principally on the east and the great new Cordilleran region on the west. After the Acadian and Appalachian orogenies the eastern margin of the continent was left free of further mountain-making disturbances, but the western margin became engrossed in profound orogeny. The tectonic map of Plate 4 spans the time from Mid-Cretaceous to the Eocene epoch of the Tertiary. See Fig. 15-9.

As shown on the map, seas encroached over the margin of the continent from New York southward to Florida and all around the Gulf of Mexico. Florida and the Bahama Islands were part of an extensive shallow platform on which various calcareous sediments accumulated.

The Atlantic Ocean basin, the Gulf of Mexico basin (Mexican Basin), and the Caribbean basin (the western part is known as the Colombian Basin) came into existence. There is considerable evidence to indicate that Europe and Africa lay in contact with or close proximity to North America and South America during the Paleozoic era and that a great breach occurred between them with the continents of the western hemisphere drifting westward. The drifting apart occurred during the Mesozoic and Cenozoic eras to open up the gap between and to create the Atlantic Ocean. It is possible that South America was closer to North America then than now and that, as the two continents moved apart, the Mexican and Caribbean basins were created. Hence, on previous tectonic maps it is stated that there possibly was no Atlantic Ocean or Gulf of Mexico, but now we can be confident of their existence.

Concerning the development of the long and broad western Cordillera we should note first the Nevadian orogenic belt, shown in red. It is the most profound belt of disturbance in the west and somewhat analogous to the older Acadian belt on the eastern margin. It developed in the thick eugeosynclinal sediments, which were tightly folded, widely metamorphosed, and then injected by tremendous batholiths. The batholithic intrusions culminated a long build-up of deformational and volcanic events that had started with the Antler orogeny. The extensive granite mass of the Sierra Nevada of California is one of the immense batholiths.

Almost all the large batholiths were intruded in Mid-Cretaceous time, which by isotope dating methods, is about 100 million years before the present.

Adjacent on the east to the Nevadian (Nevadan) orogenic belt is the long and in places narrow Laramian (Laramide) orogenic belt. It is the region of the Rocky Mountains proper. It may be seen to extend from Alaska to the Greater Antilles, and a similar belt extends southward from Venezuela and Colombia to form the Andes of South America. The Laramian belt has a number of divisions along its lengthy course, each with its characteristic structures. In large part it consists of folded and thrust-faulted miogeosynclinal sediments. The well-known Lewis overthrust of Glacier National Park at the international border between Canada and the United States is an example of one of the great faults. There the Precambrian Beltian strata have been pushed 10 to 50 miles eastward over the Cretaceous shales on a nearly horizontal thrust surface.

One of the most important structural divisions of the Laramian belt is the group of large anticlinal uplifts extending from Montana through Wyoming, Colorado, Utah, and New Mexico. Such ranges as the Wind River and Big Horn in Wyoming, Uinta in Utah, Front and Sawatch in Colorado, and Sangre de Cristo and Zuni in New Mexico are examples. They are all wonderfully scenic ranges sculptured by erosion from the large oval-shaped anticlines. Some of the anticlines were asymmetrical and even faulted along one or both sides, and by now erosion has exposed the Precambrian rocks in the center of most of them. The Rush Memorial in the Black Hills is a megalithic monument sculptured in a Precambrian granite in the core of the Black Hills anticlinal uplift.

Wide arid and semiarid basins separate the uplifts. These include the Powder River basin between the Black Hills and the Big Horn uplifts, and the Green River south of the Wind River Range and north of the Uinta Range. These basins are the characteristic cattle and sheep ranch lands of the west. They trapped much sediment as lake and river flood-plain deposits during the Tertiary and in these strata are the favorite mammalian fossil hunting grounds of the geologist. The amazing variety of animals, now extinct, that lived in these 'basins is described in Chap. 20.

Some narrow basins along the Pacific Coast sank in Late Cretaceous time within the Nevadian orogenic belt. They sank to great depth and received an equally great thickness of clastic sediments from both land areas on the east and on the west.

TERTIARY DEVELOPMENT

The seas of the Gulf and Atlantic margin of the continent south of New York retreated gradually from Late Cretaceous time as the land rose, until they finally reached their present shore line (Plate 5). In fact, the entire southern half of the continent, including Mexico, Central America, and the Antilles, has generally risen several hundred feet while the northern half has tilted downward. From Chesapeake Bay to Labrador, Hudson Bay, and the Arctic Islands on the east and from Puget Sound to Alaska and the Arctic Ocean on the west the continent has subsided and suffered considerable marginal submergence. Note the drowned river val-

leys and fiords on any detailed map. This appears as a continent-wide tilting in which north of a hinge line from Chesapeake Bay to Puget Sound the continent has tilted downward, and south of it the continent has risen. Superposed on the continent-wide tilting is a broad arching of the Rocky Mountain region from the Missouri to the Rockies and the Colorado Plateau in which 4,000 to 7,000 ft of uplift has occurred. This broad arching has affected the Great Plains, Laramian ranges, intermontane basins, and plateaus equally. It is probably a matter of expansion of the upper mantle causing the broad uplift of the overlying crust. The development of the 7.5-velocity layer (Chap. 13) may have been the cause of uplift.

Besides the broad arching of the Cordilleran region there was a tremendous outbreaking of vulcanism. Numerous volcanic fields from the Aleutians and Bering Strait to South America were built during the Tertiary. Volcanic eruptions in the western United States and Mexico were particularly intense, voluminous, and long-continued. Fissure eruptions of incandescent heavy clouds of volcanic dust were emitted that rolled over the countryside for hundreds of square miles, annihilating and burying all life. These were particularly marked in western Utah and Nevada and occurred mostly in early Oligocene time. Later great fissure basalt flows were extruded in Oregon and Washington to build the extensive Columbia lava field in Miocene time. It ranges between 2,000 and 3,000 ft thick. The Sierra Madre Occidental is a most extensive volcanic field in western Mexico of Mid-Tertiary age. The numerous high volcanic cones of southern Mexico and Central America are mostly of Quaternary age, and many are still active. The High Cascades of Oregon and Washington are also lofty and extremely scenic Quaternary cones. The Aleutian Islands have had a long Cenozoic volcanic history, and its most impressive exhibit is a long arcuate row of exquisite Quaternary cones.

Equally impressive is the breaking up of

the complex Mesozoic and Early Tertiary Cordillera by faulting. An extensive system of generally north-south faults developed in Oligocene and later time and resulted in uplifted, dropped, and tilted blocks. Adjustments along some faults are still taking place. The Great Basin province from the Sierra Nevada to the Wasatch Range is a series of fault blocks of this orogeny. Some blocks have been elevated and others depressed, but the bounding blocks, the Sierra Nevada and the Wasatch, are conspicuously uplifted beyond the rest. Each uplifted block generally defines a modern range.

As the map shows (Plate 5) the block faulting extends southward into Mexico. The slice or sliver of continental margin west of the San Andreas fault and including Baja California has moved progressively northwestward from its original position adjacent to the Sierra Madre del Sur, and as a result, the Gulf of California has opened up.

From western Montana northward through British Columbia and the Yukon a long single trench extends from the Basin and Range province. It is of downfaulted origin and is called the Rocky Mountain Trench.

The broad arching or uplift of mid- and late Cenozoic time of the Cordilleran region, the widespread vulcanism, and the profound block faulting are all believed to be the result of deep-seated, upper-mantle swelling or expansion. Some consideration to this theory has been given in Chap. 13.

A narrow belt of deformation, involving folding and faulting along the narrow Pacific margin of California, Oregon, and Washington has resulted in the Coast Ranges. The Great Valley between the Sierra Nevada and the Coast Ranges is a result of the uptilting of the Sierra Nevada block on the east and the building of the Coast Ranges on the west in late Cenozoic time. The Great Valley is mostly underlain by Late Cretaceous and Cenozoic sediments.

The Greater Antilles was a belt of volcanism and deformation in Cretaceous time

and until well into the Tertiary was mostly submerged. It gradually rose in late Cenozoic time to its partially emergent condition. A profound trench between Cuba and Jamaica and extending to Guatemala has settled along faults some 15,000 to 20,000 ft in late Cenozoic time. This is the Cayman Trench. North of this is the Yucatan, another downfaulted basin. Possibly the Mexican and Colombia basins have widened during the Cenozoic as North and South America have drifted somewhat more apart.

Plate 5 illustrates the submergent condition of the Gulf and Atlantic Coastal Plains of early Tertiary time and the emergent Arctic land areas. Since then the southern coasts have risen and became emergent, and the northern coasts have subsided and become drowned. These activities seem to be continuing. The extensive ice caps of the northern part of the continent also had an influence, and this will be noted in Chap. 21.

MINERAL DEPOSITS

Oil and Gas

Oil and gas occur exclusively in sedimentary rocks except in a very few odd places where they have seeped into igneous and metamorphic rocks. The search for oil and gas is thus concentrated on sedimentary rocks, and a large volume of literature deals with the subject. Suffice it to say that oil and gas, as hydrocarbons, gather in sediments, chiefly in the soft sediments of warm, shallow, inland seas and shallow, sheltered continental shelves and platforms and that they are derived from various plants and animals. As the sediments become consolidated and hardened, the oil and gas may be locked in place or squeezed out. It seems that the hydrocarbons were originally widely dispersed but that, by being squeezed out or by migrating through the pores of the sedimentary rocks, under favorable conditions, they have become concentrated into valuable oil or gas pools. By "pool" is simply meant a local accumulation of oil or gas that fills most of the small pores, as in a limestone reef formation or between the sand grains of a sandstone.

Much oil and gas is found in every stratigraphic system from the Ordovician through the Tertiary. There is even a little oil in Precambrian and Cambrian rock but it has probably migrated to these rocks from younger sources. Otherwise, we think that oil and gas have originated in all these long periods of time and in places have been preserved until today. So the search for oil and gas takes geologists to all places on earth where sedimentary rocks exist of Paleozoic, Mesozoic, and Cenozoic age. In some sedimentary-filled basins we have found oil and gas in formations of several ages. Even a single well may penetrate several oil- and gas-bearing formations. These hydrocarbons have been found to depths greater than 20,000 ft, but almost all the commercial ones to date occur between 2,000 and 15,000 ft below the surface.

Coal

Coal is a sedimentary rock of complex combinations of carbon, hydrogen, and oxygen and occurs as beds interlayered in shales and sandstones. The cellular structure of plant tissue may be seen in certain coals when studied under a microscope. In others, seeds, pollen grains, and pieces of pitch or resin may be recognized. These are indicators of plant origin, and we need only to observe the extensive swamps of Florida or other semitropical places to learn the origin of coal.

As luxuriant vegetation dies in swamps, the dead plants fall in the water and become soaked or even submerged. In this state bacterial decay proceeds, and the brown organic acids are generated. The acids are toxic to the bacteria and eventually eliminate them, thus bringing a halt to the decay. A brown mat composed of the partially decomposed plant material and the waste acids results. This is called *peat*,

and it is stable and durable for a long time. It only changes when it becomes buried by accumulating sands and clays, whose weight creates pressure and slowly drives out the water. The change through lignite to bituminous coal is chiefly one of reduction of water content, but there is also a slow evolution of methane gas.

It is estimated that 20 ft of dead plant matter compacts to 3 ft in the formation of peat. Then in the change from peat to bituminous coal the 3 ft of peat will compact to 1 ft of coal. It has also been estimated that the 20 ft of plant matter will take about 3,000 years to accumulate under the conditions prevailing today in a southern Florida swamp. Thus, a 10-ft coal bed would require peat accumulation for 30,000 years and a 20-ft coal bed about 60,000 years.

Another consideration is the maintenance of swamp conditions for such a long time. If peat accumulates 2 or 3 ft thick, the area will be built up so that the swamp waters will disappear. It is necessary, therefore, to postulate subsidence of the swamp region just at the rate of peat build-up so that swamp conditions will endure for a long time.

Generally the swamplands are parts of broad, slowly subsiding basins; and in the course of time the common sediments, such as clay, silt, and sand, will compose the fill. Occasionally, however, the right conditions for a swamp will prevail for a while, and a bed of peat will form and become interlayered in the clays and sands. The peats, clays, and sands later make up the sequences of coal beds, shales, and sandstones that we see in many parts of the country.

Overlying pressure alone will not advance the coals in rank higher than bituminous, and it is quite clear that the semibituminous (next higher than bituminous) and anthracite coals of the Appalachians are due to additional horizontal pressure. They and the enclosing beds have been folded, and where the folding is more pronounced, the coal is of higher rank.

The coal deposits of North America are very extensive and plentiful. There is still a most extensive supply but it is not inexhaustible. It will be the principal fuel for many years to come in the production of electrical power.

The coals of the east and midwest are of Pennsylvanian age and are generally of high-heat and good coking coals. They are classed by ranks as bituminous, semibituminous, and anthracite. The coals of the west are Cretaceous and Early Tertiary in age and are generally of lower rank, including lignite, subbituminous, and bituminous. The western coals are excellent for the production of liquid and gaseous hydrocarbons but have not yet responded commercially to the manufacture of coke suitable for blast furnace use. Figure 17-1 shows the regions underlain by commercially valuable coal beds.

In the upper beds of the Pennsylvanian coal sequences the plants show characteristics that equip them to survive during a short period of dryness. Higher still, the coal beds are gone, and hence the warm equable climates seem to have disappeared. Plant fossils in the shales reveal forms that could survive through a prolonged season of dryness or cold. This is particularly evident by the development of growth rings that had not been present in the previous lush and continuously warm swamps and by thicker leaves with protective coatings.

FIG. 17-1 Major coal basins. Black basins contain coals of Pennsylvanian age of bituminous and anthracite ranks. Stippled basins contain coals of Late Cretaceous and Early Tertiary age of lignite and bituminous ranks.

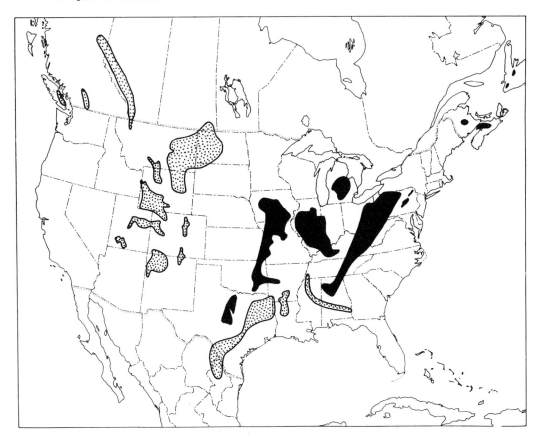

Thus, the warm, equable climate of the Early and Mid-Pennsylvanian that had existed over so much of central and eastern North America, and also of Europe, gradually gave way in the very late Pennsylvanian and Early Permian to a harsh and seasonal climate.

Evaporites

In saying that the climates were warm does not mean necessarily that they were moist, for there were warm dry areas. The Silurian and Devonian seas of Michigan, Ontario, and western New York were surrounded by desert regions, and evaporation from the inland seas was intense. The marine waters were thus concentrated at times to the point of saturation, and the precipitation of salt over the inland sea floor took place. The Williston Basin was also an extensive sea of evaporation and salt precipitation during a number of times from Silurian to Triassic. The Permian seas of Kansas, Oklahoma, Texas, and New Mexico were also in a vast desert region, and in them tremendous quantities of salt were precipitated as bottom layers. The salt layers were buried by later clays and lime muds that today are shales and limestones. The calcareous precipitates were probably largely due also to evaporation, concentration, and precipitation in the same manner as the salt. These are the so-called evaporite sequences, in which layers of shale, dolomite, limestone, salt, and gypsum are interbedded. In fact, if a body of marine water is evaporated slowly to dryness, the compounds that are held in solution will precipitate out in the following order: first, calcium and magnesium carbonate; second, gypsum ($CaSO_4 \cdot 2H_2O$); third, common salt (NaCl); and finally, potassium and magnesium chlorides and sulphates. The last constitute the valuable potash deposits of New Mexico, Utah, and Saskatchewan. Needless to say, the saline deposits are sedimentary and are mined in the same way as beds of coal. The common salt deposits in the United States alone would sustain the world for thousands of years, and the potash deposits, although yet poorly known, will meet our needs for a century or two.

Figure 17-2 shows the evaporite basins and the localities of thick salt, potash, and gypsum deposits.

Rock Phosphate

Rock phosphate is a source of fertilizer, with the phosphorous compound being chiefly calcium phosphate. The phosphate-containing rock is shale or limestone and is spoken of as phosphatic shale or phosphatic limestone. The phosphorous content ranges from a little to over 50 per cent P_2O_5. Commercial rock phosphate ranges from a minimum of 12 per cent to 32 per cent P_2O_5, depending on the mining and beneficiation conditions.

Rock phosphate occurs as beds interlayered with shale, limestone, and chert and, as such, is mined like coal. The major phosphate-bearing region and reserve is in southwestern Montana, western Wyoming, southeastern Idaho, and northern Utah, where a flourishing mineral fertilizer industry exists (Fig. 17-2). The phosphate rock is of Permian age. The special environment of formation is not fully known, but possibly it was one of waters with low oxygen content rising to shallow shelf areas from the abyssal ocean depths. Nearby extensive volcanism may have contributed to the precipitation of the calcium phosphate. The eugeosyncline lay to the west, and the region of phosphate sedimentation spread from the miogeosyncline to the shelf.

Another area of rock phosphate is in Tennessee, where beds of Devonian limestone have been altered and replaced by calcium phosphate. Still another place of rock phosphate occurrence is in Florida, where the rocks are of Tertiary age. Large phosphate reserves have just recently been recognized in the Coastal Plain sediments of North Carolina. Also, phosphatic nodules in sediments 40 miles off the coast of south-

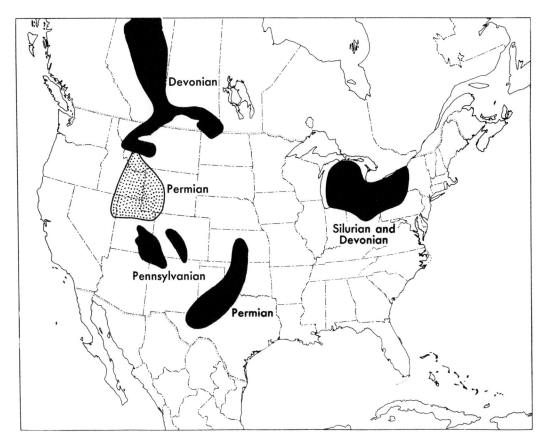

FIG. 17-2 Major evaporite (black) and phosphate (stippled) basins. Potassium salts occur in the Permian basin of New Mexico, in the Pennsylvanian basin of Utah, and in the Devonian basin of Saskatchewan. Salt beds occur extensively in sedimentary rocks of Silurian, Mississippian, Pennsylvanian, and Permian age in Saskatchewan and Alberta.

ern California in 600 ft of water may be a potential reserve.

Metalliferous Deposits

Mineral deposits of the metals are many, widespread, and of various origins. The major iron ore bodies were originally sediments but have become in part, at least, altered through metamorphism and later by weathering. Some, however, have been formed near the contact of intrusive igneous stocks. Iron-bearing solutions rose as part of the igneous activity and deposited masses of iron oxide (hematite and magnetite) at the margin of the intrusive in the adjacent sedimentary rocks.

The several great iron ore deposits around Lake Superior together with the fine coking coals of the Eastern states have been the base of our industrial economy. These and the newly discovered Labrador deposits are all of Precambrian age and of sedimentary origin. They were originally flat-lying sheets interbedded with other sedimentary rocks but have since been involved in folding and alteration. Near Birmingham in the southern Appalachians are commercial iron ores of sedimentary origin and Silurian age.

Gold, silver, lead, zinc, and copper are metals found in mineral deposits usually due to rising hot aqueous solutions accompanying igneous activity. The minerals are deposited in fissures and cavities of various kinds or particularly in place of limestone that has been removed by the same solutions. The latter we call replacement deposits. The igneous rocks are in some places hard to find, so that it is not always evident that the mineralizing solutions have come from igneous centers (Fig. 17-3). The metalliferous deposits occur in numerous, scattered, generally small deposits in the orogenic belts. There are many ore deposits in the Acadian belt, and they are probably mostly of Late Devonian age. The many ore deposits of the Rocky Mountains are of Cretaceous and Tertiary age, as part of the Nevadian and Laramian orogenic belts.

A well has recently been drilled in a hot-spring area in the Imperial Valley of southern California to a depth of 5,232 ft, and it tapped a hot brine extraordinarily high in the heavy metals, especially copper and silver, and in the rare elements. The temperature of the brine was too hot to be measured by the available instruments but is believed to be between 270 and 370°C. It is not only the deepest well ever drilled in a thermal-spring area for steam-power generation, but its water has an astonishing array of elements. Its lithium and potassium content is unusually high; copper and silver are depositing in the pipes conveying the brine; and cesium, rubidium, bromide, iodide, and several isotopes of hydrogen and oxygen are conspicuous. It would appear that the brine is almost entirely of juvenile origin (see Chap. 9) and probably the first true ore-depositing solution on record. It is certainly the kind of solution visualized by students of ore deposits to have formed the vein and replacement deposits around the intrusive igneous rock bodies.

The major uranium ore deposits of the west have been found in the structural province of large anticlinal ranges of Wyoming and the Colorado Plateau of Utah, New Mexico, and Arizona. The ore occurs as irregular and tabular masses in

FIG. 17-3 Miners drilling shot hole in conglomerate, deep in a gold mine of the Transvaal and Orange Free State. (Courtesy of Chamber of Mines, Johannesburg.)

COLOR PLATES

PLATE 1. Tectonic map of the Ordovician period.
Blue areas represent the seaways and regions of sediment accumulation. Yellow areas represent the gently emergent lands. Orange area was one of energetic uplift. Green area represents the ocean floor over true oceanic crust.

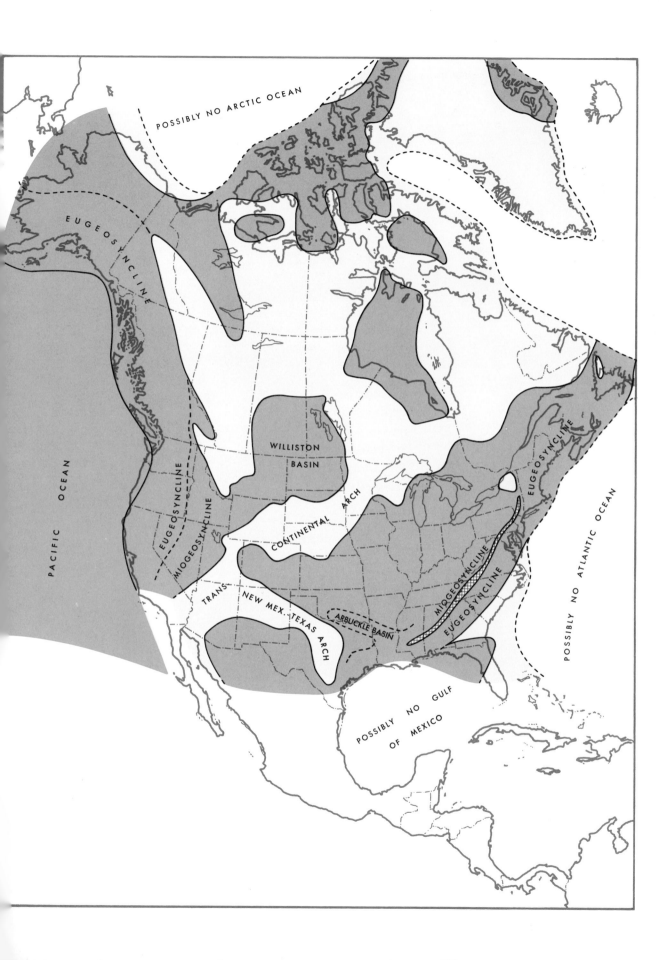

POSSIBLY NO ARCTIC OCEAN

EUGEOSYNCLINE

PACIFIC OCEAN

EUGEOSYNCLINE

MIOGEOSYNCLINE

WILLISTON BASIN

CONTINENTAL ARCH

TRANS NEW MEX. TEXAS ARCH

ARBUCKLE BASIN

MIOGEOSYNCLINE

EUGEOSYNCLINE

EUGEOSYNCLINE

POSSIBLY NO ATLANTIC OCEAN

POSSIBLY NO GULF OF MEXICO

PLATE 2. Tectonic map of the Devonian period.

Blue represents seaways and regions of sedimentation. Yellow represents gently emergent land areas. Orange represents fold belts. Red represents the Taconian (Taconic) and Acadian belts of folding, large intrusions, and metamorphism.

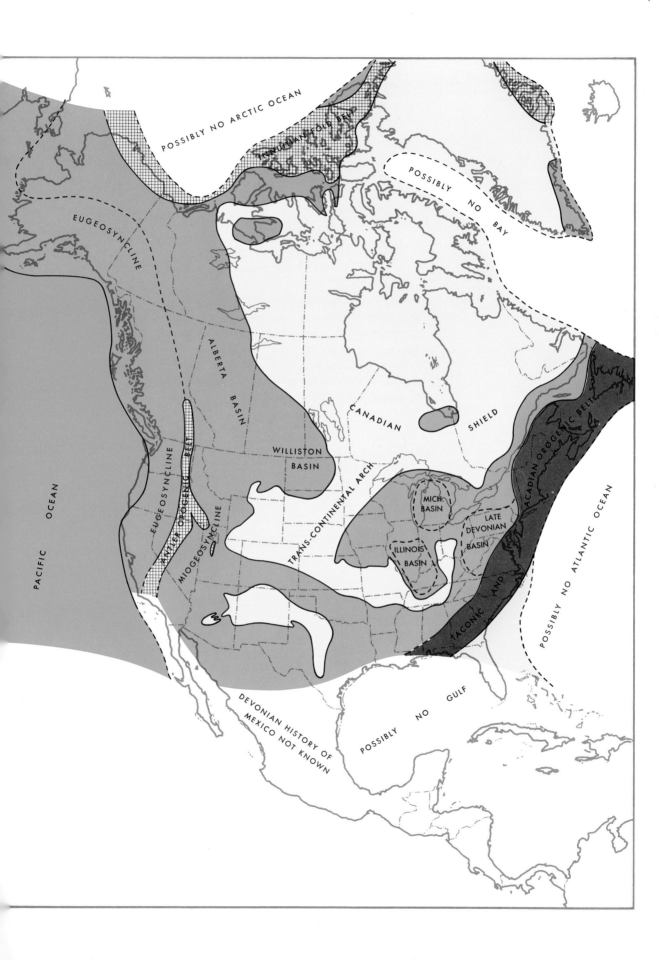

POSSIBLY NO ARCTIC OCEAN

INNUITIAN FOLD BELT

POSSIBLY NO BAY

EUGEOSYNCLINE

ALBERTA BASIN

CANADIAN SHIELD

PACIFIC OCEAN

EUGEOSYNCLINE

ANTLER OROGENIC BELT

WILLISTON BASIN

MIOGEOSYNCLINE

TRANS-CONTINENTAL ARCH

MICH. BASIN

ACADIAN OROGENIC BELT

LATE DEVONIAN BASIN

ILLINOIS BASIN

TACONIC LAND

POSSIBLY NO ATLANTIC OCEAN

DEVONIAN HISTORY OF MEXICO NOT KNOWN

POSSIBLY NO GULF

PLATE 3. Tectonic map of the Pennsylvanian period.
Blue areas represent seaways and regions of sediment
accumulation. Yellow areas represent gently emergent lands.
Orange areas represent ranges and mountain systems of
energetic uplift. Green area represents ocean floor over true
oceanic crust. The orogenic belt across southern Mexico is
Permian in age.

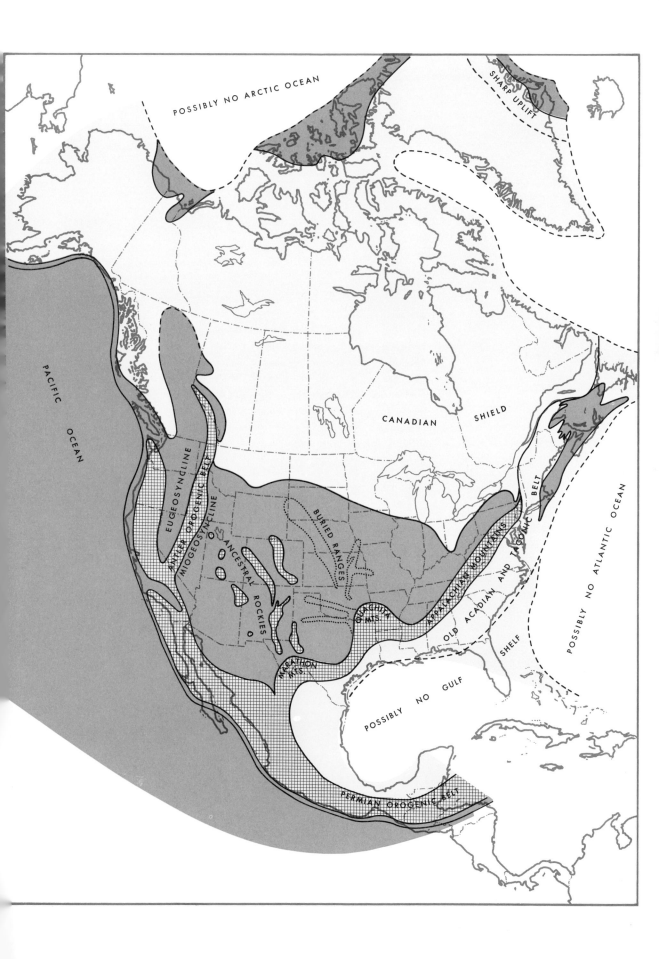

POSSIBLY NO ARCTIC OCEAN

SHARP UPLIFT

PACIFIC OCEAN

CANADIAN SHIELD

EUGEOSYNCLINE

ANTLER OROGENIC BELT

MIOGEOSYNCLINE

ANCESTRAL ROCKIES

BURIED RANGES

OUACHITA MTS.

MARATHON MTS.

APPALACHIAN MOUNTAINS

OLD ACADIAN AND TACONIC BELT

SHELF

POSSIBLY NO ATLANTIC OCEAN

POSSIBLY NO GULF

PERMIAN OROGENIC BELT

PLATE 4. Tectonic map of the Late Cretaceous and Early Tertiary periods.

Blue areas represent seaways and regions of sediment accumulation. Yellow areas represent gently emergent land. Orange areas represent regions of vigorous uplift and deformation, the Laramian orogeny. Red areas represent the Nevadian orogenic belt of strong deformation, metamorphism, and batholithic intrusions. The Late Cretaceous seas spread widely across the Laramian (Laramide) belt before deformation in Alaska, the Yukon, and Mexico. They spread still farther over the Nevadian (Nevadan) belt in Mexico in places.

PLATE 5. Tectonic map of the Middle and Late Tertiary period. Yellow represents gently emergent land. Blue represents seaways over the continental margins. Red represents regions of volcanism. Lined areas represent the regions of block faulting and trench faulting of the Basin and Range orogeny. (Where red, both faulting and volcanism; where orange, only faulting.) Coastal areas shown in orange are characterized by folding, faulting, and uplift. Green represents oceanic crust.

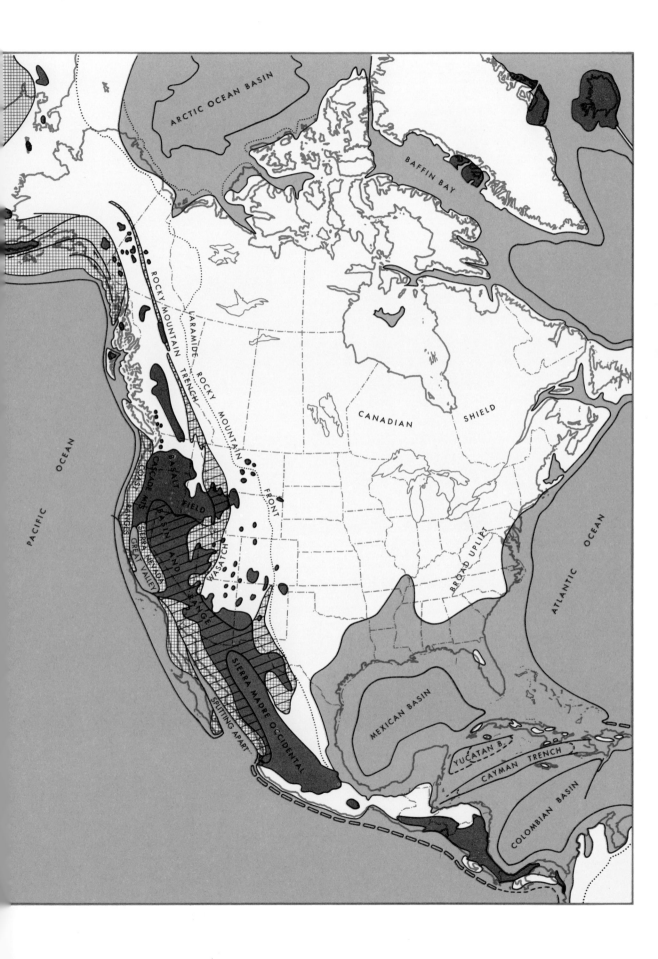

sandstone beds and has been transported and deposited by circulating ground waters through the sandstone. However, the original source of the uranium compounds seems to have been mineralizing solutions given off by cooling magmas about igneous centers, although this is hard to prove.

CLIMATES OF THE PAST

Climatic Indicators

In the consideration of the origin of coal and salt deposits it is clear that they indicate generally warm climates that existed at the time and place that the deposits were formed. Oil and gas accumulations also suggest, but in a less definite way, warm climates. There are several other indicators that have been used in reconstructing the past climatic zones. They are discussed below.

Soils are of many kinds, and each reflects a specific climate. Soils are preserved in certain sedimentary rock sequences, and where found, and if they can be understood or interpreted, indicate past climates. One type of soil widely used in climatic studies is bauxite. It develops in tropical and semitropical climates that have contrasting wet and dry seasons. Such soils are the result of leaching of much of the iron and silica that were originally present in the rocks exposed at the surface, leaving in places a concentrate or residue of alumina. They are mined as aluminum ore. Fortunately bauxites are fairly widespread around the world and are recognized as of Tertiary, Cretaceous, Jurassic, Triassic, and even Paleozoic age.

There are regions where extensive dune complexes accumulated in the past and now constitute widespread sandstone formations, such as the Wingate and Navajo sandstones of the Colorado Plateau. These testify to aridity.

The majority of marine fossils indicate warm waters and hence probably mild to tropical climates on adjacent land. Corals are one of the best indicators of water temperature because they cannot tolerate a temperature below 60°F. At least, if we take the minimum temperature for survival of today's corals we arrive at such a conclusion. Many delicate shelled cephalopods, the crinoids, and the bryozoans liked the warm tropical waters. The mid- and late-Paleozoic ferns were all warm moist climate dwellers. Many could not endure even one cold season. The amphibians and many of the reptiles needed the same warm, equable living conditions.

The major marine reef deposits, regardless of types of organism responsible for the deposit, commonly depict tropical to semitropical climates. This is deduced by noting the distribution of such reef-building activity today and by the fact that the warm waters have a higher degree of supersaturation of calcium carbonate than the cold waters and thus that more calcium carbonate is precipitated by organisms in the warm seas of low latitudes than in the cold seas of low latitudes. Modern reefs are growing principally between latitude 30°N and 30°S.

It is well known that the continents of the Southern Hemisphere suffered an intense glaciation in latest Pennsylvanian and earliest Permian time. The southern part of Africa exhibits many polished and striated rock floor surfaces and an extensive cover of glacial drift. India, Australia, and South America are much the same. This ice cap type of glaciation solely recognized in the Southern Hemisphere has evoked much thought, and one theory, especially, has been widely discussed that the continents of Australia, Antarctica, Africa, and South America were clustered together during the Paleozoic with the South Pole approximately at the hub of the ice cap and that they have since drifted apart.

It was realized by Professor Urey in 1947 that the amount of the isotope O^{18} will be slightly greater in $CaCO_3$ precipitated from cold sea water than from warm sea water, but the difference is so small that mass spectrometers of very great sensitivity and precision must be used. Temperatures have been measured of the Late Cretaceous ocean waters of central Europe, for instance, in which belemnites lived. The thick $CaCO_3$ rods of belemnites are particularly good for the analysis. It was con-

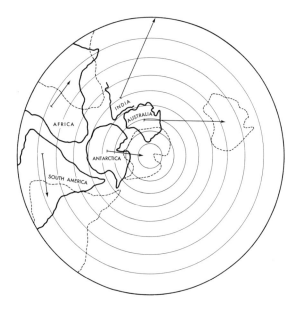

FIG. 17-4 Attempted reconstruction of the Southern hemisphere for middle Mesozoic time. Dashed lines show continents in present positions, and solid lines show postulated middle Mesozoic positions, shortly after breakup. (*After Runcorn, 1962.*)

cluded that subtropical climates probably existed on the bordering lands.

Bearing on Past Positions of Continents

The fairly good fit of South America and Africa, if closed in against each other, has piqued the curiosity of many from the turn of the century, particularly from the time of Alfred Wegener, in 1912, to the present. The Pennsylvanian-Permian glaciation of the continents of the Southern Hemisphere resolved the conclusion firmly

in Wegener's mind that the two continents did lie side by side in Permian time and shared a common ice cap. He also clustered Antarctica, Australia, and India together with them in the manner shown in Fig. 17-4 and in so doing did away with the Atlantic Ocean. He called the single great continent Pangea and postulated that the breakup started about in Triassic time and has continued until today.

The South Pole has been placed about in the center of the ice cap of Pangea, and thus the north pole in Late Paleozoic and Early Mesozoic would have been located in the north Pacific Ocean. This brings up the necessity of the postulate of polar wandering as well as continental drifting.

POLAR WANDERING

Paleomagnetism

Certain sedimentary rocks and lavas exhibit a magnetic field whose directional components can be measured. It is the small amount of magnetite and hematite in the cement of sandstones or in the red coloring of shales and argillites that holds the magnetic field, and it is presumed that at the time of sediment accumulation the tiny particles of magnetite and hematite became aligned in the earth's magnetic field. Also, when a lava cools in a magnetic field, the magnetite grains of the crystallized lava will become oriented in harmony with the field and will keep this direction unless the lava rock is heated up to a certain temperature, the Curie point, when the magnetic directions are removed. In addition, it has been determined that this field generally does not coincide with the earth's present magnetic field, so that it has been concluded that these rocks acquired a magnetization at the time they were formed that was coincident with the direction of the geomagnetic field at the time and that it has remained unchanged since.

In the past ten years S. K. Runcorn, of

England, has pressed research in the field of paleomagnetism and has presented rather impelling evidence that the earth's magnetic poles were in different positions in times past than now. Furthermore the poles have wandered over several thousand miles. It should be said at this point that the magnetic poles do not coincide with the poles of rotation, but they are not far divergent. In the past the magnetic and rotational poles were probably closer than now, because the present separation is considered an extreme condition. By following the north magnetic pole, therefore, the position of the north rotational pole in times past can be located approximately,

and this is what Runcorn and others have done.

To make a complex and long story short, the paleomagnetic north pole has been plotted according to the paleomagnetism of rocks collected from many places ranging from Precambrian to Tertiary in age. Figure 17-5 shows the successive positions of the pole determined by rocks collected in Europe and by rocks collected in North America. You will see that the paths are not coincident but separated by about 30° of longitude. Now, if Europe and North America were placed in a certain close proximity, as they are presumed to have been up until Triassic time, then the two

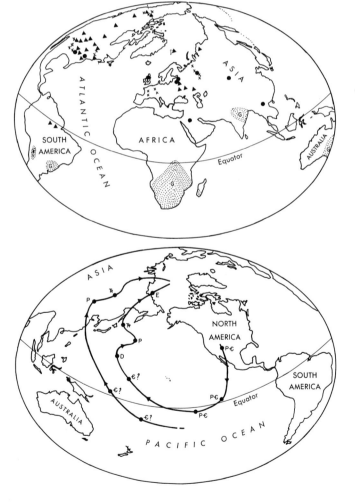

FIG. 17-5 Late Paleozoic climates and proposed paths of wandering of north pole. Upper map: X's, reefs; triangles, evaporites; filled circles, bauxite deposits; G, glaciated regions. Lower map: Paths of polar wandering. Right curve as determined from Eurasia. Left curve as determined from North America. Note incompatability of Indian glaciation with tropical climates as indicated by the climatic data. *(After Runcorn and Opdyke, 1962.)*

pЄ=Precambrian position of north pole
Є=Cambrian position of north pole
D=Devonian position of north pole
P=Permian position of north pole
Ŧ=Triassic position of north pole
E=Eocene position of north pole

paths would coincide. It is therefore suggested that North America broke away from Europe in Triassic time and has drifted westward about 30° since.

Two major criticisms have been leveled against continental drift and polar wandering, and they are difficult to refute. The first is the view that an event of such magnitude in the evolution of the crust might well have occurred but not so late in geologic time. The second is that no tenable dynamical cause for the drifting has been proposed.

Paleoclimates

A number of recent critical paleontological studies on paleoclimates, based on brachiopods, pelecypods, and reptiles and amphibians (the large ectotherms) result in the conclusion that during the major extent of Paleozoic and Mesozoic time the world was generally tropical and subtropical. The climatic zones were probably ill-defined. The Late Pennsylvanian–Early Permian glaciation in the Southern Hemisphere was an interruption to this warm, moist climatic scheme.

By Late Triassic the tropical and subtropical climates were again established on a widespread scale, and the large reptiles and amphibians spread widely across the continents (Chap. 19). They lived from Greenland and Spitzbergen to the southern tips of Africa and South America. See upper map of Fig. 17-5.

From extensive studies of mammals and plants of the Cenozoic (Chap. 20) it is concluded that a gradual cooling began in the Eocene, and climatic zones were more sharply defined than previously. This trend culminated in the glacial stages of the Pleistocene (Chap. 21).

Without sharply defined climatic zones the several climatic guides are of little help in marking the former positions of the several continents or in depicting the polar positions in times past. It should be noted, however, that certain studies, such as one

on tabulate corals of the Silurian period, lead to the conclusion that their distribution is not compatible with the present position of the continents.

Furthermore, a recent review of evaporite deposits around the world leads to the conclusion that those of Paleozoic age lay too far north to be compatible with the present distribution of similar deposits. This, presumably, allows for the Pennsylvanian-Permian glaciation in the Southern Hemisphere. The distribution data, as interpreted, do not require a drift of continents but a movement of the North Pole from a latitude of about 30°N, longitude 170°E to its present position. This evaporite-distribution study leads to conclusions somewhat contrary to most paleontologic studies.

Oxygen isotope ratios in calcium carbonate shells are different in warm water than in cold water, and thus within limits the temperature of the ocean waters at certain times and places can be determined. This was explained briefly a few pages back. By this method it appears that the equatorial regions may have been a little different in Cretaceous time than now, such that the North Pole was about 10° away from its present position. This is not much and hardly demonstrative of polar wandering.

Conclusions

The evidence other than that of paleomagnetism is thus tending not to support either continental drift or polar wandering or a combination of the two. And now, it is being contended that we must take a closer look at the evidence of paleomagnetism, but such a look would carry us beyond the scope of this book. It is a subject almost entirely in the realm of physics.

It must therefore be concluded that in this year of 1964, the theories of continental drift and polar wandering are most interesting but certainly not proved. New lines of attack will undoubtedly be found and perhaps lead to a better understanding of the theories.

Suggested Aids

Readings

Brooks, C. E. P.: *Climate through the Ages,* McGraw-Hill Book Company, Inc., New York, 1949.

Eardley, A. J.: *Structural Geology of North America,* 2d ed., Harper & Row, Publishers, Incorporated, New York, 1962.

Runcorn, S. K.: *Continental Drift,* International Geophysics Series, vol. 3, Academic Press Inc., New York, 1962.

Shapley, Harlow (ed.): *Climatic Change: Evidence, Causes, and Effects,* Harvard University Press, Cambridge, Mass., 1953.

Movie

Mining for Nickel, Rothacker Motion Picture Distribution, Time and Life Building, New York 20, 16 mm, 45 min.

Chapter 18

CAMBRIAN PERIOD

Kinds of Life

Trilobites are the most varied and abundant fossil forms of the Cambrian strata. Brachiopods are next in abundance. Gastropods and sponges are sparingly present in some beds but are not important for correlation purposes. As we step from strata of the Late Precambrian, which are generally barren of all traces of life, onto those of the Cambrian, we are not only amazed at the abundance of fossils but the complexity of the life form that they represent. Trilobites were complex animals, with well-developed musculatory, digestive, circulatory, and nervous systems.

Many species of trilobites had evolved, and they have proved highly useful in subdividing the Cambrian, because some of the species had short time ranges. Three divisions are recognized in North America, the Lower Cambrian or Waucoban, the Middle Cambrian or Albertan,

Life of the Paleozoic Era

and the Upper Cambrian or Croixan. A few typical Cambrian trilobites are represented in Fig. 18-1. Refer back also to Fig. 14-8, in which some of the forms illustrated are from the Cambrian.

Cambrian strata are widespread in North America, as well as in other continents, and fossils are usually to be found in shale or limestone units. The fossils are generally the varied trilobites and the primitive brachiopods, but the forms found in one locality are truly remarkable, because 130 species in 70 genera have been taken from the rocks there. At the turn of the twentieth century Dr. Charles D. Walcott was the leading student of Cambrian fossils and had visited and collected from the known Cambrian strata in all parts of the continent. In 1910, while searching in the Canadian Rockies, he made a momentous find. On the high slopes of Mt. Wapta, in the Selkirk Mountains of British Columbia, near the town of Field, he located a dark gray shale unit only a few feet thick that contained many fossil forms. For several summers thereafter he returned and quarried and split the shale. In all, over 36,000 specimens were taken from the quarry and deposited in the United States National Museum in Washington. Among them are fossils of soft-bodied animals so delicate and fragile that their preservation seems scarcely possible. Some are unfamiliar in living or fossil form. Worms, jellyfish, and possibly sea cucumbers are common, with some fossils showing internal organs (Fig. 18-2). Shrimplike and trilobitelike forms were found with leg appendages, antennae, and ornamentation of the carapace. Many specimens but only a few species of trilobites were noted. Our idea of life in this early period was greatly enriched by the fossils from the Burgess shale. Figures 18-3 and 18-4 depict some of the forms.

It is reasoned that the soft tissue was not subject to bacterial attack and that this was possible because the bottom waters were foul and poisonous to bacteria. Such conditions exist today in the deep parts of

Cryptolithus
Ordovician

Elrathia
Middle Cambrian x2

Peronopsis
Middle Cambrian x15

FIG. 18-1 Examples of common Cambrian trilobites.

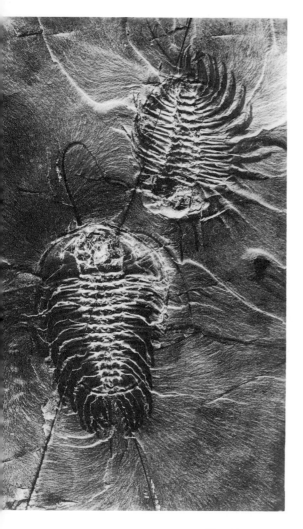

Olenoides serratus

Canadia spinosa

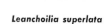

Leanchoilia superlata

Waptia fieldensis

FIG. 18-2 Some of the remarkable fossils of Middle Cambrian age from the Burgess shale, Burgess Pass, near Field, British Colombia. It should be noted that the appendages of the trilobites *Olenoides* are fossilized. This is a rare occurrence; generally only the carapace is left as an imprint. *(Courtesy of Smithsonian Institution.)*

FIG. 18-3 Diorama of Burgess shale fauna. *(Courtesy of Smithsonian Institution.)*

FIG. 18-4 Cambrian diorama. *(Courtesy of Exhibit Museum, University of Michigan.)*

certain lakes or seas where circulation does not exist and poisonous acids and gases abound. The bottom sediments would be fine clay, made black by organic matter, and would not be agitated by waves or currents. If a jellyfish should die in the surface waters it would sink to this sterile, quiet, bottom and would soon be covered with fine clay particles, which settle gently. With greater burial it would become compressed, dehydrated, and finally carbonized, leaving just carbon films of the outline and perhaps some of the parts of the animal. When the Burgess shale is split apart the fossils of such delicate forms as jellyfish show simply as carbon films on the smooth dark shale surface.

Life in Marine Waters

Jellyfish, sea cucumbers, brachiopods, and almost all the crustaceans and sponges are organisms living today in marine waters, and it is most likely that they were marine organisms in the Cambrian. The trilobites are considered marine. Fresh-water fossils are unknown from the Cambrian. The algae, including the seaweeds, were also marine. Fresh-water plants, especially land plants, did not come into existence until later in the Silurian, but fresh-water fish possibly appeared in the Ordovician. So it is believed that life originated in the oceans and eventually evolved and adapted to fresh-water and land conditions. It is also considered probable that the salinity of the oceans was about the same in the Cambrian as now, because of the similarity of the invertebrate life then to that of today.

Reasons for Sudden Abundance of Fossils

The reasons for the abundance of fossils in the Cambrian and not in the Precambrian are not clear. It has been suggested that Early Cambrian time lasted 25 to 30 million years and by "eruptive" or "explosive" evolution the trilobites and brachiopods may have developed in this time, and therefore that the evolution was not as sudden as has been supposed. It has also been contended that the more primitive forms lacked hard parts and hence were not fossilized; yet we wonder how the complicated musculature of the trilobite appendages could have evolved without skeletal parts. Again it is contended that, with only an abundant algae food supply in the sea waters and all ecological niches open for occupancy, evolution had every opportunity for expression. The marked increase in the number of animals that used calcium carbonate to build shells was possibly paralleled by the deposition of thick beds of limestone and dolomite on a large scale for the first time in geologic history. The Upper Cambrian strata especially are thousands of feet thick in western and eastern North America and are made up largely of calcium and magnesium carbonate.

A thick shell may provide protection from predators but it also reduces mobility of its host. Some animals survived and propagated because of their ability to move, and others spent much energy in building heavy shells for protection, which at the same time rendered them immobile or nearly so.

Plants and Protista

Vascular plants are very scarce as fossils in Cambrian strata, but aquatic plants (algae) are common in fossil form. Plants are the source of all animal food, direct or indirect, and therefore an abundance of animals presupposes an abundance of plants. Seaweeds were the largest forms of plant life. The protista, such as the bacteria, foraminifera, fungi, and radiolarians, have been noted or are believed to have existed.

Considering the marine life of the Cambrian, it is reasonable to assume that the world's climate was warm and equable, and the oceans likewise warm. There is little evidence of a polar distribution of climates

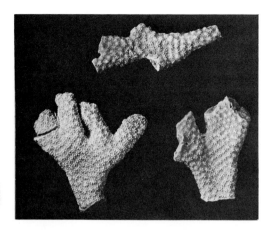

Constellaria, Ordovician

Devonaster, Devonian

Astracospongia, Silurian

FIG. 18-5 Examples of bryozoa, starfish, and sponge.

because of the world-wide distribution of the characteristic Cambrian life communities.

ORDOVICIAN PERIOD

Invertebrates

Our knowledge of life in the Ordovician is greatly expanded over that of the Cambrian. The horny phosphatic shelled brachiopods of the Cambrian were still present, but calcareous shelled forms, which were common in the Late Cambrian, became very abundant. These and colonies of bryozoans make up large parts of some strata (Figs. 18-5 and 18-6), and thus they lived on certain sea floors in great profusion. Trilobites reached the peak of their diversification, and the largest known form measured 30 in. long, coming from Ordovician strata in Portugal.

The Ordovician is noted for the graptolites (Fig. 18-7). Cephalopods became common, and some grew to be the largest invertebrates of their time, with shells 1 ft across at the aperture and 15 ft long (Fig. 18-6). These were long straight forms like a Swiss horn. Clams and snails were also present but not yet abundant. Solitary and colonial corals and crinoids have been noted in some strata. Seaweeds are the only plants yet discovered in fossil form in the Ordovician.

It should be noted that the brachiopods were much more varied, with most major divisions represented. The Cambrian specimens were mostly less than ½ in. in length and breadth, with unhinged, phosphatic shells of nearly equal size. Hinged varieties, chiefly calcareous, however, made their appearance in Cambrian time, and in Ordovician time they became dominant. They were generally larger and strongly striated or plicated; they developed interlocking anterior margins; and the two shells or valves of each individual were usually of different size. The cephalopods were of the

FIG. 18-6 Diorama of Ordovician sea floor. *(Courtesy of Chicago Natural History Museum.)*

FIG. 18-7 *Nemagraptus* (Ordovician), found ½ mile south of Luster's Gate, Virginia. *(Courtesy of Smithsonian Institution.)*

nautiloid type, some with long straight shells, some with loosely coiled shells, and some with tightly coiled shells. The septa that divide the shell into chambers were simple and smooth.

First Vertebrates

The earliest known fossil attributed to a vertebrate is a single small jaw with pointed teeth, found in Lower Ordovician strata in Missouri. The entire specimen is only about ⅓ in. long.[1] In Middle Ordovician strata in Colorado rather numerous fragments of bone and enamel have been found. Present also are tiny "teeth" called conodonts, which may or may not belong to the same animals as the bones. There is little question that the fragments of bone and enamel belonged to backboned animals. It is generally

[1] Wm. Lee Stokes, *Essentials of Earth History*, Prentice-Hall, Inc., Englewood Cliffs, N.J., 1960.

believed by paleontologists that they were fishlike animals that perhaps lived in fresh-water lakes and rivers and were washed into marine waters, where they were fossilized.

The fragmentary fossils of vertebrates in Ordovician time, however obscure, presaged an evolutionary chain that resulted in forms that dominated the oceans and eventually the land. Much more is known from the Silurian, which will be discussed presently.

Status of Life

All major groups of invertebrates had become established by the close of Ordovician time. No new phyla and very few classes have evolved since. All were marine forms and probably lived in shallow arms of the sea that had invaded the continents. We have seen that lands existed in the early Paleozoic and even mountain chains, but these land areas were probably barren except for some primitive plants (Fig. 18-8) whose existence is mostly conjecture.

The trilobites (Fig. 18-9) and worms scavaged the bottom deposits and are called "mud grubbers." The brachiopods, bryozoans, crinoids, sponges, and corals strained the waters and are called the "food sifters." They were, as now, commonly reef builders. Their favorite habitats were warm, shallow waters, some preferring quiet waters, but the corals especially liked the bold ocean front where the surf pounded violently on occasion. They are mostly shallow-water forms, and nothing is known of life in the deep waters, if it existed.

The trilobites could swim and crawl and could thus migrate. It is evident that they spread in time long distances along shallow seaways where the conditions were propitious to their existence and left many

FIG. 18-8 A giant Ordovician algal growth on Ellesmere Island, Canada. (Courtesy of Geological Survey of Canada and R. L. Christie.)

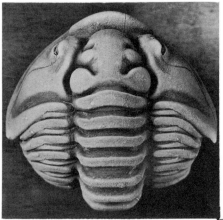

Coiled front view

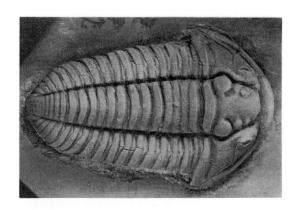

Uncoiled top view

Flexicalymene meeki

Coiled side view

FIG. 18-9 Trilobite (above) and three typical brachiopods (below) of the Ordovician.

Zygospira

Rafinesquina

Sowerbyella

FIG. 18-10 Habitat group of the corals, cystoids, cephalopods, brachiopods, clams, snails, and trilobites that inhabited Middle Silurian seas. *(Courtesy of Chicago Natural History Museum.)*

fossils on the several continents, some of which are good for intercontinental correlation. These migration routes are still nebulous or are a subject of concern in several theories of origin of the continents and ocean basins.

The corals, brachiopods, and bryozoans were attached or sedentary and thus in such form were at the mercy of the waves, currents, and settling sediment. Yet in their free-swimming larval stage they were able to spread along favorable bottom areas and in time establish themselves over wide distances. Some crinoids break loose from their stems in adult life and become free-floating. Graptolites were in part floaters and in part bottom-attached forms. The floating forms probably had no means of locomotion and hence drifted with the currents. They were abundant and at times died en masse as indicated by their tightly packed and crowded carbonized fossils on some shale surfaces. The world-wide distribution of the floating forms and rapid diversification make them excellent guide fossils. They declined rapidly after the Ordovician, probably because of their de-

fenseless nature and the rise of fishes and other predators.

SILURIAN PERIOD

Most Abundant Life Forms

Silurian time was much shorter than Cambrian and Ordovician, and the seaways were more limited over the continent. In central and eastern United States, however, the Silurian strata contain many fossils, and remains from other parts of the world add valuable new information in orderly fashion to that already furnished by the Ordovician fossils.

Brachiopods, corals, bryozoans, and cephalopods are the most important Silurian fossils, although echinoderms, sponges, graptolites, and the small ostracodes are abundant in places. Trilobites were declining in numbers and varieties (Fig. 18-10).

In the Silurian strata of outcrops around the Great Lakes, especially in Indiana, Illinois, and eastern Wisconsin, are many

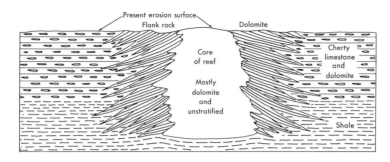

FIG. 18-11 Bioherm (reef) typical of many in Indiana, Illinois, and Wisconsin in Silurian strata.

sizable coral reefs. The well-bedded and flat-lying carbonate and shale strata give way to inclined and irregular dolomitic beds that butt up against a massive cylindrical-shaped core of coral reef rock (see Fig. 18-11). These reef heads are called bioherms and are generally a few hundred feet across. They were evidently formed by colonies of coral and perhaps other organisms living in small island assemblages in very shallow, warm seas. A characteristic coral and guide fossil for the Silurian is the chain coral *Halysites* (Fig. 18-12).

Eurypterids

Certain arthropods called eurypterids or sea scorpions characterize Late Silurian strata in the northeastern United States. Figure 18-13 conveys a good impression of these forms. Their fossils are generally a few inches long (Fig. 18-14), but one species attained a length of 9 ft from the tip of the tail to the outstretched pincers. This is the largest known arthropod, living or extinct.

Fishes

The real nature of the early vertebrates is shown by small fishlike fossils in Silurian rocks. From outcrops near Oslo, Norway, come fossils of a primitive fish with a queer pattern of scales. In other places in northwestern Europe fossils of *ostracoderms* have been found. These formidable-looking fishes were partly encased in bony plates. In spite of the poor fossil record in the Ordovician and Silurian strata it is evident that the vertebrates had arrived at a respectable status and were well underway by mid-Paleozoic.

DEVONIAN PERIOD

Invertebrates

Invertebrate life continued from the Silurian into the Devonian with all main classes

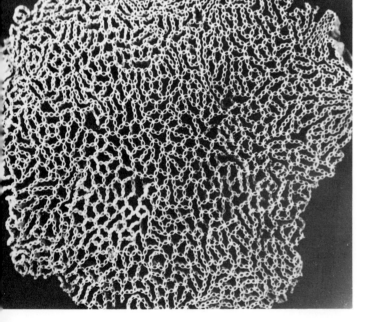

FIG. 18-12 Chain coral, *Halysites*, from Silurian strata near Louisville, Kentucky. (Courtesy of Smithsonian Institution.)

FIG. 18-13 Diorama of the Silurian sea floor showing sea scorpions (eurypterids) and associated snails, crustaceans, worms, and seaweed. *(Courtesy of Chicago Natural History Museum.)*

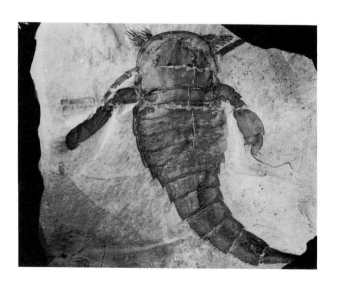

FIG. 18-14 Eurypterid *(Eurypterus lacustris Harlan)* from Silurian strata in the cement quarries near Buffalo, New York. *(Courtesy of Smithsonian Institution.)*

represented. The trilobites were on the wane but the brachiopods (Fig. 18-15) and bryozoans were very numerous. Corals reached a high stage in variety and beauty (Figs. 18-16 and 18-17). Many crinoids of exceptional grace and ornamentation were present, as well as a host of gastropods, pelecypods (Fig. 18-18), and cephalopods. Among the cephalopods are a number of good guide fossils that have been used to zone the Upper Devonian. The graptolites were gone except for one solitary stock. They disappeared entirely in the Mississippian. Corals were abundant and contributed to large reef complexes, in the pores of which much oil has been found, especially in Alberta, Canada.

The Devonian shales and limestones of New York, Pennsylvania, Ohio, and Michigan are in places full of fossils that break out of the rock in near-perfect form. Such abundance of well-preserved fossils, together with an amazing variety of them, lured a number of very capable young men into paleontology in this region in the early formative years of geology in North America, and we thus have a rich heritage of knowledge of ancestral invertebrate life, particularly of the Devonian.

FIG. 18-15 Devonian brachiopod (Mucrospirifer). Upper, impressions in limestone; lower, internal structure showing especially the brachia. This is an example of silica replacement of the calcareous parts, which can be revealed by solution of limestone in acid.

FIG. 18-16 Diorama of a Devonian sea floor showing a number of kinds of corals, both colonial and single types, bryozoans, crinoids, and cephalopods. *(Courtesy of Exhibit Museum, University of Michigan.)*

Top view

Bottom view

Hexagonaria

FIG. 18-17   Devonian corals. *(Courtesy of Smithsonian Institution.)*

Rise of the Fishes

The record of the early vertebrates thus far has been fragmentary and scarce, but now in the Devonian Period a considerable number and variety of fishes appeared. In addition to the probably jawless fishes (*ostracoderms*) of the Ordovician, the new forms called *placoderms*, and lobe-finned bony fishes had evolved. By the end of the Devonian, it should be remarked, the ostracoderms became extinct.

The ostracoderms, as far as we know, never exceeded 12 in. in length, did not possess articulating jaws, and had a well-armored head region. The trunk and tail were covered by bony plates and scales. The placoderms (Fig. 18-19) attained large size, some fossil specimens measuring as much as 30 ft long. They had well-developed jaws and a strong, bony armor, particularly around the head. The tail was asymmetrical, like living sharks. The fossils are found in deposits that certain researchers have interpreted to have been laid down in fresh or brackish water, and hence they

conclude that the placoderms evolved in fresh water. Other students, believing the deposits are of marine origin, are skeptical about the fresh-water origin of these early fishes.

The lobe-finned bony fishes had advanced jaw structure, well developed fins, and scales covering the body (Fig. 18-20). They also had the distinction, it is believed, of possessing lungs or an air bladder to assist in respiration. The paired fins were four in number on the ventral side and supported by bones resembling limbs of the amphibians and reptiles. Their teeth resembled those of the early amphibians. All told, we have the strong indication that out of this stock (the *crossopterygians*) the higher vertebrates evolved. See also Fig. 18-21. The ray-finned bony fishes of the evolution chart, Fig. 15-12, appeared in Mississippian time and gave rise to several branches, including all the modern fishes, such as salmon, trout, perch, halibut, cod, and herring.

FIG. 18-18 Devonian pelecypods. *(Courtesy of Smithsonian Institution.)*

Amphibians

The amphibians belong next above the fishes in the evolutionary scale. They lay their eggs in water, like fishes, and the eggs hatch and grow as fishlike forms through a tadpole stage. Then a metamorphosis takes place, in which buds appear and grow into legs, the tail shrinks, and air-breathing lungs develop. The animal henceforth ventures out on the land and breathes air. Most species cannot roam far from the water in which they were born, however, because their skins or bodies cannot endure prolonged aridity. They are still tied to the water and frequently swim in it or spend almost all their time in it. The salamanders and newts among the modern amphibians live in the water almost all the time, but the frogs and toads get along without water pools for appreciable periods of time. In this sense the amphibians are the first known land vertebrates and, from fossil finds, made their entry in the pan-

Orthonota

Cimitaria

FIG. 18-19 This giant placoderm was a predatory joint-necked fish of Devonian age. The armor plates and bones of three individuals were used in mounting this specimen, which is about 4 ft high. From the black Devonian shale of northern Ohio. (Courtesy of Smithsonian Institution.)

orama of life in Late Devonian time. We assume that an earlier evolutionary development took place, however. The amphibians became fairly common in the Mississippian, and in Pennsylvanian time some became as large as crocodiles.

The primitive amphibians had very weak legs, not sufficiently strong to carry the body but only to help slide it along. The tail was generally long and flattened to aid in swimming.

Land Plants

Trunks of tree ferns 3½ ft in diameter have been found in Middle Devonian rocks in southeastern New York. These same tree ferns are known in fossil form elsewhere in heights of 40 ft, so that it is evident that land plants had become strongly established by Devonian time. The ferns were the highest order of plant development of the

time and probably required a very moist climate and swampy conditions. Certain naked plants (without leaves or roots) are known from the Silurian.

MISSISSIPPIAN PERIOD

Invertebrates

Most Devonian invertebrate stocks continued into the Mississippian. In America a remarkable feature is the flowering of the crinoids (Fig. 18-22). The Lower Mississippian strata of the Mississippi Valley have yielded more than 400 species. Almost all these disappeared, apparently as abruptly as they came, for only a few survived into Middle and Late Mississippian time. Budlike relatives of the crinoids the *blastoids*, were prominent also and are considered to have reached their climax in the Late Mississippian.

FIG. 18-20 Crossopterygian fish from the Devonian. It was probably ancestral to the amphibians. Length 24 in. (Museum of Paleontology, University of Michigan.)

FIG. 18-21 This fish, known as the coelacanth fish, has an ancestry spanning 300 million years, or from the Devonian to the present. It is much like the crossopterygian of Fig. 18-20 and during a very long time has changed little. The biological world was amazed when the first of these fishes was caught in the Mozambique Channel between Madagascar and the east coast of Africa. It weighed 127 lb. From the fossil record it had been thought that these fishes became extinct at the close of the Mesozoic era. Since 1952, twelve additional specimens have been recovered.

FIG. 18-22 Diorama of the Mississippian sea floor, showing principally the crinoids and bryozoans. (*Courtesy of Exhibit Museum, University of Michigan.*)

The brachiopods were still varied, abundant, and important but now represented particularly by spine-bearing concave- convex shells, known as *productids*. The productids were world-wide in distribution. Clams and snails were numerous but not very significant; cephalopods developed greater structural complexity to their shells (Fig. 18-23); and the trilobites, although present, had become a minor element of the fauna.

Bryozoans were generally lacy, with the screwlike *Archimedes*, a common fossil of the Mississippian. Corals were common but not so varied as in the Devonian.

Vertebrates

Sharks are known in the Upper Devonian strata, and in the Mississippian there were those having rounded teeth, believed adapted to crushing shells. Sharks have cartilaginous skeletons but highly developed jaw structure. They are generally regarded as primitive fishes, but some authorities have advanced the view that they are somewhat altered forms from previously fairly well-advanced bony fishes. The Mississippian fossils are chiefly teeth, which look like shark teeth, and it is thought that the skeletons of the creatures to which the teeth belonged had lost their original bony nature.

The amphibians found the extensive warm, inland swamps and rivers of the Mississippian favorable and increased in number, but their maximum development came in the next period, the Pennsylvanian.

PENNSYLVANIAN PERIOD

Plants

America's industrial wealth is predicated on its extensive coal beds of Pennsylvanian age. The bituminous and semibituminous

---

FIG. 18-23 Typical fossils of the later Paleozoic. (Courtesy of Smithsonian Institution.)

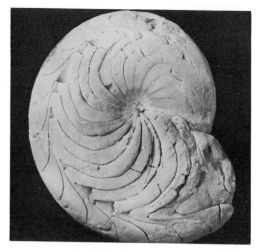

Mississippian cephalopod
(Imitoceras)

Pennsylvanian gastropod
(Shansiella)

Permian fusulina X3
(Parafusulina)

Permian pelecypods

coals of Ohio, Pennsylvania, West Virginia, Kentucky, and Tennessee have not only furnished much of the heat energy for the Appalachian region and Atlantic seaboard, but because of their fine-coking quality, they have been the basis for the steel industry of the Pittsburgh and Birmingham areas. The anthracite coal of central Pennsylvania is the very best for domestic heating purposes. The widespread bituminous coals of Illinois and of Arkansas and Oklahoma have been of primary importance to the economy of the central part of the continent. They are shipped to Utah and California to aid in steel manufacture. The Pennsylvanian coals of the Maritime Provinces supply eastern Canada.

The Pennsylvanian period was obviously one of extensive swamps that supported a prodigious plant growth, because it is in swamps that peat accumulates and later, after burial by mud and sand, turns to coal. The sequence of change is peat to lignite to bituminous coal to semibituminous coal to anthracite. The change involves the gradual loss of water and of gases, principally methane.

The fossil record of the plants is unusually complete because the underclays, the clay or shale partings of coal beds, and the overclays have preserved the many plant varieties in exceptionally fine style. Even certain plant parts are preserved in the coal itself, such as cellular structure of woody parts, pollen, and seeds. The remarkable record, of course, is available because of the extensive mining of the coal, which has brought to light many of the important fossils. This was a world principally of ferns, with their relatives the seed ferns, and of great scale trees and horsetail rushes (Fig. 18-24). The conifers and modern flowering plants had not yet evolved. Some 6,000 species of Devonian, Mississippian, and Pennsylvanian plants have been described.

The fronds of some of the ferns resemble those of today. Some were 12 ft in length and were borne as clusters at the top of long trunks of large, tree-size proportions. Other ferns were like vines.

True ferns bear spore clusters on the underside of the leaves or on specialized fronds, but some of the Pennsylvanian ferns produced seed clusters, and are known as the seed ferns.

Great scale trees, called *lycopods*, were dominant in the swamps, and attained

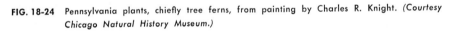

FIG. 18-24 Pennsylvania plants, chiefly tree ferns, from painting by Charles R. Knight. (Courtesy *Chicago Natural History Museum.*)

FIG. 18-25 Impression of the bark or scales of Lepido-dendron. (University of Utah Museum.)

liquely intersecting rows, whereas in *Sigillaria* they were in vertical rows. Some scale trees were short and stocky, and others soared 100 ft in the air. Branches were scarce or absent.

The horsetail rushes were represented prominently in the swamp flora. They are the jointed plants with circlets of leaves from the nodes at each joint. They had hollow pithy stems. They were much larger generally than their modern descendants, with *Calamites* being a tree whose trunk measured 2 to 3 ft across and whose height was 40 to 100 ft.

Unfamiliar plants in the Pennsylvanian flora were the *Cordaites*, which were the ancestors of the conifers or evergreens. Of slender tree proportions they bore the branches near the top with a thick mass of leaves each up to 6 in. wide and 3 ft long. It is evident that the several varieties of tree ferns grew tall and carried their foliage at the top in a struggle to get the sunlight in competition with others. The true ferns made up chiefly the undergrowth. They favored the shade.

heights of 100 ft. They had short, stiff, scaly or needlelike leaves that covered the trunk. These dropped away when dead and left scar patterns. In *Lepidodendron* (Fig. 18-25) the scars occur in two ob-

Invertebrates

The main stocks of invertebrates of the Mississippian continued into the Pennsyl-

FIG. 18-26 Habitat group of Pennsylvanian life, U.S. National Museum. (Courtesy of Smithsonian Institution.)

vanian (Fig. 18-26), and these into the Permian. The Permian forms had evolved significant differences, and therefore, almost all comments on the invertebrates of the Pennsylvanian will be left to the discussion of the Permian. A few groups, however, need special mention. These are the *fusulinids* (Fig. 18-23), which are shelled protozoans about the size and shape of grains of wheat. Although making an appearance in Mississippian rocks and continuing in places into the Permian, the fusulinids are very abundant in most Pennsylvanian sequences of strata and are useful guide fossils. They evolved rapidly

least, it persisted through the geological ages.

Vertebrates

The amphibians appeared, as far as we know, in the Devonian period. In North America our first records of amphibians of any note are Pennsylvanian fossils, but when they did enter the stage, it was in force. The Pennsylvanian amphibians were mostly ponderous, sluggish creatures that waddled and lumbered about the banks of lakes and streams. Some, however, were lizardlike with well-developed limbs and

FIG. 18-27   An amphibian from the Permian of Texas, *Trimerorhachis.* Length 24 in. (Museum of Paleontology, University of Michigan.)

and are used to subdivide the Pennsylvanian.

Insects made their debut in mid-Devonian time, but now they appear in abundance and in large sizes, such as dragonflies nearly 30 in. across the wings and cockroaches 3 in. long. Spiders were also fossilized. The thought was originally expressed by Dr. U. D. Matthew, one of the fathers of American paleontology, that the active dragonfly rather than the sluggish amphibian might seem a far superior type or a more promising candidate for the position of ancestor of the higher, more intelligent animals that were to come in the distant future, but the insect evidently had fulfilled the mechanical possibilities of which his structural organization was capable. It lead to nothing better, but at

were probably more active. Some were capable swimmers, and a few had lost their legs and were snakelike. Judging from their teeth, probably all were carnivorous, but judging from our experience with reptiles and mammals, some herbivorous ones might have been present.

The major group of Pennsylvanian amphibians were marked by a covering of plates on the head, which in the larger forms was a veritable bony armor. The head was flat and broad across the top, and the eyes were directed upward from this flat top (Fig. 18-27). They are known as the *stegocephalians,* meaning "roofed head." One form of the stegocephalians attained a head length of 4 ft and a total length of 15 ft.

The amphibians continued as an im-

FIG. 18-28   Diorama of Permian sea floor representing fossil forms taken from the Glass Mountains, Texas. *(Courtesy of Smithsonian Institution.)*

portant element of the Early Permian land fauna but thereafter they decreased in relative numbers, owing undoubtedly to the rise of the higher reptiles. The stegocephalians were scarce in the Late Permian and became extinct in the Triassic.

PERMIAN PERIOD

Changing Climates

The Pennsylvanian was a time of mild and equable climate, with little indication of latitudinal climatic zones. Such a warm and moist climate had existed from Cambrian times to the Permian in many parts of the world, but now, cooler climates began to appear, and eventually a glacial epoch on continents south of the equator set in. The Permian fossils reflect such a change. The plant varieties had diminished, and different regions were marked by differentiated groups. Greater dryness in places set in. In fact, there were desert conditions in North America in all the periods from the Silurian on, but not necessarily cold regions. Southwestern United States was a region of excessive evaporation in Pennsylvanian time, when the thick salt and gypsum beds of the so-called Paradox Basin of Utah and the Central Colorado Basin were deposited. Arid conditions persisted here through the Permian also. The great coal-making swamps of the Pennsylvanian had disappeared from North America, and plant fossils in Permian beds of the southwest attest to desert conditions there. Coal was formed in South Africa and Siberia in Permian time, however.

FIG. 18-29 Various kinds of spiny brachiopods secured from the Glass Mountains, Texas. These remarkable fossils are composed of silica and were released from the enclosing limestone by dissolving the limestone with hydrochloric acid. *(Courtesy of Smithsonian Institution.)*

Plants

The *cordaites* are considered possible ancestors of the conifers. These and various primitive conifers became well established in the Permian, along with the ferns. Primitive pines, spruces, and other cone-bearing types were present. This, then, marked the beginning of a great advance in the plant world.

Invertebrates

The important elements of the Permian marine invertebrate fauna are the cephalopods, brachiopods, bryozoans, corals, and fusulinids (Fig. 18-28). Each includes forms that are highly distinctive. Some of the specialized brachiopods have long, delicate spines protruding from the shells (Fig. 18-29). The ammonoid cephalopods had developed elaborate ornamentation, and reef communities built great porous masses of limestone in the Permian seas of the Southwest. These strata have proved to be prolific sources of oil and gas in west Texas and southeastern New Mexico.

Professor R. C. Moore[2] reports that the thick and complete sequence of Permian strata in the western Texas region will soon be one of the best-known biologically in the world, because about 5 million well-preserved fossil specimens have been collected and are being studied. This elaborate

[2] Personal Communication.

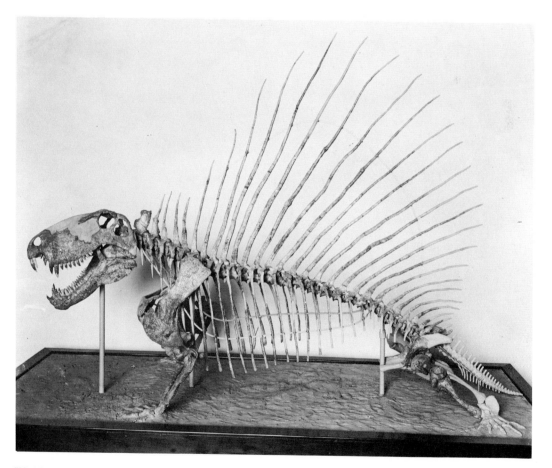

FIG. 18-30 Mounted skeleton of the Permian "sail lizard" reptile *Dimetrodon gigas* in the U.S. National Museum. It has since been discovered that the tail of this animal is longer than the restoration shows. *(Courtesy of Smithsonian Institution.)*

FIG. 18-31 Permian reptiles and amphibians, from painting by Charles R. Knight. *(Courtesy of Chicago Natural History Museum.)*

FIG. 18-32 Mammallike reptiles *(Lycaenops)* from the Permian of South Africa. Note characteristic *Glossopteris* plants. From painting by Charles R. Knight. *(Courtesy of Chicago Natural History Museum.)*

knowledge of the fossils has practical value in correlation, which is basic in the search for oil.

Professor Moore also reports that about 12,000 beautifully preserved insect fossils have been obtained from a Lower Permian limestone in central Kansas, from which almost all the main divisions have been identified. The insects were thus established, much as now, by the close of the Paleozoic.

Vertebrates

A prominant group of early amphibians was called the *labyrinthodonts* because of the infolding of the enamel of the teeth. They probably came from the crossopterygian fishes.

A certain Permian vertebrate, called *Seymouria,* has the morphological characters of a connecting link between the amphibians and the reptiles and probably evolved from the labyrinthodonts. The skeleton combines features of the amphibians and the early unspecialized reptiles. It appears more like an amphibian but is believed to have laid eggs in sand on land in small numbers, like the reptiles. It is one of the varieties of early reptiles known as the *cotylosaurs.*

The evolution of the reptiles from the amphibians is a momentous one because the dependence on a water habitat was broken. This allowed the new forms to spread more freely over the land and provided the impetus to numerous later significant adaptations to land environments. The step forward is seen mostly in the nature and development of the egg. Fish lay their tiny eggs in large numbers in some sequestered place on the bottom of a pool, lake, or stream. If the water dries up, the eggs perish. The so-called amniotic egg evolved and permitted complete land existence. Such an egg has a tough outer shell and shell membrane and an amniotic membrane enclosing the amniotic fluid. In this fluid the embryo floats, protected from

injury and dessication. It is also provided with a food supply, the yolk. Such eggs were larger and much fewer in number. The reptiles generally lay them in a pocket in the sand, where they hatch. The young fend for themselves immediately without parental care.

Scales were substituted for moist skin, and improvements in the circulatory, respiratory, and excretory systems all enabled the reptiles to search for new food supply and occupy the many different land habitats.

A peculiar Permian reptile was the *pelycosaur,* which had bony spines protruding up from the vertebrae and connected with cartilage and skin to form a bizarre fin (Figs. 18-30 and 18-31). The bones of the fin had an unusual number of blood vessels, and hence it is postulated that the fin might have been a body temperature controlling device. They were carnivorous, lived entirely on land, and became extinct before the end of the Permian.

Perhaps, most significant among the Permian reptiles was a type with certain mammalian characters. These were the *therapsids* (See Fig. 18-32). They had teeth that were differentiated into the incisors, canines, and molars like the mammals, and the skull was also mammalianlike. The first mammals, appearing in the Triassic, are believed to have sprung from this stock.

To recapitulate, the fishes evolved into the amphibians by way of the crossopterygians and labyrinthodonts, the amphibians into the reptiles through a Seymouria-like animal and the reptiles to the mammals by way of the therapsids. The stage was set in late Paleozoic time for the explosive evolution of the reptiles, and this, indeed, happened. The diversity and adaptive radiation of the reptiles is amazing. The mammals, however, remained obscure and diminutive all through the Mesozoic and then ascended into dominance over the reptiles in the Cenozoic.

Suggested Aids

Readings

Moody, Paul A.: *Introduction to Evolution,* Harper & Row, Publishers, Incorporated, New York, 1962.

Romer, A. S.: *Man and the Vertebrates,* vol. I, Pelican Book Company, Baltimore, Md., 1954.

Stokes, Wm. Lee: *Essentials of Earth History,* Prentice-Hall, Inc., Englewood Cliffs, N.J., 1960.

Models

Evolution of the Fishes. Ten models each 6¾ in. long in display case. Wards Natural Science Establishment, Inc., P.O. Box 1712, Rochester 3, New York.

Chapter 19

TRIASSIC PERIOD

Life in the Beginning of the Mesozoic

Had Rip Van Winkle gone to sleep in the evening of the Paleozoic and awakened on the morn of the Mesozoic he would have said, "Where am I?" The inland seas were gone from the eastern and central parts of the continent. The swamps had vanished, mountains had been built along with great volcanic piles, and these were being eroded away. Climates differed from place to place and were generally more stringent than in the warm, moist Pennsylvanian. The Permian, of course, had been a time of great physical change, and many forms of life had undergone considerable hardship. With changing physical conditions all organisms either adapted to the new conditions, migrated to more favorable places, or died off. Certain stocks, once abundant, became extinct or were continued by a few generally conservative

Life of the Mesozoic Era

lines, and then, some of the groups that survived began immediately to make noteworthy and in part startling evolutionary changes.

We note the complete disappearance of the trilobites and blastoids, along with certain archaic types of crinoids, bryozoans, and corals. The brachiopods suffered a great decline. The cephalopods known as ammonites had a rapid development, with the spawning of many new species. The reptiles took to several major habitats—the river flood plains, the swamps, the air, and even the ocean. The monstrous dinosaurs dominated the animal world, and the Mesozoic is often called the Age of Dinosaurs or the Age of Reptiles. The conifers and cycads took over from the tree ferns, and in the latter part of the Mesozoic the modern flowering plants became exceedingly abundant and varied and, with the evergreens, crowded the ferns into an insignificant part of the total flora.

FIG. 19-1 Characteristic cycads of the Jurassic period. Also primitive birds, flying reptiles, and small running bipedal reptiles. Painting by Charles R. Knight. (Courtesy of Chicago Natural History Museum.)

The Late Devonian mountain building had been more profound than that of the close of the Paleozoic, at least in North America, so that we cannot blame the great change in life on mountain building. But the continent did become largely emergent during Permian time, and there was much new land to conquer. The plants and the vertebrates, especially, met the challenge, but the marine invertebrates suffered. Even so, all phyla, almost all classes and orders, and many families and genera survived the transition from the Permian to the Triassic.

Plants

As far as numbers are concerned we should probably say that the cycads were most important. It has been estimated that two-fifths of the flora of the Mesozoic, especially of the Jurassic, were cycads. Cycads in general have a woody trunk with a large central pith cavity. The trunk is short and bulbous or keg-shaped in some species, but in others it is long and high. It is covered by a mat of hanging dead leaves or marked by a pattern of scars of the former positions of attachment of the leaves. The top is a graceful crown of long palmlike leaves that have a strong stem axis and numerous narrow elongate leaflets on either side. Abundant in the Mesozoic were two cycadlike groups, the *Bennettitales* and the *Cycadeoidales*, which are now entirely extinct. They bore flowerlike structures, in which a circle of male spore-bearing stamens surrounded a pear-shaped female organ provided with numerous seed ovules, similar to the modern flowering plants. Some 40 species have been recognized in Triassic deposits near Richmond, Virginia. See Fig. 19-1.

The conifers or cone-bearing evergreens, which made a primitive start in the late Paleozoic, flourished in the Triassic and thenceforth to the present. They are the pines, spruces, cedars, firs, etc. The petrified tree trunks of the well-known Petrified Forest of Arizona and elsewhere in the

FIG. 19-2 Polished sections of petrified wood. Left specimen is a Jurassic cycad, and right specimen is a Triassic conifer.

Colorado Plateau are mostly of the family *Araucariaceae*, which now survive only in the Southern Hemisphere. Literally thousands of logs lie exhumed or partly exposed there. They were buried in the muds and sands of Triassic river flood plains and in the modern erosion cycle are being unearthed (Fig. 19-2). They are mostly shorn of any branches and hence probably were carried down the courses of long rivers from distant forests and, in the process of river transport, had the branches and part of the root system worn or torn off. The petrified logs in the Petrified Forest average about 3 to 4 ft in diameter, but some attain a measure of 7 ft in greatest diameter and a length of 125 ft. They are mostly broken into segments, owing undoubtedly to the jointing that occurred in the sediments in which they were buried, after petrification.

In eastern United States a few narrow, downfaulted basins caught red Triassic sediments, and in places of the basins peat-forming swamps existed. The peat is now a poor grade of coal, but it was mined somewhat in the early colonial days. Plant fossils from these beds reveal that ferns were the dominant type, and even many of large size had survived like their Pennsylvanian ancestors. Horsetails of fair size and abundance were also present.

Invertebrates

Marine invertebrates are known only from the western margin of the continent. Marine waters invaded the continent from the west coast as far inland as central Utah and western Wyoming and brought with them a new and most interesting ammonite fauna. Some were identical with those found in the Himalayas across the Pacific. Clams and brachiopods are present but generally not important.

Vertebrates

The Triassic marks the beginning of expansion of the reptiles. Numerous three-

FIG. 19-3 Restoration of an amphibian, *Buettneria bakeri*, from the Triassic of Texas. *(Museum of Paleontology, University of Michigan.)*

toed birdlike tracks in the red siltstones of the Triassic basins of the Atlantic continental margin range in size from ½ to 18 in. long. These tracks were first thought to be those of birds, even gigantic birds, but now they are regarded as those of the early stocks of the so-called ruling reptiles, or dinosaurs. The southwestern Triassic beds have yielded the skeletons and plates of a terrible-looking aquatic reptile like a huge crocodile. It is called phytosaur and inhabited the sluggish streams and river flood-plain ponds in considerable number.

Amphibians were competitive with the rising reptiles in the Triassic, as the broad and thick-skulled group, the *stegocephalians,* attained their maximum size (Fig. 19-3). Hereafter the amphibians lost ground rapidly and became insignificant.

The bony fishes were evidently numerous (Fig. 19-4).

JURASSIC PERIOD

Seaways and Land

The Jurassic period continued nearly like the Triassic, with the eastern and central parts of the continent emergent. In the absence of interior seas, deltas, swamps, and broad agradational river flood plains the chances of fossilization were poor, if not nil, over these parts of the continent.

The Pacific margin was the site of a long basin of subsidence and of thick accumulation of sediments. Also a broad sea extended from the Arctic to the Gulf of Mexico along the site of the present Great Plains and Rocky Mountains. Its sediments contain fairly abundant marine invertebrate fossils. Near the close of Jurassic time the region of the seaway had become emergent and streams from west-lying mountains were spreading flood-plain sediments far

FIG. 19-4 Bony fishes *(Semiconotus capensis)* from the Triassic sedimentary rocks of South Africa. The bony fishes were evidently numerous in the Triassic.

and wide. All the way from Alberta, through Montana, the Dakotas, Wyoming, Colorado, eastern Utah, northern Arizona, and New Mexico was covered with the variegated muds and sands, which are known today as the Morrison formation. These are pointed out particularly because they are the repository of many bones of the great dinosaurs.

Invertebrates

The coiled ammonites evolved further from those of the Triassic and new types with a variety of new external ornamentation effects and with an increase in the elaborate crenulations of the sutures, which are the junction of the septa with the outer shell (Fig. 19-5). The rate of change was rapid, and the species are widespread. Hence, the Jurassic ammonites make excellent guide fossils. Some Late Jurassic forms were as large as tractor tires.

Belemnites were common and widespread. They are dense, cigar-shaped rods pointed on one end, that formed an internal support for squidlike animals (Fig. 19-6). The belemnites and squids are relatives of the ammonites, and all are cephalopods.

Echinoids are represented by sea urchins. The crinoids were represented by forms having long pentagonal stems. The cross-section appearance of the segments of the stem appear like stars, and the genus is called *Pentacrinus.*

Foraminifers, sponges, corals, bryozoans, brachiopods, snails, and various arthropods make up a host of species that are known from Jurassic deposits. The Jurassic beds are divided into a number of divisions, and these as time units are recognized around the world on the basis of the good guide fossils.

Plants

The cycads became so abundant in the Jurassic that the period has been called

Harpoceras Jurassic

Scaphites Cretaceous

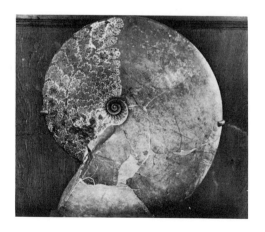

Placenticera **Cretaceous**

FIG. 19-5 Jurassic and Cretaceous ammonites.

FIG. 19-6 Belemnites (squidlike forms), oyster bed, and sea weeds of the western Jurassic seas. Note faint form of ichthyosaur in the murky water. *(Courtesy of Chicago Natural History Museum.)*

FIG. 19-7 *Protoceratops* and its eggs. This is a dinosaur that lived in Cretaceous time but illustrates a reptilian type with weak legs, hardly able to support its weight. From painting by Charles R. Knight. *(Courtesy of Chicago Natural History Museum.)*

the Age of Cycads (Fig. 19-1). But from a botanical standpoint the *ginkgo* is more interesting. It lived abundantly and became distributed all over the world, whereas today only one species lives, which is native to China and Japan. Since its discovery in a monastery garden it has been introduced to the United States and Europe. There is probably a ginkgo on your campus that enjoys the distinction of being the oldest living kind of tree. It has a relatively smooth bark, bears broad, subtriangular leaves with veins radiating from the pointed base, and may reach a height of 80 ft. It stands apart from other plants in its specialized method of seed fertilization.

The ferns were still abundant in places in the Jurassic but of moderate size.

Reptiles

Locomotion. The early reptiles, like their amphibian ancestors, had weak legs, with the upper part from the shoulder to elbow and from the pelvis to knee extended outward from the side, and then from the elbow and knee joints the lower part turned downward. The legs could not support the body or only momentarily so during a quick lunge (Fig. 19-7). The legs simply helped to slide the body along, and the walk was slow and laborious. Observe the locomotion of the existing alligators or the turtles. The next improvement is a change in attitude of the legs and a strengthening of them. They carry the body above ground, extend directly downward, and swing forward and backward in vertical planes. The length of the stride is increased, and the animal has gained considerable speed and agility. Some of the dinosaurs exhibited this proficiency, but never to the extent of many of the later mammals. Some reptilian groups, like the lizards, turtles, and crocodiles and alligators, have improved their legs little and, although holding on competitively in certain environments, have never amounted to much.

Speedy locomotion was obtained by one group of reptiles by running on the hind legs. How this started is suggested by a lizard called the "mountain boomer" in our arid southwest. When frightened and maximum speed is necessary, the front end

FIG. 19-8 Duck-billed dinosaur, *Anatosaurus annectens* Marsh, from the upper Cretaceous Lance formation of Niobrara County, Wyoming. *(Courtesy of Smithsonian Institution.)*

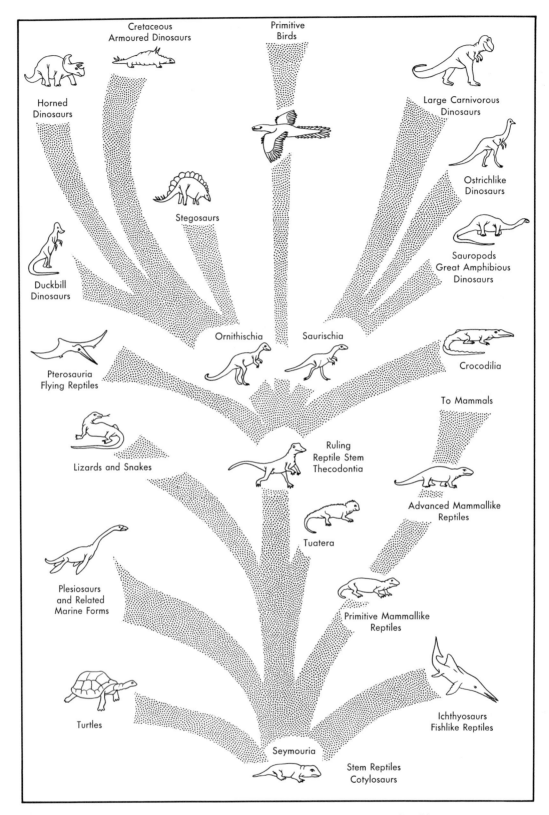

FIG. 19-9 The family tree of reptiles. In general the position from bottom to top signifies older to younger forms, but not entirely. A number of branches have continued on to the present.

of the body is lifted from the ground and the well-developed hind legs carry the entire body during the swift burst of speed. The front legs are relieved of duty and probably because of this lesser importance have become smaller then the hind ones. After the run is over, the four-footed posture is again assumed. The elevation of the front part of the body to a bipedal posture is accomplished by the leverage of the heavy tail. The hind legs and pelvis thus serve as a fulcrum of balance for the body of fairly equal weights fore and aft. (Fig. 19-8).

Ruling Reptile Stem. The bipedal locomotion is of critical importance in any attempt to understand the evolution of the dinosaurs and related groups, for they all stemmed, it is now concluded, from a fairly conservative reptile that had taken to a form of locomotion much like that of the mountain boomer. This reptile and associates are called the *Thecodontia*, and they are regarded as the precursors of the "ruling reptiles." For an idea of the appearance of the Thecodontia, see Fig. 19-9. The animal pictured here was about 1 yd long, and although it looked somewhat like a large modern lizard, it had an internal structure like the dinosaurs. The hind legs, particularly, were strong and modified.

Study Fig. 19-9. You can see that the primitive reptile, *Seymouria*-like, is portrayed as the stem line from the amphibians and that a number of major orders have evolved from it, one of these being that of the Thecodontia. From the Thecodontia all the grotesque and extremely varied dinosaurs came, as well as the *Pterosauria* or flying reptiles, the birds, and the crocodiles. The crocodiles are a degenerate form of the ruling reptiles, yet are with us today though all the rest are extinct:[1]

These sluggish creatures have wandered far from the bipedal pathway which their early ancestors had taken, although they have still,

[1] A. S. Romer, *Man and the Vertebrates,* vol. 1, Pelican Books, Baltimore, Md., 1954.

one may note, the long hind legs and short front ones that are characteristic of the group. They alone of ruling reptiles, however, have survived, secure in their specialized position in the world, while their more ambitious reptilian cousins have had their splendid day and have gone.

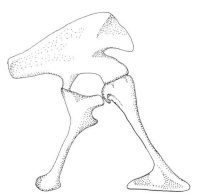

Saurischian (Reptilelike)

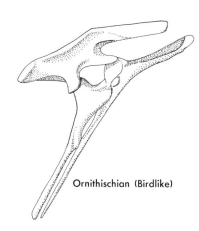

Ornithischian (Birdlike)

FIG. 19-10 Right pelvic bones of dinosaurs, showing the contrast between the two great orders. (After Romer, 1954.)

Primitive birds evolved from the Thecodontia during the Mesozoic and flowered into the modern birds in great variety and abundance in the Cenozoic Era.

The two major branches of the ruling reptile stem were the *Ornithischia* and the *Saurischia*. See Fig. 19-9. These had quite different pelvic structures, and although each spawned extremely contrasting sub-

FIG. 19-11 *Triceratops and Tyrannosaurus, from painting by Charles R. Knight. (Courtesy of Chicago Natural History Museum.)*

FIG. 19-12 Giant sauropod dinosaur, *Diplodocus*, from the upper Jurassic Morrison formation in the Dinosaur National Monument, Uintah County, Utah. *(Courtesy of Smithsonian Institution.)*

FIG. 19-13 *Brontosaurus, a huge plant-eating dinosaur. From painting by Charles R. Knight. (Courtesy of Chicago Natural History Museum.)*

FIG. 19-14 A group of vertebrae of *Brontosaurus*. University of Utah Museum. Nearest vertebra is about $3\frac{1}{2}$ ft high.

branches, the continuity of inheritance of the unique pelvises in each group furnishes the main guide in classification. The Ornithischia had birdlike pelvises, and the Saurischia had reptilelike pelvises. See Fig. 19-10. It should be emphasized, however, that the birds are not descended from the Ornithischia; they are essentially cousins, each coming along separate branches from the common ancestors, the Thecodontia.

Saurischia. The reptilelike dinosaurs were already abundant in the Late Triassic. Little change was needed to convert the Thecodontia into comparatively small, swift-running, flesh-eating bipeds. Bipedal flesh eaters continued to be the main stock of the saurischians until their demise at the end of the Cretaceous period, and many kept to a small size. *Compsognathus*, for example, was about the size of a rooster and was rather abundant in the Jurassic. The main line of the carnivorous dinosaurs tended to evolve larger individuals, however, and some by the end of the Jurassic were large enough, it is believed, to venture to prey upon the gigantic herbivorous

FIG. 19-15 Large bipeds on right are herbivorous ornithischians (duck-billed dinosaurs). From painting by Charles R. Knight. *(Courtesy of Chicago Natural History Museum.)*

dinosaurs that had appeared by this time. *Allosaurus* was one of these truculent carnivores, and his bones are most numerous in the Morrison formation. The trend culminated in the Cretaceous with the huge bipedal carnivore *Tyrannosaurus rex*, "king of the ruling reptiles" (Fig. 19-11). He stood some 19 ft high and had a skull of massive structure more than 4 ft long that was armed with numerous sabrelike teeth for biting and tearing. The hind legs were large and powerful, but the front legs had atrophied to tiny useless appendages with two fingers. The primitive amphibian and reptilian number of toes and fingers was five, and although in the course of time and change we note the loss and modification of the digits, there never was a gain in number, except in some of the marine reptiles.

By Late Triassic time certain reptile-like dinosaurs were tending to a plant diet, as indicated by their teeth. At the same time they were becoming large and four-footed. From these developed the largest four-footed animals that ever lived on land. Of these, *Diplodocus* holds the length record of 87½ ft, but he was comparatively slimly built and weighed a modest 25 to 35 tons (Fig. 19-12). *Brontosaurus* was somewhat shorter but equally as heavy (Figs. 19-13 and 19-14). The giant of these ponderous beasts was *Brachiosaurus*, which is estimated to have weighed 50 tons and could look over a three-storied building.

The monumental, arched construction of the back bone over the supporting hind legs was necessary to carry the weight of the enormous body (Fig. 19-13). The hind legs, were, of course, massive also. The feet seem to have been huge pads with two or three large claws. The small head looks absurd on the huge body. The nostrils on some species are high on the skull above the eyes, suggesting that the animal could breath while submerged in water with only the top of the head exposed. In fact, it is generally believed that these great herbivores were amphibious and spent most of their time in luxuriant swamps cropping bottom vegetation. The buoyancy of the water would help immensely in supporting the weight, which might be a bit excessive

FIG. 19-16   The plated dinosaur *Stegosaurus*, from painting by Charles R. Knight. (Courtesy of Chicago Natural History Museum.)

FIG. 19-17 Skeleton of *Stegosaurus* from the upper Jurassic Morrison formation in Albany County, Wyoming. Compare with restoration in Fig 19-16. *(Courtesy of Smithsonian Institution.)*

for any lengthy journey on land. They must have eaten continuously with their small head to keep the huge body in fuel. The teeth were feeble and few, and the jaws weak, indicating that the fodder was soft and abundant.

Ornithischia. Although the ornithischians started as carnivorous bipeds they all soon turned herbivores and continued that way until their extinction in Late Cretaceous time. Almost all had lost their front teeth and had found a replacement in a stout horny beak. The teeth in the back of the jaws were better fitted for chewing.

The duckbill bipedal dinosaurs were abundant in the Cretaceous. They had a broad beak like a duck, were massively built, and probably amphibious. Some individuals evidently died on a desert floor, where their bodies dried to a mummified condition. This, when buried by river muds, left a fossil that shows the tendons and natural details of the skin (Fig. 19-15).

Some of the ornithischians reverted to a four-footed mode of life, but in each, their bipedal ancestry is clearly shown by the large hind legs and short front legs. The four-footed herbivores were slow and could

only survive in the face of their carnivorous contemporaries by developing a formidable armor, and this they did in bizarre ways. *Stegosaurus,* for instance, developed a double row of stout, sharp, bony plates that extended along the back from head to tail. The tail was equipped with two pairs of sharp, heavy spikes, with which it could deal terrific blows (Fig. 19-16 and 19-17).

Ankylosaurus had a broad flat body studded with a heavy series of bony nodules forming a protective shell. It has been called a reptilian tank. See Fig. 19-15.

Triceratops appeared in the Late Cretaceous with a concentration of head armament. A broad skirt of bone from the back of the skull protected the otherwise vulnerable neck from the flesh eaters, and three formidable horns pointed forward (Fig. 19-18). As long as *Triceratops* could keep face to face with the attacker perhaps he was safe (Fig. 19-11).

Flying Reptiles. One line of reptiles took to the air. These are called the pterosaurs and also pterodactyls, meaning wing-fingered. We find fossils of them in the Late Jurassic strata of Germany in a formation called Solnhofen limestone. Here a number

FIG. 19-18 Horned dinosaur, *Triceratops*, from the upper Cretaceous Lance formation Niobrara County, Wyoming. (*Courtesy of Smithsonian Institution.*)

of forms of life were preserved under conditions so delicate that the structures of jellyfishes and the wing skin of the pterodactyls show. One flying reptile fossilized in the Solnhofen limestone was about 3 ft long with a long beak and sharp teeth and a long tail tipped by a horizontal rudder (Fig. 19-1). The hind legs were thin and weak, but the front legs were strong and, in fact, served as the wings. The first three fingers were short and had claws for clutching. The little finger was lost, but the fourth was strong and long and served as the sole support of the wing. The wing was completed by a thin skin, which stretched from the bones of the arm or front leg to the flank of the animal.

The transition from the stem reptiles to the flying reptiles was undoubtedly through the bipeds, in which the front legs, or arms, were freed from walking and hence could be used for other purposes. In some cases the front legs degenerated, but in the pterodactyls we note the modification as wings and a build-up to much more powerful structures than the hind legs.

In Late Cretaceous time a toothless flying reptile, *Pteranodon*, with a short tail and delicate, hollow, light bones developed a wing spread of 27 ft (Fig. 19-19). Even so it may not have weighed much over 50 lb.

Marine Reptiles. A number of branches from the main trunk of ancestry of the reptiles took back to the sea from whence their forebears came. After the long journey of evolution from the aquatic fishes to land-living and air-breathing reptiles, some sought fish as food, progressively became good swimmers, and again adapted to an aquatic habitat, in fact, to life in the great oceans. Their reversions were of different kinds and of different degrees of perfection. In some the adaptation was as perfect as that of the porpoises and whales; in others it was comparable to the seals and walruses, for these are parallel adaptations to a marine mode of life by some of the mammals. Legs were remodeled for paddling, and the body was refashioned for aquatic locomotion, but the lungs, after having replaced the gills, could never be converted or replaced. Like their mammal counterparts, the marine reptiles were air breathers and always had to surface for air, no matter how complete their adaptation was otherwise.

Let us take a brief look at the *plesiosaurs* (Fig. 19-20). They had a bulbous body, with the four legs converted to great strong paddles or flippers. A gigantic early form from Australia had a fairly short neck but a head nearly 10 ft long and measured 42 ft from head to tail. The snout was well equipped with sharp-pointed teeth. Another group of plesiosaurs evolved long necks and small heads with the 76 neck vertebrae in the last form. It is conjectured that the mode of swimming itself was not good enough to pursue and catch the elusive fishes, but with the long agile neck or snout, the feat was accomplished in good style. The plesiosaurs were common in the Jurassic seas and survived until near the close of the Cretaceous.

The *ichthyosaurs* were the most highly adapted marine group to an aquatic exist-

ence and well deserve the name "fish reptile." They reached a maximum length of 15 ft. Various species spanned the Mesozoic before becoming extinct. The outside appearance was very fishlike (Fig. 19-20). The skeletons show the head set closely on the shoulders and the legs so small and remodeled to flippers that they could only have served to direct the course of the reptile through the water. A number of fossils in black shales in southern Germany show the flesh and skin outline with a large dorsal fin like that of a fish. The creature undoubtedly swam in fishlike fashion by undulations of the body and tail.

The ichthyosaurs were so completely adapted to a marine life that it was early realized that a problem of reproduction existed. Reptiles are egg layers, and those which take to the sea must return to land at least to lay their eggs in the sand above the water line. The turtles that live in the sea do this. But the ichthyosaurs would flounder and die on the beach should they attempt to come out of the water. Their small flippers or fins would be of no use whatsoever for land locomotion. So, along with the complete adaptation to an open sea life, the ability to retain the eggs in the mother's body until hatched was developed, and the young were born alive

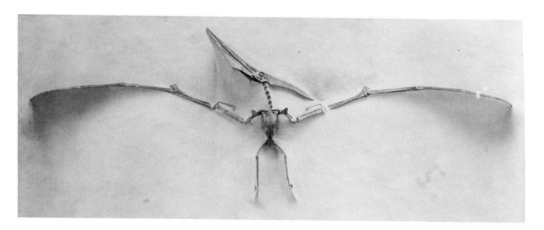

FIG. 19-19 Restored skeleton of the flying reptile *Pteranodon* from the upper Cretaceous Chalk deposits of western Kansas. (*Courtesy of Smithsonian Institution.*)

FIG. 19-20 *Plesiosaurus and Ichthyosaurus,* from painting by Charles R. Knight. *(Courtesy of Chicago Natural History Museum.)*

in the water. A number of specimens are now known that show a cluster of young ichthyosaurs inside the rib case of the adult.

There were also the long-tailed marine lizards, the *mososaurs,* that are known only from the Late Cretaceous. These were also excellent swimmers and they lived on

fishes, some of fair size, judging from the numerous sharp conical teeth (Fig. 19-21).

Primitive Birds

Also found in the Solnhofen limestone are two creatures about midway between the thecodonts and the true birds. One is

FIG. 19-21 *Mososaurus,* the giant sea lizards, sea turtles, and the flying reptile *Pteranodon,* from painting by Charles R. Knight. *(Courtesy of Chicago Natural History Museum.)*

called *Archeopteryx* and one *Archeornis*, and each was about the size of a crow. The tail was the reptilian type but with a double row of feathers spread laterally down it. Rather feeble wings were fitted with short feathers and three clawed fingers (Fig. 19-1). The breastbone was small, indicating weak flying muscles. The bones were not hollow, and the jaws were armed with teeth. It is evident, therefore, that *Archeopteryx* and *Archeornis* were not far removed from the stem stock of the ruling reptiles.

CRETACEOUS PERIOD

Plants

The flowering plants (Angiospermae) made their entry in force in Early Cretaceous time, although pollen grains from a Jurassic coal in Scotland are regarded as those of the angiosperms. The angiosperms consist of the monocotyledons and the dicotyledons. In the monocotyledons the seed sprouts in a single leaflet, and as it grows, the stem lacks a differentiation of cellular structure into pith, wood, and bark. The leaves have parallel veins. This group includes the grasses, cereals, palms, lilies, etc. The dicotyledons start with two leaflets, exhibit pith, wood, and bark, and have leaves with a network of veins. These are the shrubs, herbs, oaks, maples, elms, etc.

The Early Cretaceous varieties identified are referred to 16 modern families. Many of the same species living today were present in the Late Cretaceous, and since some of the modern species are limited to specific climatic belts, it is possible to discern the climate that existed where some of the fossil floras are found. For instance, the present dogwood, fig, tulip tree, persimmon, sycamore, breadfruit tree, and eucalyptus mainly inhabit moderately warm climates, so that it is expected that the Cretaceous relatives of these, even though some are extinct, would have lived in about the same climates.

The sequoias, whose modern survivors are the giant redwoods, were common in the Cretaceous.

By mid-Cretaceous time the angiosperms had become the most abundant plants, and now the ferns were reduced to a minor role. The advance of the modern plants presaged the momentous rise of the mammals and is of great significance in geologic history.

Invertebrates

All main groups of the larger marine invertebrates are known in fossil form in Cretaceous rocks. The pelecypods were prominent in the form of thick-shelled oysters, large concentrically ribbed clams, and corallike reef builders called rudistids. These last were twisted or conical forms, some 4 ft long and 1 ft in largest diameter. The Cretaceous is noted for ammonites,

FIG. 19-22 Coiled and straight ammonites and various gastropods and pelecypods on a Cretaceous sea bottom. Fossil assemblage from Coon Creek, Tennessee. *(Courtesy of Chicago Museum of Natural History.)*

some tightly coiled, some loosely coiled, and some straight (Figs. 19-6 and 19-22). All had extremely complex sutures and ornate ribs, nodes, and spines. They were evidently making a last showy stand, because none are known from the Tertiary. The shallow seas teemed with foraminifers, and their small shells form sizable parts of certain chalk formations. Abundant in the chalk also are diatoms and coccoliths, both remains of simple floating plants.

Vertebrates

Birds. A brief outline of the various groups of Mesozoic vertebrates has been given under the heading Jurassic Period, and the histories given there were mostly carried through the Cretaceous. It need only be added that the birds had also already assumed to conquer new environments, and although still primitive in Cretaceous time in terms of modern birds some lines had already undergone considerable modification. Fossil birds are rare, but we get a glimpse of extreme adaptation with resulting modification in

FIG. 19-23 Extinct bird *Hesperornis*, from the upper Cretaceous Chalk formation of Logan County, Kansas. The skull is now known not to belong to the bird but is one of a *Plesiosaurus*. (Courtesy of the Smithsonian Institute.)

Hesperornis, a wingless swimming and diving bird (Fig. 19-23). It had powerful hind legs rigged as paddles, and only very rudimentary wings. It had a long neck, but the skull mounted on the neck is now known to be one of a plesiosaur. If its true skull were about like the plesiosaur shown, the individual was 5 ft long. So specialized was *Hesperoris* that paleontologists doubt that it could have managed to get about on land.

The Last of the Ruling Reptiles. A question that occurs to every imaginative mind after reviewing the monstrous and brawny creations of the Mesozoic is, Why did so many die off and fail to survive the transition into the Cenozoic? None of the dinosaurs, the marine reptiles except the turtles, or the flying reptiles lived after the Cretaceous. What caused their extinction? We must first observe that size and strength do not necessarily ensure survival, because the ascendency of the mammals over the reptiles in the Cenozoic demonstrates the power of the mind. Still the reptiles ruled for 100 million years while the mammals existed as timid, hunted, nervous, and cautious animals mostly of rodent size. The low mentality of the reptiles fitted them poorly to cope with unusual circumstances; they reacted only in set, instinctive patterns. Their body processes were probably inefficient and required an almost constant intake of food. Also it must be remembered that the reptiles are cold-blooded and suited to the lush warm swamps and river flood plains of the lowlands. Much upland and mountainous country had evolved by Late Cretaceous time, and as far as we know, the dinosaurs had not been able to occupy it. Possibly some stocks of the mammals, biding their time during the long reign of the great reptiles, had adapted to life in the uplands. Their warm blood, fur coats, and solicitous care of their young permitted them to survive seasonal changes, which, undoubtedly, the dinosaurs could not endure. If we observe the Late Cretaceous and Early Tertiary paleogeographic maps of Chap. 17 we note that the vast inland sea of the region of the present Great Plains and Rocky Mountains disappeared by the close of the Cretaceous. The ranges of the Rockies were rising with catchment basins in between for the debris eroded from the mountains. The lush vegetation of the Cretaceous swamps had mostly disappeared, and all manner of the modern angiosperms and conifers had spread over the plains and on the uplands and mountains. The mammals were finding this new frontier much to their liking. They were made for it and began to prosper in a hundred radiate branches. The uplands were erosional regions, and chances of fossilization of these new, efficient, and vigorous mammals were slim. Hence we know practically nothing about them. At the same time the only places that the amphibious, herbivorous dinosaurs could tolerate were shrinking, and the survivors were being crowded into limited areas. Even these limited areas were developing conditions that caused the ponderous beasts considerable discomfort. For example, let us follow the changing conditions in central Utah. The Mesaverde sandstones, shales, and coal beds attest to favorable conditions for the swamp-loving dinosaurs in this, the latest of Cretaceous time. The numerous great footprints in the coal beds show that the dinosaurs were still doing right well. A broad upland and mountainous region was growing to the west, however, and the dinosaurs must have been forewarned by slight seasonal changes and the shrinking of their swamplands. The shore of the inland sea oscillated back and forth but generally withdrew, and river flood-plain muds and sands, the North Horn formation, were spread over the swamps. Soon, and approximately by the beginning of Cenozoic time, the swamps were gone, and so the sauropods, duckbill dinosaurs, and armored dinosaurs, all amphibious, disappeared also. The conditions were even inhospitable for the herbivorous horned dinosaurs and they disappeared in the night. Without herbivores to prey on, the terrible carnivores perished also. Probably the alert and agile mammals, now adapted to the lands adjacent to the limited swamps, were making hay in preying on the eggs and young of the reptiles, and they hurried the demise of the dinosaurs. Thus ended the reign of the reptiles. Of some 20 orders of Mesozoic reptiles only 4 major ones survived: (1) the turtles, (2) crocodiles and alligators, (3) lizards and snakes, and (4) Rynchocephalia. Off the coast of New Zealand on a few islets is the Tuatara, scientifically known as *Sphenodon,* a lizardlike reptile. It is the sole surviving member of the Rynchocephalia. Its anatomy suggests that it is a survivor of an archaic group from which the ruling reptiles, lizards and other types, evolved. It, with the three groups mentioned above, now all very much subordinate to and dominated by the mammals, are the sole survivors of the impressive reptiles of the Mesozoic era.

Suggested Aids

Readings

Colbert, E. H.: *The Dinosaur Book,* McGraw-Hill Book Company, Inc., New York, 1951.

Moore, R. C.: *Introduction to Historical Geology,* McGraw-Hill Book Company, Inc., New York, 1958.

Raymond, Percy E.: *Prehistoric Life,* Harvard University Press, Cambridge, Mass., 1939.

Romer, A. S.: *Man and the Vertebrates,* vol. 1, Pelican Books, Baltimore, Md., 1954.

Simpson, G. G.: *The Major Features of Evolution,* Columbia University Press, New York, 1953.

Stokes, Wm. Lee: *Essentials of Earth History,* Prentice-Hall, Inc., Englewood Cliffs, N.J., 1960.

Filmstrip

The Coming of Reptiles, Encyclopaedia Britannica, FSC 714, 715, and 716.

Chapter 20

THE AGE OF MAMMALS, BIRDS, AND FLOWERING PLANTS

The Cenozoic era is preeminently the age of the mammals. They succeeded the reptiles of the Mesozoic in a convincing and thorough way. The culminating triumph of the mammals was the production of man, who now threatens either to annihilate himself or to overpopulate the earth. The mammals have evolved along most imaginable lines and have conquered all earthly environments. The reptiles arrest a person's attention because of their grotesque, ugly, terrifying, and stupid-looking forms, but the mammals catch your fancy by their alertness, beauty, grace of motion, parental care of their young, and in the case of a domesticated few, a sense of protection of and affection and fidelity to their human masters.

The Cenozoic was also the age of birds, and many of us find much fascination in the life and diversity of our feathered friends. Mother nature has given them all a

Life of the Cenozoic Era

sleek coat of feathers, which in some is fancy and colorful. They help control the insects, and the domesticated ones furnish man part of his staple food supply.

The Cenozoic is not only the age of mammals and the age of birds, but it is also indeed the age of the angiosperms or flowering plants. By the process of photosynthesis the plants make their own food, and the plants are the food directly and indirectly of the mammals and birds. It is possible that the explosive evolution of the mammals would not have taken place had not the angiosperms evolved, with only the conifers, ferns, and mosses existing, but in some mysterious way it seems as though the tremendous expansion of the flowering plants during the Late Cretaceous prepared the way for, and assured the prosperity of, the mammals. So, it is just as appropriate to say that the Cenozoic is the age of the flowering plants as the age of mammals.

CHARACTERISTICS OF MAMMALS

Reproduction

All mammals but the most primitive bear their young alive and nurse them. Postnatal care is characteristic. The young of several orders of mammals are born with sufficient growth to walk immediately, and it takes a high degree of organization of the mother's body for the nourishment of the embryo to such a stage of development.

Warm Blood

Mammals and birds are warm-blooded; that is, the body temperature is generally above that of the environment. In the case of mammals the temperature is controlled and regulated by means of sweat glands, hair, and the circulatory and respiratory systems. The aerated and impure blood streams are kept separated by a four-chambered, two-way heart, with the stream on one side coming from the lungs and on the other in transit to the lungs. In the reptiles the two blood streams are partially mixed in the heart, which leads to inefficiency. Hair and sweat glands are properties of the mammals but not of the reptiles.

Brains

The brain of the reptile is very small indeed. It is exceeded in size in some species by an enlargement of the spinal cord in the thoracic or pelvic region of the backbone. In the mammals the brain is much larger, even in the most stupid of them. As the more intelligent mammals evolved, the cerubellum remained about the same in size, but the cerebrum, or forebrain, originally dedicated to smelling, grew immensely. In the case of man, it almost completely covers the cerubellum. The degree of crenulation or folding of the cerebrum is in general an indication of the degree of intelligence. The folding provides more area for its outer layer or cortex, which is the seat of intelligence. In fossil skulls only the brain cavity remains, but this provides a measure of size, and in some specimens, the crenulations may be made out on the inside of the brain or on mud casts of the brain chamber. By means of the enlarged cerebrum the mammals are able to retain impressions, to analyse situations, and to act accordingly. The clarity and definition of their sight and hearing are believed to have improved as the cerebrum grew in size.

Skull

The skull of the mammals represents a consolidation of bone parts from the reptiles and shows conspicuous new developments. For instance, the lower jaw of the reptiles has normally seven bones, whereas the mammals have but one, and this articulates with a different skull bone than in the reptiles. The large jaw muscles attach to a pierced temporal region, leaving a bar or arch at the edge of the cheek. The mammals have a bony partition separating nasal and food passages to the back of the throat. This feature is important to continuous breathing. Needless to say, the brain case has expanded greatly. Lastly, the skull in the mammals articulates with the backbone by a pair of condyles, whereas in the reptiles a single round bony knob, or condyle, is present.

Teeth

Mammalian teeth differ from those of the lower vertebrates in two ways: first, mammals have only two sets of teeth, the milk teeth and the permanent teeth, whereas the lower vertebrates have an indefinite number of replacements; and second, the teeth in the tooth row of the mammals are of three kinds, designed to perform different functions, whereas in the lower vertebrates all the teeth are about the same shape and serve essentially the same purpose. In the ancestors of the higher mammals the dentition came to have a set formula (number, differention, and order) and it is expressed in terms of half a jaw, either lower or upper. As seen in Fig. 20-1, there were three front sharp, nipping or biting teeth, the incisors; one large piercing tusk, the canine; four premolar teeth behind this; and lastly three molars. This gives a total of 44 teeth in the basic formula. Now, as the various orders of mammals adapted to different environments and changed their eating habits, conspicuous modification of this early dentition occurred. Take your own teeth for instance. Laterally from the center line or axis of your jaw there are two incisors instead of three, your canine is still present but sufficiently small so that it is not conspicuous; you have two premolars, instead of four, which you call "bicuspids," and you have two molars or grinding teeth up

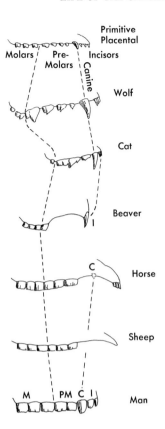

FIG. 20-1 Comparative dentition of certain selected mammals.

to late adolescence or early maturity, when the third one starts to grow. Your jaw generally does not have room at the back for this final molar, so that it becomes impacted and you are in trouble. This is the price you pay for being such a highly specialized mammal. Man's jaw progressively decreased in size as he evolved, and although the teeth diminished in size also, they now lack room, and our common dentition troubles stem from crowded teeth.

In the radiate lines of mammalian evolution teeth were lost but rarely added. The teeth were spread and refashioned in a number of ways, with the premolars and molars developing cusps and ridges in many patterns. So all told, there is a great variation possible, and the mammals about measured up to the challenge in developing an almost infinite variety. In the hands of the specialized paleontologist one molar tooth may suffice to identify the species. Not only this but the teeth are most common parts of a skeleton found in fossil form. They are more durable than bones in the face of both chemical and mechanical weathering. We commonly find teeth scattered in the mudstones of ancient lakes or river flood plains, and they suffice to tell us something not only about the life of the time but about the relative age of the formation. The mammals evolved so rapidly in so many lines that their remains are some of the best guide fossils of the Cenozoic. Teeth, therefore, make good guide fossils.

Locomotion

Get down on the floor and do a push-up. Note the expenditure of energy necessary to hold your body off the floor with elbows out and arms bent in a right angle. This is the reptile stance. Now lift up all the way with body supported on straight arms. Not so much effort is required to hold the body off the ground this way, which is the general mammalian leg position. Swing your elbows back so that they bend backward, not sideward, and with your knees bending forward in the line of the body, you are now ready to walk on all fours like most mammals. But you don't walk on all fours easily because your body has undergone a number of changes to fit it for bipedal locomotion.

In the mammals the muscles of the legs can be used almost entirely for locomotion, and not mostly for holding the body off the ground. Certain skeletal and muscular evolution accompanied the new leg functioning, and with increasing brains intelligent direction was given to the activity, and the much more efficient body gave rise to speed endurance and quick reactions. Such alert and active animals could only head for important things. As we shall see, much modification of the legs oc-

curred as the mammals adjusted to new environments.

MAJOR ORDERS OF MAMMALS

The evolution of mammals during the reign of the dinosaurs resulted by Late Cretaceous time in the two great living groups, namely, the marsupials and the placentals. The marsupials are the more primitive and were the most abundant in the last days of the dinosaurs.

A typical marsupial is the living opossum, which is similar to the Cretaceous forms. When mammals first began to bear their young alive, in transition from the egg stage, the young were tiny and immature, but they managed to crawl up the mother's body and gain entrance to a pouch on the belly. There they found shelter, warmth, and nourishment from teat glands, the same as now in all the many kinds of marsupials. The young grow in the pouch until they are ready to start life on their own.

The weakness of the marsupials lies in the almost embryonic helplessness of their young upon birth, but the placentals overcame this flaw, and in Cenozoic times easily dominated the marsupials. The allantois membrane, which surrounds the egg of the reptile, has come into contact with the walls of the uterus in which the developing embryo lies, and through the walls of this fused area, called the placenta, food and oxygen are transmitted from the mother to the embryo. This permits it to grow to a far higher stage before birth than was possible before. Then, with a considerable period of protection by the parent after birth the complicated mechanisms of body and brain can mature into an able and efficient adult. Students of the mammals believe that it was the development of the efficient placenta, which occurred by Late Cretaceous time, that led, more than anything else, to the future success of the placentals. The marsupials could not compete well with their placental cousins.

THE PLACENTALS

Ancestral Placentals

The ancestral placentals appear to have been small insect eaters and would resemble certain of our modern insectivores, such as the mole and the hedgehog. These have persisted, owing to a very specialized and isolated form of life.

The small mouselike shrews are a generalized type of placental mammal with ancestral Mesozoic overtones. Of special interest are the tree shrews of the Old World tropics, because they have certain anatomical characteristics common with the primates and are believed to represent the remote stem from which monkeys, apes, and man came.

The placentals were ready to blossom because of their able, alert, and efficient organisms, and when the dinosaurs faded, their spread was astonishingly rapid. During the very Early Tertiary (Paleocene epoch) there was a speedy differentiation from the insect eaters along many radiate lines, and by the Eocene epoch the main lines of mammalian evolutionary history were established (Fig. 20-2). The great array of higher living mammals sprang from the early insectivores, of which now only a few survive.

Carnivores

We should review the main and common groups of placentals in order to be on speaking terms with their relatives in fossil form as Cenozoic life is discussed. The carnivores will be considered first. It took only an increase in size before some of the insectivores siezed as prey their smaller cousins and thereby became flesh eaters or carnivores. Perhaps, some of these cousins became herbivorous and became the sub-

ject of prey. We are speaking of the dog family, cat family, bears, weasels, hyenas, and aquatic carnivores such as the walruses.

The carnivore has to make the kill mainly with his teeth. On the other hand, flesh is simple to digest and need not be well chewed. As a result the changes of note and of particular interest are in the teeth. The incisors are highly useful in biting and are well developed; the canines are long, large, and pointed, and serve as stabbing weapons; the molars are modified for cutting, and in the cats the chewing power is gone entirely. A pair of teeth, upper and lower, are sharp-ridged and pass by each other as shears; they do not meet directly as a chopping or crushing mechanism. Study the dentition patterns of Fig. 20-1. Dogs, coyotes, wolves, and their kin follow a carnivorous diet less strictly than cats, and have kept all their molars except one upper pair, and have retained some chewing surface. The bears, as you know, like berries, and have forsaken in part their flesh-eating habits. In one season they may live entirely on fish, for instance, and in another on various plant parts. They have, thus, redeveloped considerable chewing power in the molars.

As for the skeleton of carnivores, it has remained rather similar to the early ancestors. A carnivore must be speedy to catch its prey, it must be supple, and it must retain claws to grapple with its prey and, in the case of the dogs, to dig in the ground. It is along these lines that a light skeleton has evolved.

During the Paleocene and Eocene epochs of the Tertiary period the carnivores were scarcely distinguishable from their Late Cretaceous insectivore ancestors. These were the creodonts, or archaic carnivores. The molars in all species of creodonts were modified for shearing, but different combinations of the molars were selected for the purpose. The brain was small, and the legs were comparatively short. It apparently mattered little that they were thus dull and rather slow runners, because their con-

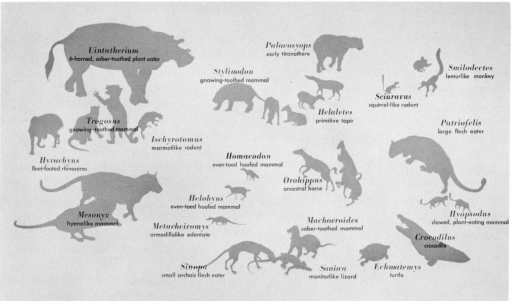

FIG. 20-2 This mural painting by the artist Jay H. Matternes shows the better-known mammals and contemporary reptiles, together with the associated flora of middle Eocene time in the geographic region of Wyoming. The animal restorations are based on study of the skeletal remains from the Bridger formation of southwestern Wyoming. The animal arrangement shown is, of course, a compromise with space and is not intended to imply that so diverse an assemblage lived together in so small an area. Such a grouping of herbivores, for example, would be quite out of place with the large predators. Moreover, it may be further remarked that the coloring of the animals employed by the artist is entirely conjectural, as no evidence for this is prepared in the fossil record. The animals represented are shown on the accompanying chart. The floral environment shown is based on studies of the fossil plant remains from the Green River formation, an interfingering lake facies of the Bridger formation. Included are ground and climbing ferns, arrowhead, water hyacinth, water lilies, palmetto and other palms, and a variety of deciduous trees, such as sweet gum, legumes, and sycamores. From this and other evidence it is clear that the region was warmer and better watered than now. (Courtesy of Smithsonian Institution.)

temporary herbivorous associates were feeble of brain and perhaps even slower of gait.

Hoofed Mammals

General Characteristics. The hoofed mammals, or ungulates, include most of the large herbivorous mammals. They are horses, cattle, deer, rhinoceroses, camels, hippopotamuses, etc. The ungulates are a great and varied group and stand quite apart from the carnivores. There are two main divisions, the odd-toed *perissodactyls* and the even-toed *artiodactyls*.

Leaves, grain, and grass must be chewed

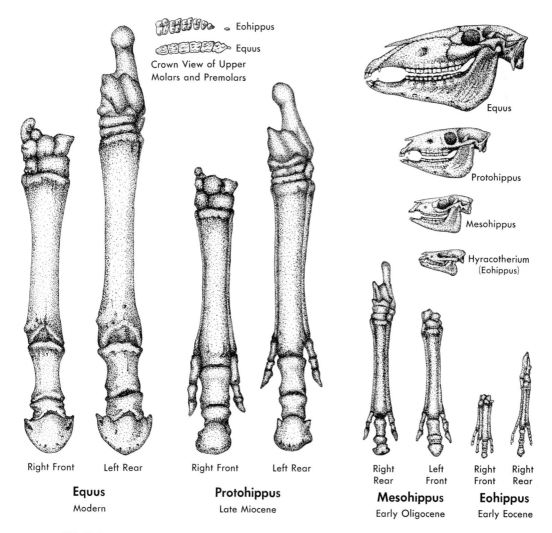

FIG. 20-3
Skeletal parts showing evolution of the horse. "Evolution of the horses from Eohippus, the dawn horse, to Equus, the modern wild horse. Only four stages are shown, but there are a number of others that demonstrated apparently an unswerving directness in the ascent. Two side branches are also known from fossils. This is the merest outline sketch of a marvelous story of progressive modification and adaptation to changing conditions. All parts of the structure must at every stage, throughout all the changes, have been coordinated into a harmonious whole, so that the animal could thrive and maintain itself against competition. *Hyracotherium (Eohippus)* must have been as perfectly fitted to its environment as are the modern species of Equus. Evolution was the response of changing needs." *(W. B. Scott, 1937.)*

FIG. 20-4 Four-toed horses and uintatherium of the Uinta Basin in Eocene time. From painting by Charles R. Knight. (Courtesy Chicago Natural History Museum.)

before passing into the mammalian stomach, and the molars and premolars rose to the task. They became large with high flat crowns for crushing and grinding. The larger molars resulted in a row of considerable length, and this required a lengthening and deepening of the jaws. The canines were hardly of any use and generally became small or disappeared except for the tusks of pigs. The incisors became adapted in various ways for cropping leaves or grass.

In most ungulates the development of hoofs went hand in hand with the evolution of long limbs for speedy running. If the herbivores are to escape their enemies, the carnivores, they must be able to outdistance them in the sprint or develop some protective armament like antlers, horns, or tusks. Antlers and horns have generally not served very well, and it has been speed for the most part that has brought the greatest protection to the ungulates. Speed has been attained chiefly by the elongation of the wrist and finger (ankle and toe) bones, with the animal actually running on the tip of his toes. The horny claws became the hoofs, which are short and broad and surround the end of each toe. In addition the limbs swing only fore and aft.over a wide angle and are very efficient for the forward motion. The first joint of the limb (the humerus and femur) is short and operated by powerful muscles, adding leverage and drive to the rest of the leg.

It seems obvious that one or two hoofed toes would do better than four or five, and thus we see in the course of evolution all through the Cenozoic era the gradual shrinking, shortening, and loss of the outer toes. The "thumb" of the front legs and big toes of the hind legs disappeared early. Beyond this, two major trends set in: one in which the middle toe was strengthened leading to the three-toed (rhinoceroses) and one-toed (horses) types (Fig. 20-3) and one in which an axial development occurred between the third and fourth toes, each becoming equally strengthened and dominant. This produced the two-toed or "cloven-hoofed" pigs, deer, cattle, etc. The second and fifth toes (first and little fingers) are seen as vestigial organs or have disappeared.

In forms like the hippopotamus, where heavy, ponderous bodies have evolved, the limbs have altered to match and are much different from fast-running limbs. They are short, straight, and thick. The foot is broad and stumpy, generally with no loss of toes and a pad beneath forming a bottom to the pillarlike limb.

Odd-toed Forms. The living perissodactyls include the horses, zebras, rhinoceroses, and tapirs. Two early Tertiary groups, now extinct, are the *titanotheres* and *chalicotheres*. In these forms we note a trend from five toes to four or three (Fig. 20-4) and from three to one. The horse's limbs are reduced to one finger (or toe) the rhinoc-

eros to three, and the tapir to four. Just the thumb (or big toe) has been lost in the tapirs. As carriage comes to be more and more on the tips of the digits and as the wrist and finger bones lengthen, the thumb first loses contact with the ground, and then the little finger. Without use they atrophy and soon become vestigial. Then, finally, the weight is carried on the second or middle finger, and the first and third become nonfunctional and decrease in size.

Probably the most classic evolutionary example of vertebrates is that of the horse. This is so because the fossil record through the Eocene, Oligocene, Miocene, Pliocene, and Pleistocene is fairly complete, and the transformation of limbs, skull, and teeth clearly displayed. With the morphologic changes came a gradual increase in size. The graphic story of Fig. 20-3 is better than words and should be studied carefully.

Even-toed Forms. The even-toed artiodactyls were not as abundant as their odd-toed rivals in the early days of ungulate development but have become increasingly abundant and probably stand at the peak of their development today. They include the cattle, sheep, goats, deer, camels, giraffes, antelope, pigs and peccaries, and hippopotamuses. The modification of limbs was a parallel with that of the odd-toed forms except that the two central digits,

FIG. 20-5   A small deerlike animal, *Leptomeryx,* that lived in great numbers during Oligocene time. This skeleton is composed of the bones of two individuals collected at Plum Creek, Niobrara County, Wyoming. *(Courtesy of Smithsonian Institution.)*

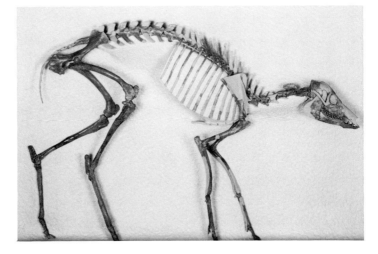

FIG. 20-6 Miocene plains mammals, from painting by Charles R. Knight, showing camels, rhinos, horses, giant pigs, and the great clawed mammals, *Moropus*. *(Courtesy of Chicago Natural History Museum.)*

the third and fourth, came to share the weight equally and develop as the strong toes while the others faded away. The "cloven hoof" of the sheep or cow consists in reality of two closely related, almost symmetrical hoofs (Fig. 20-5).

The pigs are the most primitive of the artiodactyls. They are still four-toed, although the side toes are considerably reduced, and they "eat anything from potatoes to rattlesnakes." The pigs had their origin and history of development in the Old World; the peccaries passed their early history in North America but are found to-

FIG. 20-7 Pliocene rhinos, mastodons, and oreodonts, from painting by Charles R. Knight. *(Courtesy Chicago Natural History Museum.)*

day mainly in South America.

The pigs have large canine tusks from the upper jaw that curve outward and even upward (Fig. 20-6). They are a defense mechanism at this stage, but in one species they turn upward, pierce the nose part of the skull, continue to grow, and even curve backward in a spiral in front of the eyes. Such a useless end product in the scheme of evolution constitutes a puzzle, indeed. The tusks of the peccaries grow straight downward in normal fashion.

A more important division of the artiodactyls than the pigs and one that contains the cattle and other groups previously named is that of the ruminants, or cud chewers. The side toes in these have tended to disappear, and living members of the group have but two functional digits. An early form of the ruminants was the Oligocene *oreodont*. It swarmed the western plains in enormous numbers. They were like the pigs in general proportions but had teeth closely related to the cud-chewing types (Fig. 20-7).

The camels and closely related llamas make another classical evolutionary group. Their original home was in North America, and they appeared early in the Cenozoic (Fig. 20-6). By Pleistocene time the llamas had established their home in South America, and the camels had migrated to Asia, where they have persisted until today. They became extinct in North America, however, in the Pleistocene. This is the same story as that of the horses, which were reintroduced by the conquistadors. Why the hardy camels and horses became extinct in North America, where they originated, is a mystery.

Elephants

Another noted evolutionary group is the *proboscidians*. The elephants are the only living representatives of this diversified, ponderous, grotesque, but remarkable family. They are the largest living land creatures and are only exceeded by some of the dinosaurs and one extinct giant rhinoceros. The elephants are classed as one of the stocks of the hoofed mammals but, being somewhat incongruous with the more typical ungulates, are called subungulates. They are, of course, noted for their trunks. They have stout pillarlike limbs ending in a broad padded foot to carry the great weight.

FIG. 20-8   Mastodon skeleton mounted in the Exhibit Museum of the University of Michigan. (*Courtesy of L. B. Kellum.*)

FIG. 20-9   Molar teeth of mastodon, *Mammut ameri-canum.* (Courtesy of Smithsonian Institution.)

The teeth are most exceptional. There remain only two upper incisors, which extend forward as the long curved tusks. The nose, above and between the tusks, is extended to form the long flexible proboscis. The mastodon (Fig. 20-8) has three molars up and down for grinding (Fig. 20-9), but in the mammoth (20-10) only one molar is in place at a time, that is, one on each side, up and down. These are very large, high-crowned, grinding teeth with numer-

ous cross ridges (Fig. 20-11). The grinding surfaces wear a great deal, and in fact, the tooth moves up or down into place as it is worn away. Soon the tooth is ground down to the roots, but at this time a new tooth is ready and moves in to take the place of the old tooth, whose stump is discarded. The new teeth form one after another in the back part of the jaw and gradually swing into position as needed. Three molars serve the animal in each jaw position during its lifetime.

From the fossil record it is clear that the proboscidians originated in Africa. Their primitive ancestors had become established there in earliest Cenozoic time. A form no larger than a good-sized hog, called *Moeritherium*, and with few but unmistakable elephant characteristics, is regarded as the most primitive ancestor. It seems to have given rise to three divergent and incongruous groups, the marine sirenians or sea cows, the conies or woodchucklike creatures, and the proboscidians. At this time Africa was isolated from the rest of the world by seaways, but by latest Eocene time a land connection somewhere was established and the probiscidians made a

FIG. 20-10   Mammoth and woolly rhinoceros, from painting by Charles R. Knight. (Courtesy of Chicago Natural History Museum.)

FIG. 20-11 Crown view of molar tooth of a mammoth. *(Courtesy of Smithsonian Institution.)*

triumphant entry into Eurasia and eventually to the Western Hemisphere. They evolved into a number of bizarre forms and reached the Pleistocene ice age in large numbers as the mastodons and mammoths. The mammoths lived until the close of the ice age in Siberia and northern North America, to a time only 10,000 years ago or even less. A number of specimens of the woolly mammoths have been found in natural cold storage in Siberia. The individuals apparently fell in fissures in the frozen ground covered by tundra and were trapped and frozen. Wolves then and now have feasted on the flesh, so that some of the remains are partial but more than sufficient to give a fairly complete knowledge of the appearance and food habits of the great shaggy but handsome beasts (Fig. 20-12). Some years before World War II at a scientific conference in Russia the attendants were served portions of mammoth steak at a unique banquet.

In reviewing the life of the Cenozoic on later pages of this chapter, more will be said about the elephant family.

Rodents

The rodents include the squirrels, gophers, beavers, rats, mice, porcupines, guinea pigs, hares and rabbits, and many other forms. They exceed in number of living individuals and in number of species all other types of mammals combined. They are found in almost every land area of the globe and do well in almost any environment. It is redundant to say they have been successful. They are nearly all vegetarians and are noted especially for their chisellike gnawing teeth, which are four in number, two incisors in the upper and two incisors in the lower jaw (Fig. 20-13).

Being small animals in general, they have not attracted the interest of paleontologists until recently. The large mammals were much more spectacular. But now they are the concern of a number of research workers. One rodent from the Pleistocene was a giant beaver, as large as a half-grown black bear.

Bats

The only mammalian group to take to the air and develop true wings is that of the bats. Like the flying reptiles the wings are formed of a web of skin. The thumb is free, clawed, and a clutching organ, but the other fingers are utilized in the support of

FIG. 20-12 Piece of skin with hair from shoulder of the Beresovka mammoth, Beresovka River, northeastern Siberia. *(Courtesy of Smithsonian Institution.)*

FIG. 20-13   Rodent skull fossils from western Tertiary sediments. *(Courtesy of Smithsonian Institution.)*

the wing membrane and usually have lost their originally clawed end joints. They are generally insect eaters. Bats, like other mammalian groups, developed early, for fossil skeletons showing well-developed wing supports have been found in Eocene rocks.

Whales

Consider the degree of adaption to an aquatic life of the following series of mammals: polar bear, sea otter, seal, and porpoise or whale. Although the polar bear has been seen 50 miles from shore and is unquestionably an adept swimmer, he is quite at home on all four legs on land (Fig. 20-14). The sea otters and seals make major migrations at sea and seem intermediate between the polar bear and whale in an adaptation to a marine life. The seals' limbs are modified into powerful paddles and a streamlined body (Fig. 20-15). They have great difficulty getting about on land, and only come out of the sea to breed and have their young. Finally, the whale and porpoise are completely remodeled to an aquatic habitat, with torpedo-shaped body, tail fin for propulsion, and the loss of hind

limbs except for internal vestiges and front limbs as steering flippers. They have become completely divorced from their former land life and are helpless if stranded on a beach. Only in that they breathe air do they show any marked functional relation to their former terrestrial existence. Hair has been abandoned as a covering, and instead, a thick layer of blubber affords insulation against the constant cold waters of the high-latitude seas that they frequent. Teeth have been completely remodeled to peglike structures for catching squid and fishes or lost entirely and supplanted by whalebone for sifting out the plankton of the surface waters. These latter include paradoxically the largest of the whales and the largest animals by far that have ever lived. The blue or sulphur-bottomed whale is estimated to reach a maximum weight of 150 tons. Recall the biggest of the herbivorous, amphibious dinosaurs of 50 tons.

We have no fossil record of the transition of the early mammals into the whales, porpoises, and dolphins. In Eocene time a sea-serpent type of whale existed, slimly built and some 70 ft long (Fig. 20-16). Whale bones are common fossils in marine sedimentary layers of Miocene and younger age. During the late Pleistocene the whales moved up the St. Lawrence embayment into the Lake Champlain area, where their bones are found.

The reversion of the mammals to the sea parallels that of the reptiles, and the processes of adaptation are certainly reminiscent. Once air-breathing, neither group could change, although body morphology was notably altered to the ancestral fishlike form.

Edentates

The edentates are the anteaters, armadillos, and tree sloths and are mentioned because they are the surviving remnants of a queer lineage through the Cenozoic that evolved in an isolated continent, South America. The anteaters are toothless, and the others have a degenerate type of rear teeth, with an absence of them in front. The mouth of the anteaters is nothing more than a small terminal opening from which a long sticky tongue protrudes to scoop up termites. The feet are fitted with long heavy curved claws to dig into termite nests.

The tree sloths of the South American forests spend most of their time hanging upside down from the branches of trees whose leaves are their diet. They hold on by long curved claws, two or three in number.

The armadillos have a protective armor of rows of bony plates over the back and sides and even over the top of the head. These are the only mammals with such a carapace and are certainly odd evolutes.

Primates

The primates include the lemurs, monkeys, great apes, and man. Since these forms build part of man's family tree, they will be treated in a separate chapter (22) on later pages. They are basically arboreal forms and are characterized by an opposing fifth digit on hands and feet, designed for grasping, and flat nails instead of claws. The brain, of course, becomes the largest in proportion to the size of the body of any mammal. Cenozoic fossil remains of the primates are more rare than those of any other order of mammals. This is true in general of animals that live in forests, where chances of burial in sediment and consequent preservation are practically nil. This is unfortunate because we are most interested in our own immediate ascent.

FIG. 20-14 Polar bears north of Barter Island, showing fairly good adaptation to aquatic habitat, yet retaining good quadruped locomotion on land. *(U.S. Navy photograph; courtesy of Dr. James A. Whelan.)*

FIG. 20-15 Seals on St. Paul Island of the Pribilofs. Note modification of front limbs to flippers and difficulty of locomotion on land. (Courtesy of U.S. Navy; by Dr. James A. Whelan.)

PALEOCENE, EOCENE, AND OLIGOCENE MAMMALS

Fossil Localities

The large ranges of the Rockies were beginning to rise in the Late Cretaceous inland seaway and hastened the abandonment of the continent by the marine waters.

Ranges like the Beartooth and Big Snowy of Montana, the Big Horn, Wind River, and Sweetwater of Wyoming, the Uinta of Utah, the Front Range and Uncomphagre Plateau of Colorado, and the Sangre de Cristo of New Mexico are examples. Between were broad plains or catchment basins for the sediments washed from the uplifts. Much sand and silt was carried eastward during the Cenozoic from the rising Rockies by tributaries of the Mississippi and deposited as broad outwash plains. The intermontane basins and the early Great Plains teemed with the carnivorous and herbivorous mammals of the Tertiary, and the aggrading rivers buried many carcasses and preserved them for our study today. We now live in an erosion cycle, when these former deposits are being dissected, and the bones are being exposed. The Badlands of South Dakota have been a collector's haven for seventy-five years, and each spring and early summer, after a winter's weathering, new material is found on the barren mud-rock slopes. Much of the following account of Cenozoic mammals is put together from fossil finds in the Great Plains and in the basins of Wyoming, Montana, Utah, Colorado, and New Mexico.

The Cretaceous and Early Tertiary Cordilleran land area, which is now essentially the Great Basin, was the site of much volcanism, but amidst the travail of repeated eruptions, the mammals roamed in large numbers. In the deposits of lakes and streams of some of the intervolcanic areas, like the John Day Basin of Oregon, fossils are plentiful.

Kinds of Mammalian Fossils

Only three orders of mammals were present in the Late Cretaceous, namely, the insectivores, the marsupials, and some small rodentlike forms called the multituberculates. Fifteen orders were present in Paleocene time, but all were primitive, unspecialized, and relatively small. Divergence into the carnivore and hoofed types was not yet

FIG. 20-16 Whales of the Eocene seas. From painting by Charles R. Knight. *(Courtesy of Chicago Natural History Museum.)*

clearly evident. The small Paleocene forms were similar in both Europe and North America, so that it is presumed that a land connection existed across which the common varieties could migrate and disperse. The Alaskan-Siberian bridge was the most likely route, but students of Tertiary mammals prefer a connection across the North Atlantic by way of Spitzbergen and Greenland at times. There are fairly deep water gaps in this route, so that the amount of crustal emergence and subsidence that needs to be postulated is large and makes one wonder if a complete land bridge could have existed there.

The fifteen orders of the Paleocene con-

FIG. 20-17 Oligocene titanotheres, turtles, and creodonts, from painting by Charles R. Knight. *(Courtesy of Chicago Natural History Museum.)*

FIG. 20-18 Assemblage of Oligocene mammals based essentially on skeletal remains from the earlier part of the White River formation of South Dakota and Nebraska. Among the odd-toed hoofed mammals there are, in addition to the large titanothere *Brontotherium*, three different kinds of rhinoceroses, an ancestral tapir, and a group of the small three-toed horses *(Mesohippus)*. Oligocene time is characterized by a great diversity of even-toed hoofed mammals. Except for the large piglike *Archaeotherium*, most of these, such as the camel *Poebrotherium*, the leptomerycids, hypertragulids, and merycoidodonts, are comparatively small. Also represented are certain flesh eaters, including the saber-toothed *Hoplophoneus*, an insect eater, a rodent, and a rabbit. The floral environment is based on nearly contemporaneous fossil plant remains from the Florissant beds of Colorado. Among the trees are the willow *Salix*, the exotic *Ailanthus*, and an immature shrub of *Fagopsis*. Shrubs in the foreground include *Oreopanax*, *Rose*, *Potentilla*, *Ribes*, and *Mahonia*. The small bundles of grass are *Stipa*. The open savannah type of environment portrayed is regarded as subhumid. *(Courtesy of Smithsonian Institution.)*

tinued into the Eocene, and ten new ones were added. The miltituberculates became extinct at the end of the Paleocene possibly for lack of ability to cope with more modern types of rodents that had come along. The primitive but true carnivores, called creodonts, were the so-called "new carnivores" of the Paleocene and Eocene. They had a pair of shearing teeth on each side, and the brain was small. The limbs were short and speed consequently slight. The smaller creodonts seem to have been like weasels in their habits, whereas others were more wolf- or lionlike. The larger forms survived until the end of the Oligocene and may have preyed upon the titanotheres. A contemporary carnivore skull has been found in Mongolia 1 yd long, and this may have been the largest carnivorous land mammal of all time. No creodonts survived the Oligocene.

A member of the swine family attained the height of 6 ft at the shoulders in the Oligocene and early Miocene (Figs. 20-6 and 20-18). The elongate skull bore bony protuberances below the eyes and on the underside of the jaw. The tusks were stout but not long. The brain was surprisingly small, and although strong and belligerent, these giant pigs must have been profoundly stupid. Some of the creodonts may have preyed on the slow short herbivores called *Coryphodons* and *Phenacoduses*, which had claws and long tails like the carnivores but teeth adapted for eating vegetation.

The dawn horse, *Eohippus*, appeared in

the early Eocene (Fig. 20-4), as well as early tapirs and rhinoceroses. In late Eocene the early even-toed hoofed animals seemed to explode on the scene and to spread widely. Of these were the ancestors of the deer, camel, and pig. The great unitatheres (Figs. 20-2 and 20-4) reached a climax in late Eocene time and then disappeared. The titanotheres were also present in Late Eocene time and prospered during the Oligocene (Figs. 20-17 and 20-18) but then disappeared. They looked something like the modern rhinoceroses and were as large or larger. They must have been abundant, judging by the number of fossil bones found. Rodents, insectivores, whales, bats, and even early primates are known from the Eocene. The ancestry of

the bats and whales is not known, but the primates are thought to have come from the early insectivores.

In some of the Oligocene fossil beds of the western United States the most abundant forms are the oreodonts. They are restricted to North America and are known from late Eocene to early Pliocene time. They were the size of a small sheep and combined, curiously, characters of the pig, deer, and camel.

MIOCENE, PLIOCENE, AND PLEISTOCENE MAMMALS

The families that will be mentioned here all had their beginnings in the Early Ter-

FIG. 20-19 Assemblage of mammals that lived in early Miocene time on the Great Plains. Although this number and variety of mammals would not have been found in so small an area, the environment is otherwise compatible. The animal restorations are based for the most part on skeletal remains from the Harrison formation of western Nebraska. The vegetation includes willows and cottonwood trees, hackberry, aromatic sumac, cattail, and a short grass of the genus *Aristida*. The association of plants was determined from fossil leaves, seeds, and pollen from lower Miocene deposits of the region. The following animals are depicted: *Steneofiber*, burrowing beaver; *Merychyus*, small even-toed hoofed mammal; *Moropus*, clawed mammal related to horses; *Daphaeonodon*, large wolflike dog; *Promerycochoerus*, grazing piglike mammal; *Stenomylus*, small camel; *Parahippus*, three-toed horse (group in foreground); *Diceratherium*, pair-horned rhinoceros; *Syndyoceras*, antelopelike mammal; *Dinohyus*, giant piglike mammal; *Stenomylus*, small camel; *Oxydactylus*, long-legged camel. Mural by Jay H. Matternes. *(Courtesy of Smithsonian Inst.)*

tiary but were most prominent in the Late Tertiary (Miocene and Pliocene) and in the Pleistocene.

The camels began as far as the fossil record goes in late Eocene time as tiny creatures like a small lamb, but each hind foot already had only two functional toes. There were vestiges of the other two, and the front feet had four toes. By Miocene time they were slim, graceful creatures, resembling antelopes and closely paralleled the evolution of the horse except that each limb emerged with two equal toes instead of one. One genus developed browsing habits like giraffes, as attested by long necks and long legs (Fig. 20-19). From its ancestral home in North America a group of camels migrated to the Old World, where, in the desert regions of central Asia and northern Africa, it is represented by

one living genus. Another group found its way to the cold high mountains of South America and remains there as the llamas. The extinction in the Pleistocene of the camels in North America, where they originated, concludes the story on a sad note.

The deer family had its beginnings in the Oligocene and spread to Eurasia early. The wapiti, or the so-called elk in America, is a product of the evolutionary tree, but the true elk is a European evolute. We are indebted to the Old World for the moose and caribou, which migrated to North America in the Pleistocene. See Fig. 20-25.

The cattle family is represented in North America by the bison, musk ox, and wild sheep. The bison, which roamed the plains in countless numbers in the early days of exploration of the West, seems to have suddenly appeared in the Pleistocene. All

FIG. 20-20 Diorama of a group of mammals of early Pliocene time based on skeletal remains from several western states, particularly of the high plains region. Among the more spectacular forms gathered about a swamp or water hole are a variety of bizarre antelope-like animals, some with forked horns on the snout and others with a horn protruding from the back of the head. Standing in the water is *Amebelodon*, a mastodon with shovellike tusks in its lower jaws (see Fig. 20-7 again), and the short-legged rhinoceros *Teloceros*. A true cat and a saber-toothed cat, a short-faced dog, a rodent with horns on its snout, rabbits, and peccaries also appear in the foreground. On the hillside in the background are ancestral horses and camels. The following animals appear in the diorama: *Telecoceras*, rhinoceros; *Amebelodon*, mastodon; *Borophagus*, dog; *Pseudaelurus*, cat; *Machairodus*, saber-toothed cat; *Prosthennops*, peccary; *Pliohippus*, horse; *Merycodus*, deer; *Procamelus*, camel; *Epigaulus*, rodent with horns; *Hypolagus*, rabbit; *Cranioceras*, deer; *Synthetoceras*, deer. (Courtesy of Smithsonian Institution.)

FIG. 20-21   American mastodon, from painting by Charles R. Knight. *(Courtesy of Chicago Natural History Museum.)*

domestic cattle and sheep come from Asiatic species.

The elephants, as previously noted, evolved in Africa and entered Eurasia for the first time in late Eocene time. They proved hardy and adaptable and became numerous in both warm and cold climates, spreading widely over the earth. Different kinds were known in the Miocene epoch, with one type having no tusks on the upper jaw, but large, downward, and backward curving tusks on the lower jaw. Other forms had two tusks from the upper and two from the lower, all projecting fairly straight ahead. A genus from the Pliocene strata of Nebraska had two flat, shovellike tusks from the lower jaw projecting 6 ft out in front, and it is conjectured that these were used for grubbing succulent roots in swampy ground (Figs. 20-7 and 20-20).

The proboscidians flourished around the borders of the continental ice caps of North America and Eurasia during the Pleistocene, when they attained maximum size and wandered about in large herds. With their protective hairy coats, high heads, and great tusks, they are depicted in paintings by the artists as majestic beasts standing in judgement of the world about them, or with rage in their small red eyes and trunks raised ready for the crashing attack. There were two main divisions: the true elephants or mammoths and the American mastodons (Figs. 20-8, 20-10, and 20-20). The elephants are those previously described, which had developed the peculiar method of molar tooth succession—one grinding molar at a time in each jaw. The mastodons, on the other hand, had three large-cusped, crushing and grinding molars in place throughout the adult life and were stockier than their cousins the elephants. They are presumed to have weighed as much, nevertheless, as the modern Indian elephant. Mastodon remains have been found by the hundreds in the bogs of the Northern states, and it is therefore evident that it lived around the boggy lakes made by the retreating glaciers and in the adjacent forests. Nearly every time a trench is made for a water, gas, or oil line, or an excavation for some other purpose is dug in one of the peat- and marl-filled glacial lakes, some bones of the mastodons are found. One specimen taken in New York had in addition to the bones a quantity of long, shaggy, dark brown hair. See Fig. 20-21.

Several kinds of true elephants were present in North America during the Pleistocene: the imperial elephant, 13 ft high and

The culmination of the carnivorous cat family occurred in the Pleistocene epoch with the evolution of *Smilodon*, the sabretoothed tiger (Fig. 20-22). It had great upper canines curved like scimitars 8 in. long. These would seem to block the entrance of food to the mouth, but we find that the lower jaw could open so wide as to lay back against the throat, and then possibly, the great canines could be used for stabbing their prey. The skeleton in-

FIG. 20-22 A Pleistocene water hole, from painting by Charles R. Knight, depicting typical forms that lived contemporaneously in the West, especially in California. *(Courtesy of Chicago Natural History Museum.)*

with long, gracefully curving tusks; the Columbian elephant, somewhat smaller than the imperial; and the hairy or woolly mammoth. The last had a thick coat of coarse long, black hair, with a dense, brown, wool covering beneath. It is the specimens of this animal that have been preserved in deep freeze in the Siberian tundra.

Again, we close on a rather sad note, that this abundant clan of great and majestic herbivorous mammals became extinct only yesterday, so to speak. They survived to the close of the last glacial stage of the Pleistocene, to a time, presumably, not more than 10,000 years ago.

dicates a most powerful beast. The sabretoothed tigers ranged through western United States into South America, but in one place, within the present city limits of Los Angeles, we are most fortunate in having a repository of bones of the collective fauna of the time, of which *Smilodon* was a respected member. Here in an oil seep, on a property known as Rancho la Brea, like thick tar oil has been exhuding and mixing with the silt and sand since some time in the Pleistocene. A small lake of the asphalt had formed, in which presumably, some unwary animal got stuck. It became the prey of several contemporary carnivores, which themselves got stuck, floundered, and decayed. Their bones are perfectly preserved, however, and many complete specimens have been obtained, which are on exhibit in a number of museums about the country.

Dr. Romer, an authority on the fossil vertebrates, imagines that the great tusks of the old cats fitted them for dealing with the thick-skinned proboscidians. A quick kill by a bite on the neck of the huge mammoths and mastodons is impossible, but a deep stab and slash might produce profuse bleeding and eventual death. Hence we see in the artists' paintings of the Pleistocene Rancho la Brea trap a great mammoth mired hopeless in the tar, with a sabre-toothed tiger on his flank, also becoming submerged.

It was a world of giants but not a very friendly family around the tar pits and water holes (Fig. 20-21). Examples have been found there of the dire wolf, a humpless camel, a horse (*Equus occidentalis*), a peccary, the California grizzly bear, a short-faced bear, a lionlike cat (*Panthera atrox*), the imperial elephant, the American mastodon, the great ground sloth, a vulture with a 12-ft wing spread, and a bison. Most are now extinct.

The dire wolf was larger than the present wolf and undoubtedly a powerful predator. It should be noted that the dogs are the central line of carnivore evolution among the mammals, but a number of lines became extinct as time passed through the Cenozoic.

The great Irish deer was a noble animal that lived in western Europe during the Pleistocene (Fig. 20-23). A curious example of evolution due to isolation is the moa of New Zealand, a huge flightless bird also of the Pleistocene (Fig. 20-24).

SOUTH AMERICAN ISOLATIONISTS

South America was isolated from the rest of the world through much of the Cenozoic.

A group of early immigrants from North America were left alone in South America by the breaking down of the isthmian bridge in Late Cretaceous time and proceeded to evolve in their own way. Thus over 70 million years South America becomes a most remarkable experimental laboratory, if we can obtain and read the fossil record. In Late Eocene and Early Oligo-

FIG. 20-23 The Great Irish Deer, from painting by Charles R. Knight. It lived in middle Pleistocene time in western Europe and had the largest antlers of any known deer, some specimens having a spread of nearly 10 ft. (*Courtesy of Chicago Natural History Museum.*)

cene a few so-called "island hoppers" made their way in from North America by way of a string of volcanic islands that seem to have grown up. The newcomers undoubtedly caused quite a stir for a while with the local denizens but, after certain adjustments, also proceeded on their evolutionary way. In Pliocene time volcanism began to build the Costa Rica–Panama Isthmus, and for a while more island hoppers

FIG. 20-24 The moa, a giant flightless bird, from paintings by Charles R. Knight. Several varieties of moa lived during the Pleistocene in New Zealand, and some survived until the early colonizers came, who, sadly, put an end to them. *(Courtesy of Chicago Natural History Museum.)*

got in. When the isthmus grew to solid land a wave of migrants from North America reached South America, and a few of the peculiar forms from South America made their way through the jungle sieve to Mexico and the western United States.

At the time of dismemberment from North America, South America had some marsupials that developed into carnivorous varieties and then became extinct, but only a few primitive placentals were in existence. The edentate ancestors of the armadillos and sloths were there also, and some primitive South American types of monkeys and rodents appear to have entered a little later. But a line of peculiar archaic ungulates were there at the time of separation and evidently had the field to themselves, because they evolved into a bewildering array of hoofed types. As far as known, there were no carnivores to prey upon them. There were rhino-hippo types, hopping rabbit types, and even a monodactyl horse type. As in North America, they tended to become larger with time and culminated in size in the Pleistocene. Then came the catastrophe.

With the establishment of the land bridge

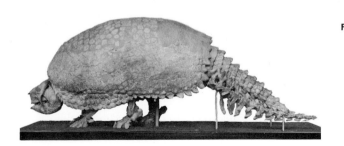

FIG. 20-25 *Glyptotherium arizonae.* This peculiar mammal with the turtlelike shell has no living representatives but is distantly related to the armadillo. This skeleton is composed of the bones of three individuals found in early Pleistocene deposits of the San Pedro Valley, Arizona. *(Courtesy of Smithsonian Institution.)*

FIG. 20-26 Ground sloths and glyptodonts, from painting by Charles R. Knight. (*Courtesy of Chicago Natural History Museum.*)

between continents the great cats and wolves made their way into South America and soon disseminated the hordes of peculiar ungulates. The North American horses, tapirs, deer, and llamas moved in also and took over the best feeding grounds, so that the somewhat archaic ungulates of the homeland disappeared. Not one survived the Pleistocene. In other places of the world, as previously recounted, various families or genera became extinct or had their ranges severely restricted, but here in South America "a whole section of several orders of the world's long-established mammalian

population was absolutely wiped out."[1]

The endemic edentates of South America spawned some exceptional varieties by the late Cenozoic. The *glyptodonts* were distinguished by a heavily armored body, being relatives of the armadillos, with the largest attaining a length of 9 ft (Figs. 20-25 and 20-26). They succumbed under the onslaught of the North American carnivores. Another unusual edentate was the ground sloth, of which the largest species attained a length or height of 20 ft and

[1] A. S. Romer, *Man and the Vertebrates,* vol. 1, Pelican Books, Baltimore, Md., 1954.

FIG. 20-27 Fossil fish, *Phareodus testis* (Cope), from the great freshwater Green River Lake in Sweetwater County, Wyoming, during Eocene times. (*Courtesy of Smithsonian Institution.*)

weighed as much as an elephant (Fig. 20-26). They were equipped with enormous claws and walked on the outer side of their feet, especially the front feet, with the claws curved inward. These giant ground sloths withstood the sabre-tooth tigers and dire wolves and made their way into the deserts of Mexico, Arizona, and Nevada. They ate the tough desert vegetation. With hair and tendons found mummified and droppings profuse in caves of southern Nevada, it appeared that they existed until fairly recent times, but with carbon-14 dates on droppings in a cave of the Grand Canyon region of northern Arizona there is good reason to believe that they lasted until the Indians put an end to them.

And so, in a fragmentary way, is written the story of the animals that became isolated in South America.

FISHES

Almost all the sport and food fishes of salt and fresh water today are the bony teleosts. They rose to overwhelming prominence in the Tertiary and apparently are holding this position very well in modern times. The sharks of Paleozoic and Mesozoic note are still strong competitors in the warm marine waters (Figs. 20-27 and 20-28).

INVERTEBRATES

The pelecypods and gastropods finally came into their own in the Cenozoic. One needs only to collect shells from a beach to realize that today these groups are by all odds the most variable and abundant. So it was also during the Tertiary. The brachiopods and cephalopods had become exceedingly rare at the same time as the pelecypods and gastropods flourished. We should note, however, that certain common Cretaceous pelecypods were gone at the beginning of Tertiary time, such as the large *Inoceramus* clam and some of the oysters. The ammonite cephalopods bowed out completely, and the only true shelled forms that survived are the beautiful pearly nautilus. The squids, octopus, and cuttlefish are surviving cephalopods, but without hard external shells they are nearly want-

FIG. 20-28 Modern (teleost) fishes, a pair of rays, and aquatic vegetation as may have been seen in a fresh-water lake of Eocene age in southwestern Wyoming. Fossils from the Green River formation. (*Courtesy of Chicago Natural History Museum.*)

ing in the fossil record, and their ancestry poorly known.

The microscopic Foraminifera forming part of the ocean plankton contributed in significant measure to the siltstones, shales, and limestones of the Cenozoic and evolved many varieties of tests, some of them rather fantastic. The many species of these tiny protozoans have proved very useful to the petroleum geologist, who finds them among the drill cuttings from oil wells and correlates the strata by means of them. An elaborate system of classification has been worked out, and many guide fossils designated.

We live in a world of arthropods. The insects, crabs, lobsters, shrimps, and ostracodes encompass more species than all other living animal forms together. Articles in magazines and newspapers occasionally depict the overrunning and annihilation of the human race by the insects.

Fossils of insects and ostracodes are especially abundant in the Tertiary strata. The insects are chiefly of academic interest, but the ostracodes are used as guide fossils.

Metasequoia

Liquidamber

Mahonia marginata

Alnus larseni

FIG. 20-29   A few plant fossils of Miocene age.

PLANTS

Fossils of plants are abundant in many sedimentary rocks of Cenozoic age. The delicate leaves are most likely preserved in lake sediments to which localities they have been blown by the wind. The angiosperms were in complete dominance, after having established themselves in Late Cretaceous time in an impressive way. And they migrated and adapted themselves to all environments in an almost infinite variety of forms. Anyone need only take an elementary course in botany to appreciate the diversity of form and function of the flowering plants. Most significant is the observation that the Cenozoic flora is essentially the modern flora (Fig. 20-29). Many early Cenozoic genera are the same as those of today; only the species are different. In this way they can be used somewhat as guide fossils to the Tertiary but they are most helpful in recognizing and establishing the climates of the Cenozoic. For instance, the early redwoods were established under the climatic conditions that they now enjoy in California in the arctic islands of northern Canada in Eocene time. As the weather turned colder there, the redwoods migrated southward to the Great Lakes region, and thence were driven westward to the Pacific Coast, where they are making their last stand today.

By mid-Cenozoic time the Great Plains and Rocky Mountain region had begun to rise. In the early Cenozoic the floors of the large intermontane basins rested at elevations of about 1,000 ft above sea level, and the region of the Great Plains was at sea level as the Cretaceous inland sea withdrew. The intermontane basins rose to about 4,000 ft. This brought on semiarid conditions. Meeting such a turn in events were the grasses that had evolved, and they spread luxuriantly over the open plains, thus creating the prairie lands. Here was a new world for the mammals to conquer. The ungulates came out of the forests, and on the plains speed was their forte. The larger horses, the antelope, and the camel evolved. Speed and endurance meant protection. Others, like the bison, were not so fast, but had size, horns, and numbers for defense against the carnivores. The wolves and coyotes followed suit and made out fairly well, also developing great running ability and cunning intelligence in the pursuit.

Suggested Aids

Readings

Romer, A. S.: *Man and the Vertebrates,* vol. 1, Pelican Books, Baltimore, Md., 1954.

Scott, Wm. B.: *A History of Land Mammals in the Western Hemisphere,* The Macmillan Company, New York, 1937.

Simpson, G. G.: *Horses,* Oxford University Press, New York, 1951.

Simpson, G. G.: *Meaning of Evolution,* Yale University Press, New Haven, Conn., 1949.

Stirton, R. A.: *Time, Life and Man—the Fossil Record,* John Wiley and Sons, New York, 1959.

Wonders of Life on Earth, Life Magazine, 1960.

Filmstrip

Age of Mammals, Encyclopaedia Britannica, FSC-717.

Chapter 21

THE PLEISTOCENE AND ITS GLACIAL CLIMATES

Toward the end of the Tertiary period the climate of the
earth began to cool, and eventually great ice caps developed
on several continents. See Fig. 21-1. Almost all high
mountains became extensively glaciated. We will be concerned chiefly in this chapter with the extent of the
glaciers, the fluctuating climate, and succession of stages
of glaciation that make up the Pleistocene epoch. Other
interesting aspects of the glacial epoch are, first, the causes
of the glacial climates; second, the amount of lowering
of annual temperature necessary to produce the ice caps
and extensive valley glaciers; third, the absolute ages
(time in years) of the several glacial stages during the
Pleistocene; fourth, the amount of lowering of the ocean
level at the time of maximum glaciation; fifth, the extent
to which we are at present out of the last glacial stage or,
perhaps, progressing back into the next glacial stage; and
sixth, the amount that the earth's surface has been

Glaciers and Climates
of the Pleistocene Epoch

FIG. 21-1 Maximum extent of glaciers during the Pleistocene epoch in the Northern Hemisphere.
Ice caps are lined areas.

depressed under the weight of the great ice caps and the bearing of this deformation of the crust on our understanding of the earth's interior.

As the earth's climate turned cool and warm a number of times, as the glaciers waxed and waned, and as the sea level fluctuated over several hundred feet, the biological world was profoundly affected. The adaptations, migrations, and evolution of new forms during this time constitute in many people's minds the most exciting period of earth history. The Pleistocene is preeminently the age of man, for during this time he made his major evolutionary strides and spread to many parts of the world. Human cultures and religious systems began to take shape near the end of the Pleistocene, and the great and small political units evolved. Lastly the stage was set for the age of steel and machinery, utilization of natural energy and science.

THE CONTINENTAL GLACIERS

Scandinavian Ice Cap

An ice cap centered over Scandinavia and spread southeastward across the Baltic Sea to Moscow and beyond, southward across the North German Plain to Berlin, and westward across the North Sea to and across Great Britain. The limits are marked by the terminal moraines and associated

✦ Degree to which the drainage system has been developed. The youngest moraine will be very hilly or hummocky, with many lakes and swamps and a completely aimless stream pattern, if any at all. The oldest moraine will be much subdued and will have very few lakes and a well-integrated drainage system.

✦ The relative position of the four terminal moraines is in itself an indication of relative age. In places it can be seen that one

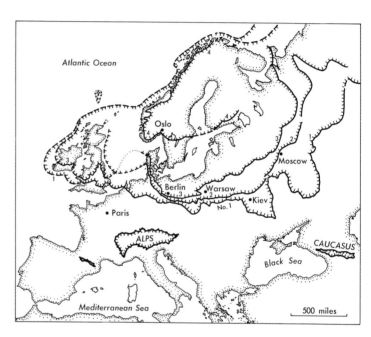

FIG. 21-2 Four stages of the Scandinavian ice cap. The hachured lines represent the terminal moraines of each stage; 1 is the first glacial and 4 is the last. The Alps and Caucusus had several stages.

features, which are shown in Fig. 21-2. It has taken geologists of the North European countries many years to trace out these moraines in the field. It will be noted that four moraines of different ages are charted. The oldest moraine, labeled 1, lies farthest east, south, and west, and shows the position of the most extensive spread of the ice lobes of the ice cap. Three younger terminal moraines lie successively back of the outer moraine. The different ages are determined by such criteria as the following:

✦ Degree of soil formation. The oldest moraine will have the thickest and most mature soil.

till rests on another, with such features as a layer of loess or a soil between. The stratigraphy of glacial deposits has played an important role in the deciphering of the several stages of glaciation.

From the relation of one moraine on another, with a thick and mature soil forming the top of the lower moraine, it must be concluded that the ice front withdrew a considerable distance to the north or disappeared completely for a long time while the soil formed. In fact, the science of soils is so advanced that soil scientists can say about how long it took to form the soil in question and what kind of a climate existed while the weathering was taking place.

With this ability and with the evidence of fossils it is concluded that the climate warmed up appreciably between ice advances and that it stayed warm for periods longer than those during which the glaciers existed. Hence, the interglacial stages are as important as the glacial. See Fig. 21-3.

By means of varves (laminations in fine sediments of glacial lakes) it has been determined that the ice sheet that deposited moraine 4 of Fig. 21-2 retreated north of Stockholm about 9,000 years ago. By means

from a few million to three billion years are determinable by such techniques as the potassium-argon or the strontium- rubidium method, and the carbon-14 method supplies dates from a few hundred years back to about 30,000 years successfully. We are anxiously awaiting the discovery of a method that will date in terms of years deposits of mid- and early Pleistocene age and thus determine when the Pleistocene started and how old certain human fossil material is that has been found in deposits

STAGES		Estimated duration in years on basis of soils
WISCONSIN GLACIAL	Mankato Cary Tazewell Iowan	25,000–30,000 (C^{14} dates)
Sangamon Interglacial		150,000
ILLINOIAN GLACIAL		100,000
Yarmouth Interglacial		300,000
KANSAN GLACIAL		100,000
Aftonian Interglacial		200,000
NEBRASKAN GLACIAL		100,000
Earlier little-known glacials and interglacials		

FIG. 21-3 Pleistocene stages of the Great Lakes region. Ages are approximate and taken from several sources.

of the carbon-14 method of dating, this advance of moraine 4 is believed to have started about 25,000 years ago and thus had its existence during the period 25,000 to 9,000 years before the present. Now, the other three glacial stages are much older and, from the evidence of soil formation, probably lasted several times longer than this latest one. Thus the Pleistocene is variously estimated to have started 300,000 to 1,000,000 years ago. No method of isotope dating has been worked out yet which is reliable or which can be used on the minerals or materials available from the moraines to determine ages in the interval of 50,000 to a few million years ago. Ages

older than the last ice advance. See Chap. 22.

North American Ice Cap

The Canadian Shield of North America was the center of ice accumulation during the Pleistocene, and its lobes overran much of New England and flowed down the depressions of the Great Lakes into western New York, Michigan, Ohio, Indiana, and Illinois to the Ohio River and across Minnesota and the eastern parts of North and South Dakota to the Missouri River. See Fig. 21-4. A part of Wisconsin was sufficiently high that the ice flowed around it, and it escaped glaciation. It is called the Wisconsin driftless area. The ice spread westward to the Canadian Rockies and merged with the valley glaciers of the Rockies (Fig. 21-1). The moraines of the continental glacier meet the moraines of the valley glaciers of Glacier National Park on the high plains just east of the park in north-western Montana. Here the stages of glaciation of the mountains have been re-

The northern coast of Labrador is one of deep fiords down which valley glaciers discharged into the sea.

The Canadian Shield, except in protected depressions, has been abraded clean of soil and alluvium by the ice cap, and in many places where by chance the surface has been left covered by a little ground moraine, the striations and groves are still intact, although where exposed they have

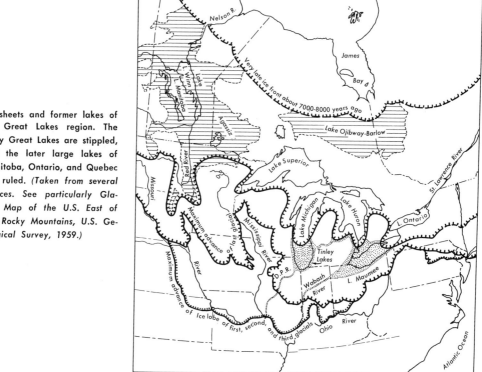

FIG. 21-4 Ice sheets and former lakes of the Great Lakes region. The early Great Lakes are stippled, and the later large lakes of Manitoba, Ontario, and Quebec are ruled. (Taken from several sources. See particularly Glacial Map of the U.S. East of the Rocky Mountains, U.S. Geological Survey, 1959.)

lated in part to the stages of glaciation of the continental glacier.

There may have been two centers of ice accumulation, one west and one east of Hudson Bay. The ice sheet spread northward to the islands of the Canadian arctic, where several small ice caps remain today as well as many valley glaciers from mountain ranges. The Greenland ice cap was probably larger than that of today but did not coalesce with the great Canadian cap.

generally crumbled away. The shield's rocks are igneous and metamorphic, such as granites, gabbros, and gneisses. Some rather unusual ones crop out in specific localities. Examples are the iron formation rocks, the Keweenawan native copper-bearing volcanic rocks, and the jasper conglomerate. *Erratics* of these formations are found on the Paleozoic limestones and shales of New York, Ontario, Michigan, and other Great Lakes localities, and by charting the distribution of erratic boulders derived from some singular known locality, the path of flow of the ice may be determined.

At first, five terminal moraines in the Great Lakes region were recognized and mapped, but they did not match the four terminal moraines in northern Europe. It is generally believed that the climatic changes were world-wide in effect and not limited to specific regions. Therefore, the glacial stages of North America should correlate with those of Europe. The tendancy today is to group the fourth and fifth stages of the Great Lakes chronology together (the Iowan and Wisconsin) and to recognize the Iowan as an early pulsation of the Wisconsin. Thus, there are four glacial stages both in North America and in Europe. But this does not leave the problem of correlation without difficulty. At the culmination of each glacial stage much water is stored in the ice caps, and sea level is lowered several hundred feet. All rivers whose base of erosion is controlled by sea level will be affected, and thus the response will be synchronous along all shores of all continents. Sea-level changes should reflect world-wide average climatic changes better than any other geologic register. Now, students of the Mississippi River and delta recognize five episodes of entrenchment and and five of valley fill and believe that this represents five stages of glaciation.

The writer is of the opinion that the Nebraskan stage in North America and the Günz stage in Europe are not the earliest glacial stage of the Pleistocene. They mark the farthest advances, but he believes still earlier moraines of minor ice advances have been obliterated by these most extensive ones. It is possible that river entrenchment and fill may not everywhere be so destructive of earlier cycles and that five, six, or more cycles may be discerned in certain deltas. It seems likely that, if the Pleistocene climate is one of cycles of alternating warm and cold, the intensity of the temperature changes would grow from a mild beginning to a medial one of greatest difference, and

thereafter gradual decline would set in. The morainal record of the continental glaciers as we see it appears to begin midway in the story with the stage of greatest ice advance. This subject will be pursued further under the heading Cause of Glacial Epochs and Stages.

GLACIAL LAKES

Synchronous with the glacial stages in a number of places large fresh-water lakes came into existence. As the glacier fronts of the Wisconsin stage withdrew northward, several lakes of varying outline and outlets evolved as predecessors of the modern Great Lakes, and a fascinating story has been worked out concerning them. In the western United States, especially in western Utah and Nevada almost half the area was covered with magnificent fresh-water lakes, with colder flora and fauna to match. Incident to the impounding of the lakes and the withdrawal of the ice, great floods occurred on the Columbia and Snake Rivers. Lake Winnipeg of Manitoba is the remnant of a late Wisconsin lake larger than all the Great Lakes combined. The Missouri and Ohio Rivers were deranged and deflected from their original courses by the ice. The glaciers thus had a marked effect on our geography.

Evolution of the Great Lakes

A divide exists in northern Ohio, Indiana, and Illinois, south of which drainage is to the Ohio and Mississippi, and north of which it is to the Great Lakes and the St. Lawrence. As long as the ice front was south of the divide, the melt-water streams flowed directly to the Ohio and Mississippi Rivers. When the front withdrew, however, north of the divide, then an impounding condition was established, with high ground to the south and the ice lobes damming the depressions on the north. The lakes that were formed at a fairly early stage when the Des

Plaines and Wabash outlets prevailed are shown in Fig. 21-4. It should be understood that the depressions or basins of the Great Lakes were present before the glacial epoch and that the expanding ice cap overran the depressions.

As the ice withdrew further, an outlet through the Mohawk Valley of western New York to the Hudson River was uncovered. For a while the Chicago outlet into the Des Plaines and Illinois Rivers and thus to the Mississippi prevailed, but eventually the Mohawk and Hudson Valleys discharged most of the drainage. Lake Duluth overflowed through the St. Croix outlet into the Mississippi, which was a much larger river then than now.

When the ice front had withdrawn to a position north of Lake Huron, an outlet to the St. Lawrence across southern Ontario was uncovered, and almost all the drainage escaped through this route for a while. But as the ice was melting and withdrawing, a remarkable phenomenon started to occur. The crust of the earth, where it had been covered by the ice, started to rise. Since the

beaches that had been carved horizontally are tilted up to the north, a careful study of all the beaches of the succession of early lakes makes it clear that the uplift occurred in progressively greater amounts to the north (Fig. 21-5). The crust where the present northern shores of Lake Huron and Lake Superior now exist has been elevated 600 ft, and the southern Hudson Bay area at least 900 ft. At the time the southern Ontario outlet was uncovered it was the lowest spillway, but after appreciable uplift had occurred, a southern outlet through Lake Erie again was established. This time, however, the water was over Niagara Falls and through Lake Ontario to the St. Lawrence. When the ice first uncovered the St. Lawrence Valley, it was sufficiently depressed so that the marine waters invaded it as far as the Lake Champlain lowlands, where fossil whale bones have been found in the sediments of the estuary. The continuing rise of the land has drained the lowlands since.

Finally, the ice withdrew to a position north of the drainage divide between the

FIG. 21-5 Shore lines of high lake levels, ancestral to Lake Michigan.

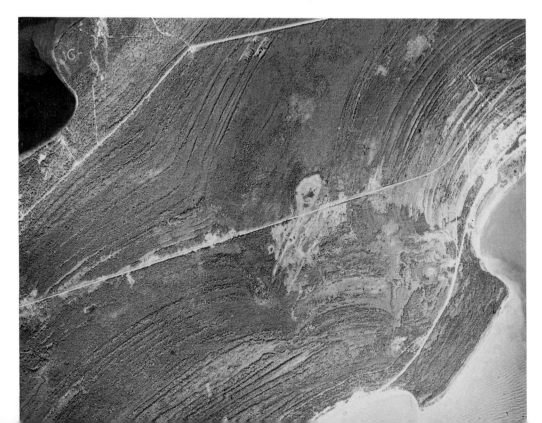

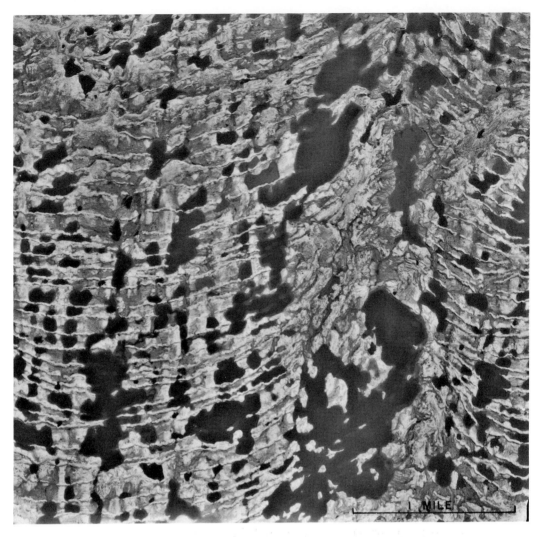

FIG. 21-6 Recessional moraines in western Quebec, within 50 miles of Hudson Bay. The once great ice cap had nearly vanished by this stage, and the front of the last remnant was withdrawing rapidly. Possibly each moraine represents the deposits of winter and spring while the front held stationary. During the summer and fall the front would withdraw to the next position. If so, the general retreat across the area of the photograph occurred in about 50 years. *(Courtesy of Geological Survey of Canada and Ed Schiller.)*

Great Lakes and St. Lawrence on the south and Hudson Bay on the north (Fig. 21-6), and another group of lakes was impounded. These were larger than any of the lakes of the Great Lakes depressions, and the two most extensive ones are known as Lake Agassiz and Lake Ojibway-Barlow (Fig. 21-4). With the disappearance of the ice cap completely, these magnificent lakes drained away into Hudson Bay, leaving only a number of relatively small lakes in various scattered depressions. Lake Winnepeg, truly a great fresh-water lake in its own right, is one of these, and Lake Manitoba another.

Lake Bonneville

The western United States contained many lakes at one time or another during the Pleistocene epoch. See Fig. 21-7. Some filled pre-existing desert depressions, and some were impounded by ice and morainal dams. A few remnants remain today. Lake Bonneville is best known of the glacial lakes and will be briefly described as an example.

The Great Basin of western Utah, Nevada, and eastern California is one of interior drainage except on the south, where the desert streams flow to the Colorado River. The condition of interior drainage had been determined by many faults which had displaced blocks of the crust upward and downward across the region but which especially had elevated the Sierra Nevada on the west and the Wasatch Mountains and High Plateaus of Utah on the east. The faulting started in mid-Tertiary time and in places has continued to the present. With the onset of glacial climates a few glaciers developed in some of the ranges within the Great Basin and in the Wasatch Mountains and Sierra Nevada. The glaciers of the high Sierra Nevada were particularly large, and four stages of valley glaciation have been recognized there. It is still not entirely clear, however, how these stages relate to those of the classical Great Lakes chronology.

With increased precipitation, cooler climates, and less evaporation, the interior basins filled with water, and two large lakes and several small ones formed. The large lake in western Utah has been called Lake Bonneville, and the main lake in western Nevada is called Lake Lahontan. See Fig. 21-7.

A valley glacier in the Wasatch Mountains descended to the waters of Lake Bonneville, but the relation of the stages of glaciation to the stages of Lake Bonneville is not very clear, and there is also uncertainty about the correlation of the stages of

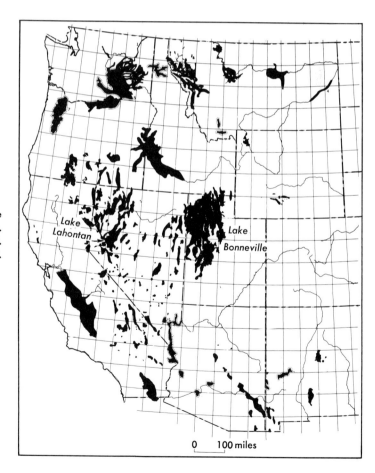

FIG. 21-7 Pleistocene Lakes of the Western United States. (Compiled by Feth, U.S. Geological Survey Prof. Paper 424B, 1961.)

0   100 miles

FIG. 21-8 Beaches of Lake Bonneville around hills in northern Utah.

valley glaciation in the Wasatch with those of the Great Lakes. Almost all geologists who have worked on the history of Lake Bonneville, however, proceed on the assumption that the lake rose with the advance of the glaciers and sank as they retreated and therefore responded closely to world-wide climatic changes.

The highest shore carved by Lake Bonneville is 1,000 ft above its remnant, Great Salt Lake (Figs. 21-8 and 21-9). The next major shore is 310 ft lower. A trenched pass at the north end of the lake heads a valley that flows into the Snake River, and it has been proposed that the lake, after fashioning the highest beach, overflowed the pass and cut it 310 ft deep. This lowered the lake level the same amount. The overflow was of

giant flood proportions, and much havoc was wrought down the Snake River. In places the Snake River Canyon was not able to contain the flood waters (Fig. 21-10), and they overflowed and scoured the upland basalt flows, leaving them barren of silt and soil and in marked contrast to the adjacent rich agricultural lands today. The velocity of flow was high as may be seen in places by the giant boulders strewn along the bed (Figs. 21-11 and 21-12). By assuming a velocity of flow through a certain canyon cross section of the Snake River, which was filled to the top at maximum flood stage, the amount of water discharged in one year can be approximated. The amount of water drained from Lake Bonneville can be calculated fairly accurately, and thus by divid-

FIG. 21-9 Shore lines of Lake Bonneville on the east side of the Pilot Range, western Utah. B, Bonneville shore line; P, Provo shore line; S, Stansbury shore line; G. Gilbert shore line.

FIG. 21-10 Canyon of the Snake River near Twin Falls, Idaho, which was filled to overflowing at the highest stage of the flood.

ing the total loss by the loss per year, it has been estimated that the flood started, reached a climax, and subsided slowly in the short time of 200 to 300 years. This is but a tick of the clock of geologic time.

FIG. 21-11 Bed of torrential flood down Snake River Canyon. Current was from right to left.

It has recently been shown by Bright[1] that the major river flowing into the Bonneville Basin, the Bear, first flowed directly into the Snake but was dammed and diverted into the Bonneville Basin by basalt outpourings. This caused a rather quick rise of the lake to the Bonneville level and to overflowing.

Sometime after the flood, the climate had begun to warm up, and in a while all outflow ceased. Thereafter, the lake slowly desiccated, with a number of minor ups and downs, to the present saline residue, Great Salt Lake. The present condition was reached about 10,000 years ago, according to C[14] dates. The exact time of the great flood has not been established, but it was approximately 20,000 years ago. All the history of Lake Bonneville here recited is

[1] Robert C. Bright, "Pleistocene Lakes Thatcher and Bonneville, southeastern Idaho," Ph.D. thesis, University of Minnesota, 1963.

Wisconsin (last glacial), and the overflow was near the culmination of this glacial stage.

WEATHERING SINCE THE LAST GLACIATION

As previously indicated, the major ice caps, glaciers, and glacial lakes had nearly vanished by 11,000 to 10,000 years ago. Smoothly abraded and somewhat polished surfaces were left in many places. These surfaces have been subject to weathering since uncovered by the melting ice, and in the case of granite, the process of hydration of the feldspars has caused conspicuous crumbling. Note the crumbling of granite in Fig. 21-13. Here the surface had been ground off fairly smooth by the glaciers, but weathering has since roughened it considerably. Actually a layer about 3 in. thick has been removed by crumbling, as shown by a close up of part of the area of Fig. 21-13. See Fig. 21-14.

VERTICAL MOVEMENTS OF CRUST

As the ice melted and withdrew from the Great Lakes region, the earth's crust responded by rising. We are sure from a number of similar observations that the crust had first been depressed under the weight of the ice, and with the disappearance of the ice the crust has risen. The phenomenon is like a ship in water. When loaded, the ship is depressed; as its cargo is unloaded, it rises. We conclude that the crust is lighter than, and supported on, a heavier subcrustal material, the mantle. Moreover, the mantle behaves like a liquid when stressed for a long time by a weight, such as an ice cap.

An impressive example of the vertical movement of the crust under load is that of the Scandinavian region. Figure 21-2 shows the ice cap over Scandinavia and northern Europe, and Fig. 21-3 shows the amount of uplift that one of the older beaches has undergone to date since the ice began to melt. As noted in the discussion of the early Great Lakes of North America, the shore lines were tilted, and this is the basis for measuring the uplift in Scandinavia. Because seaways and uplifted shore lines can be traced all around Scandinavia, the domal uplift can be nicely and fairly completely documented. The central part has risen 520 m, or about 1,700 ft, and sea-level gauges during historical times indicate that the uplift is still going on. It is expected that an additional rise of 210 m will occur. See Fig. 21-15. All this is interpreted to mean that the earth's crust was depressed 750 m during the last glacial maximum. The load of ice necessary to cause this subsidence would amount to a thickness of 2,650 m or 10,430 ft. Thus the ice in the Bothnia Sea region was almost 2 miles thick.

Another factor to consider, however, is the great viscosity of the mantle of the earth. We can see that, if a certain beach carved horizontally 6,800 years ago has been tilted up 250 m since, the adjustment is very slow, and this is due to the high viscosity of flow of the mantle. It will take several thousand years more for the uplift to run its course.

The vertical adjustment of the crust in response to loading and unloading is called *isostasy*. Geophysicists recognize from gravity measurements that the earth's crust is well adjusted to load in almost all places

FIG. 21-12 Close-up of large boulders of basalt on bed of Snake River at flood stage.

FIG. 21-13 Weathering of granite since glacial abrasion, chiefly due to hydration of feldspar grains. Wasatch Mountains, Utah. See Fig. 2-10.

and that it is out of balance and seeking adjustment in only a few places, particularly those where ice caps formerly existed. Because loads and rates of adjustment are approximately known, the viscosity of the mantle can be computed, and this is important when the interior of the earth is considered and the cause of mountain building sought. See Chaps. 13 and 17 for further information on crustal deformation.

CAUSE OF GLACIAL EPOCHS AND STAGES

Number of Theories

My colleague, Professor Wm. L. Stokes, has remarked that, since 29 theories of the cause of glaciation have been proposed, he might as well make it an even 30 by propounding another. I am not sure that 30 theories have been proposed to date, but surely the number will prove surprising to most students who inquire into the subject for the first time. The considerable number might indicate that there are several approaches to the problem with scientists of several professions taking a whirl at it; and this is true. Astronomers, meteorologists, geophysicists, and geologists have all contributed their ideas. This considerable number

might also suggest that none of the theories proposed explains all the facts about the earth's glaciations. This is the position taken by the authors of several recent textbooks. Before proceeding with a brief resumé of some of the theories, it is perhaps worthwhile to summarize the climates of geological time so that the problem will be better understood at the onset.

Review of Climatic Changes

We know much more about the last glaciation than those of the Permian or the Precambrian. No history of individual pulsations, interglacial times, separate ice lobes, or geography of glacial lakes is known from the Permian or Precambrian glacial epochs.

Table 21-1 is a modification of one published by Brooks in his text *Climate through the Ages*. It shows the climates that have existed from Late Precambrian time to the present.

Four epochs of glaciation are recognized: one during a part of the Middle Precambrian, one during a part of the Late Precambrian, one in the Late Pennsylvanian and Early Permian, and one in the Pleistocene. The first occurred between 2,200 and 1,700 million years ago, the second between 800 and 600 million years ago, the third about

FIG. 21-14 This is an inclusion in the granite which has not weathered appreciably since glacial abrasion but which has retained its abraded surface. The surrounding granite has weathered back about 3 in. Wasatch Mountains, Utah.

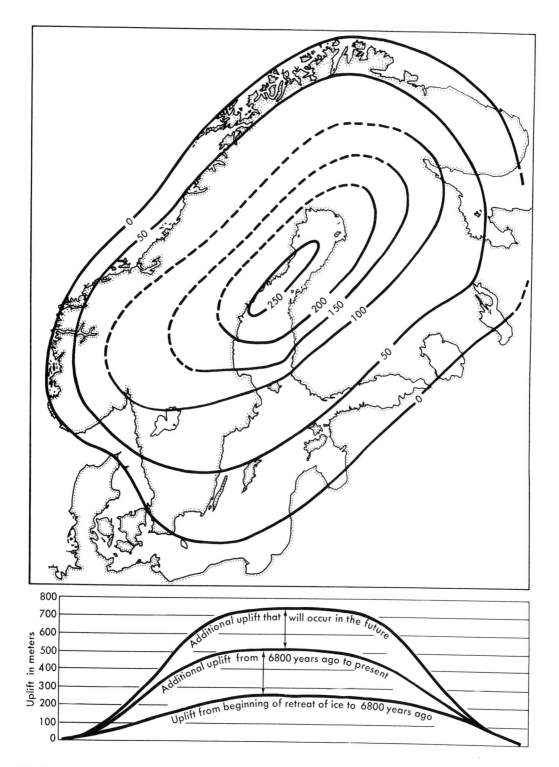

FIG. 21-15 Contour lines in meters showing the amount of uplift of one of the early beaches in the Baltic Sea region that was eroded by the waves after the ice retreated to the high central part of Scandinavia. Also, chart showing the postulated uplift before the beach was eroded, the amount of uplift exhibited by the beach, and the postulated amount that has yet to occur. *(After Flint, 1947.)*

Table 21-1 CLIMATES OF THE GEOLOGIC PAST

Millions of years ago	Geologic period	Climate
1	Pleistocene	Glacial in polar and temperate latitudes
	Tertiary:	
	Pliocene	Cool
	Miocene	Moderate
	Oligocene	Moderate to warm
	Eocene	Moderate, becoming warm
	Paleocene	Moderate
	Cretaceous	Moderate
	Jurassic	Warm and equable
	Triassic	Warm and equable
270	Permian	Glacial at first, becoming moderate
	Pennsylvanian	Warm at first, becoming glacial
	Mississippian	Warm and equable
	Devonian	Moderate, becoming warm
	Silurian	Warm
	Ordovician	Moderate to warm
600–800	Cambrian	Cold, becoming warm
	Late Precambrian	At one time, glacial
2,200–1,700	Middle Precambrian	At one time, glacial

SOURCE: Modified from C. E. P. Brooks, *Climate through the Ages*, McGraw-Hill Book Co., New York, 1949. See discussion in chapter 17.

270 million years ago, and the fourth started about 1 million years ago and is probably still with us. These figures do not indicate a regular periodicity in recurrence; if anything, they suggest an increasing frequency.

From the record of terminal moraines in North America and northern Europe there were four glacial maxima in the Pleistocene, with warm interglacial stages between. Some of the interglacial stages may have been warmer than the present. Evidence is beginning to accumulate that there were earlier climatic fluctuations in the Pleistocene than the so-called Nebraskan, or "earliest" glaciation. For instance, Wiseman,[2] in the study of the deep ocean bottom cores, recognized 10 distinct temperature minima, with each lowered ocean temperature stage presumedly corresponding to an ice age. Regardless of how many stages of glacial advance and recession, it appears that a fundamental property of a glacial epoch is a fluctuating climate in which several cycles occur.

Another conclusion that may be drawn from the fossil record is that for at least nine-tenths of geologic time the average temperature of the continents has been higher than it is today. Between the long warm epochs there have been short epochs of glaciation.

One group of theories explains the glaciations by variations in solar energy received by the earth. Another group of theories is built around the control of climates by the oceans. Variations in the proportions

[2] J. D. H. Wiseman, *The determination and significance of past temperature changes in the upper layer of the equatorial Atlantic Ocean*, 1954, Royal Soc. Proc., ser.A., v. 222, pp. 296-323.

of land and sea, variations in the height of the continents from time to time, variations in the oceanic connections and circulations, and the shifting of the entire crust in relation to the axis of rotation have been developed to explain the onset of a glacial epoch and the oscillation of climate within the epoch. A singular theory contends that there have been times of excessive volcanism and that changes in the amount of volcanic dust in the atmosphere affect the climate.

Carbon Dioxide Theory

The theory of variations of carbon dioxide in the atmosphere will be recounted in some detail, and the problems, arguments, and a few of the counter proposals will be given because the data given and the analyses made are most instructive and set the stage for the student to go to the original writings about the numerous theories, if he desires.

The carbon dioxide theory of climatic change was widely accepted fifty years ago, then generally discredited, but new research suggests that the reasons for rejecting the theory may not be valid. Here are the basic considerations:[3]

✦ Because of the relatively low temperatures at the earth's surface and in the atmosphere, nearly all the outgoing radiation from the earth is in the infrared region of the spectrum.

✦ The three most abundant gases of the atmosphere are oxygen, nitrogen, and argon. However, none of these absorbs appreciably the infrared radiation. If these were the only gases in our atmosphere, our climate would be considerably colder.

✦ Three gases occur in the atmosphere that, although present in small amounts, do absorb strongly over a portion of the infrared spectrum. These are carbon dioxide,

water vapor, and ozone. Carbon dioxide is fairly uniformly mixed in the atmosphere, but water vapor and ozone are variable from time to time and place to place. The action of these three gases, and carbon dioxide in particular, may be compared to a greenhouse where the transparent glass admits the rays of the sun with their heat but prevents the escape of the outgoing heat waves from the plants and earth.

✦ As carbon dioxide increases, the outgoing radiation is trapped more effectively near the earth's surface, and the temperature rises. According to Plass, the latest calculations show that, if the carbon dioxide content were doubled, the surface temperature would rise 3.6°C and, if the amount were cut in half, the surface temperature would fall 3.8°C.

Various authorities estimate that, if the annual temperature should fall 1.5 to 8°C, another glacial maximum would occur. Similarly an annual rise of 4°C would bring a tropical climate to almost all the earth. These postulates are denied by others who contend that warmer oceans mean more evaporation, greater precipitation, and in certain places greater snowfall, with resulting glaciation. Going along with the assumption for the time being, however, that annual world-wide reduction in temperature is conducive to a glacial epoch, it would seem that, if the carbon dioxide content were cut by one-half, a glacial stage would ensue. Is this possible, and has it occurred in the geologic past?

In order to estimate the change of carbon dioxide in the atmosphere, the so-called carbon dioxide balance must be understood. The atmosphere loses carbon dioxide today, owing to photosynthesis in plants, in the amount of about 60 billion tons per year. If the balance is steady, precisely the same amount is returned by the processes of respiration and decay of organic material. In times of great coal and oil formation some may be retained by the earth, but at the present time the amount is

---

[3] Gilbert N. Plass, "Carbon Dioxide and the Climate," *American Scientist*, July, 1956, pp. 302-316.

negligible. This loss is calculated to be 0.01 billion tons.

Carbon dioxide may be added from the interior of the earth by hot springs, fumaroles, and volcanoes. At times great volumes of the gas have been taken from the atmosphere by the formation of extensive limestone and dolomite deposits. These two factors, one that adds and one that subtracts, may upset the balance momentarily and change the amount in the atmosphere. At present they are probably equal, one contributing 0.1 billion tons and the other subtracting 0.1 billion tons.

Man has recently added a new factor and upset the balance. The combustion of fossil fuels in 1954 added 6 billion tons of carbon dioxide gas to the atmosphere, and the amount is doubling every ten years. This factor is larger by far than any contribution from the organic or inorganic world, and thus man is increasing the carbon dioxide in the atmosphere at the rate of 30 per cent a century.[4] The possible influence on the climate is frightening. We have already noted a recession of glaciers in all parts of the world in the last fifty years, the average annual temperature has risen 2°C in Norway since 1930, and the I.G.Y. estimates that the Greenland ice sheet is suffering a net loss of 22 cu miles of ice per year.

Now, the theory's first premise is that, during times of continental elevation or mountain uplift, the weathering processes were greater, and greater amounts of carbonates were laid down in the shallow oceans. This reduced the carbon dioxide content of the atmosphere sufficiently so that a glacial stage was brought on. The second premise is that, once the atmosphere has been prepared for a glacial epoch by the reduction of carbon dioxide, there will follow a series of oscillations of cold and warm climates, such as those of the Pleistocene. It happens this way.

At the time of maximum Wisconsin glacier development about 5 per cent of the ocean waters were stored in the ice. This ice contains little carbon dioxide, and hence the carbon dioxide of 5 per cent of the ocean waters will have been liberated to the atmosphere. It must be understood that a vast amount of carbon dioxide is contained in the ocean waters; in fact, about fifty times more than in the atmosphere, and the two are in balance unless something happens to throw them out of equilibrium. If thrown out of balance, it will take tens of thousands of years, owing to the slow circulation and interchange of deep water with surface water of the ocean, to restore the balance. The carbon dioxide added to the atmosphere by the loss of 5 per cent of the ocean's water would cause the climate to warm up, and the glaciers would melt. As the glaciers melt, the ocean's volume increases, carbon dioxide is absorbed, the amount decreases in the atmosphere, and another glacial stage is brought on. And so the climate oscillates as long as the total atmospheric-ocean content of carbon dioxide is held reduced.

Plass estimates that this total budget would need to be reduced about 7 per cent to bring on the oscillating condition. As soon as the total is restored to the preglacial amount, the oscillations cease, and the glacial epoch is over.

This theory, as well as others, has been criticized on the grounds that it assumes that a colder climate is accompanied by increased precipitation and a warmer climate by decreased precipitation.[5] If the sun's radiation is decreased, the earth's surface becomes cooler, and the energy available to drive the general circulation of the atmosphere is reduced. A decreased circulation means, presumably, less precipitation. Hence colder climates, although contributing to greater snow preservation, will also result in less snow, and the condition necessary for a glaciation does not necessarily develop. The several theories of vari-

---

[4] *Ibid.*

[5] Wm. Lee Stokes, "Another Look at the Ice Age," *Science,* vol. 122, no. 3174, October, 1955.

able solar energy definitely run afoul of this conclusion.

The carbon dioxide theory in new dress offers a plausible explanation of the desired situation of greater precipitation with cooler climates and lesser precipitation with warmer climates. It is pointed out that with a lesser amount of carbon dioxide in the atmosphere the upper surface of a cloud loses heat energy faster to space and is cooler. Furthermore, the upward flux of radiation from the earth that strikes the lower surface of the cloud is greater. These two factors contribute to a greater temperature difference between the top and bottom of a cloud and increased convection in the cloud. This makes for greater precipitation. Thus with decreased carbon dioxide in the atmosphere there will be colder climates and greater precipitation.

It needs to be shown that times of extensive limestone and coal deposition preceded the principal glaciations recognized in the geologic record. The record of the Late Precambrian is incomplete, but we may say that there was some limestone but no coal. We therefore find little reason why there was a decrease in the carbon dioxide content of the atmosphere preceding the glaciation. A great build-up of carbonate formations from Late Cambrian time to the Early Pennsylvanian occurred, and then the greatest of coal-forming periods followed in the Pennsylvanian. The Early Permian glaciation of the continents in the Southern Hemisphere then occurred, so that the required sequence of events seems to hold here. The Cretaceous and Early Tertiary were extensive coal-forming times, but not the Middle and Late Tertiary. Neither was the Tertiary particularly a time of limestone deposition. It is difficult therefore to account for the Pleistocene ice epoch by limestone and coal deposition and a consequent decrease in the carbon dioxide content of the atmosphere.

The only significant geologic phenomenon that preceded the Pleistocene glaciations

was major uplift of the continent of North America, especially the western part. Uplift of other continents is generally recorded also, and if this event can be related to a decreased carbon dioxide content in the atmosphere, then the theory is supported; otherwise not. Plass contends that mountain building and increased weathering represent the increased formation of carbonates. Brooks argues that the greater the proportion of land surface to ocean surface, the cooler the climate, and if so, the Late Tertiary and Pleistocene were certainly times of continentwide uplift. The lowering of temperature enough to develop ice caps due to this cause might bring the carbon dioxide oscillations into operation and give us the several glacial maxima of the Pleistocene.

Ocean Control Theory

Stokes[6] presents a plausible discussion of the cause of glaciation in long-term changes of precipitation traceable to thermal variations in the ocean. He contends that greater precipitation is the initiating cause of a glacial stage and that this comes, as previously mentioned, from warming oceans. Glaciers develop in certain mountain ranges and high latitudes, and colder climates are a result, not a cause. The cold-water rivers flowing from the glaciers gradually cool the oceans, evaporation and precipitation decrease, and the glaciers wane. With the melting of the glaciers the oceans warm, and a new glacial stage is underway. This is the ocean control theory of the oscillations. In 1957 Stokes further pointed out that at the beginning of the Pleistocene, approximately, the Isthmus of Panama was established, thus connecting North and South America and cutting off the Pacific Ocean from the Gulf of Mexico. Also the Gulf Stream into the North Atlantic was probably intensified. With this event, increased precipitation in the adjacent con-

---

[6] *Ibid.*

tinental areas occurred, and this was all that was necessary to start the growth of the great ice caps.

Migration of Poles and Ocean Circulation

Ewing and Donn[7] count on the shifting of the crust over the interior of the earth and the consequent migration of the poles in relation to the continents to bring on glaciations. When the poles reach opportune positions, extensive glaciation results. It is the temperature of the surface layer of the ocean that regulates climates, they contend, like Stokes, rather than external solar conditions or the variable amount of carbon dioxide in the atmosphere. For instance, they say that, if the ice pack of the Arctic Ocean should melt, free circulation of surface waters from the Pacific to the Atlantic would result, the surface temperature of the Atlantic would decrease, and adjacent continental glaciers would develop. When the arctic region is frozen over, the surface temperature of the Atlantic is increased, and an interglacial stage results. This is just the opposite to the effect that Stokes visualizes.

Cores taken from the bottom sediments of the Arctic Ocean reveal a few thin barren lenses of fine sediment at the surface, but directly under this is a layer with abundant Foraminifera. The Foraminifera reflect warmer surface waters, and the situation in which they lived, namely, an ice-free ocean, changed suddenly, so it seems, to the present frozen-over ocean. Carbon-14 dates on the Foraminifera range from 18,000 to 23,000 years. This corresponds, apparently, with the Wisconsin maximum. Thus, during the last glacial stage it appears that the Arctic Ocean was ice-free and warmer.

The mechanism by which oscillations between glacial and nonglacial climates are explained is a shallow sill that divides the Arctic and Atlantic Oceans between northern Greenland, Spitsbergen, and Norway. See Fig. 21-1. When the sea level was lowered during a glacial maximum, a serious reduction in the interchange of water between the two oceans occurred. The reduced inflow of warm Atlantic water, together with the cooling effect of the glaciers, eventually allowed a new Arctic Ocean ice sheet to form. Then the Atlantic waters warmed up more than formerly, and an interglacial stage ensued. The cycle was repeated several times.

The theory may be weakened by the discovery by the Russians of a deep gap in the sill through which the Arctic and Atlantic waters may move rather freely. Stokes and Ewing and Donn's theories, although in conflict on a basic assumption, are in decided contrast to the carbon dioxide theory and represent an interesting trend in thinking on the cause of glacial epochs. For further information see the references listed below, and seek help from your instructors.

---

[7] Maurice Ewing and William L. Donn, "Past Climates and Drifting Continents," in J. F. White (ed.), *Study of the Earth*, Prentice-Hall, Inc., Englewood Cliffs, N.J., 1962.

Suggested Aids

Readings

Dorf, Erling: "The Earth's Changing Climates," *Weatherwise*, vol. 10, April, 1957.

Ewing, Maurice, William L. Donn, Gilbert N. Plass, and Edwin H. Colbert: "Past Climates and Drifting Continents," in J. F. White (ed.), *Study of the Earth*, Prentice-Hall, Inc., Englewood Cliffs, N.J., 1962.

Flint, Richard F.: *Glacial Geology and the Pleistocene Epoch*, 2d ed., John Wiley & Sons, New York, 1957.

Stokes, Wm. Lee: "Another Look at the Ice Age," *Science*, vol. 122, no. 3174, October, 1955.

Chapter 22

WHAT IS MAN?

Man is a placental mammal of the order of primates, family of Hominidae, genus of *Homo,* and species of *sapiens.* He is the sole survivor on the Hominidae family tree. All races of man today, regardless of color, size, hair, shape of head, or kind of eyelids, are of one species. This defines his position in the biological world, but there is more that we would like to know.

It is commonly pointed out by anthropologists that man is set apart from other mammals by the size of his brain and by his intelligence. He remembers his own past experiences and prepares for the future accordingly. He is a wielder of weapons and a user of tools. He makes tools after a pattern and designs them with foresight. He has a language and transmits his knowledge by speech. Beyond parental solicitude for his young, he has

The Rise of Man

moral and ethical fiber; he is, to different degrees, unselfish and kind to his fellow men. He is a mystic or spiritualist, and an artist. With all these characteristics he created culture, the substance of human society.

He has eyes that focus sharply and see in three dimensions. Much of his good fortune springs from his erect posture; he walks easily on two legs and thus has his deft fingers free for many uses and acts denied the lower animals. His creations in art, music, literature, and science are testimony to his marvelous brain and versatile fingers. Man is paradoxically a most generalized, versatile, adaptive mammal by reason of a highly specialized brain.

With these characteristics of man in mind, we will next proceed to review the races of man on earth as they were in early historical times and then to trace the lineage of man back into the past, as well as we can, by the fossil record. We will see that the traces of early man are very meager and that what we know is hardly more than a few glimpses from time to time of a 70-million-year pageant.

MAN IN EARLY HISTORIC TIME

Races and Their Characteristics

Attempts to characterize racial groups are based on color or complexion; facial features, such as eyelids, nose, and lips; hair; stature; skull characteristics and proportions; metabolic activity and biological functioning; and blood types. Language and cultural characteristics are to be used with caution, because there has been so much migration and mixing. There is general agreement among the authorities that the major racial groups of *Homo sapiens*

Table 22-1 CLASSIFICATIONS OF THE HUMAN RACES

Howells	Romer	
1. White	Caucasoid	Mediterranean (longheads); mediterranean characteristics strong in Polynesians and Hindus
		Alpine (broadheads)
2. a. Early Mongoloid b. Late Mongoloid	Mongoloid	
3. a. Negro b. Bushman c. Pigmy	Negroid	Sudan Negro Forest Negro Zulus and Kaffirs Bushmen and Hottentots Oceanic Negro: Melanesians Papuans Pygmy Tasmanians
4. Australian	Australoid	

SOURCE: William W. Howells, "The Distribution of Man," *Scientific American,* September, 1960, and A. S. Romer, *Man and the Vertebrates,* vol. II, Pelican Book Co., Baltimore, Md., 1954.

are the whites, the Mongoloids, the Negroids, and the Australoids. Classifications of Howells and Romer are compared in Table 22-1.

Negroids

The homeland of the Negroids is Africa south of the Sahara, where they evidently evolved and hence can be called true natives. Their characteristics are familiar: the hair is black, short, kinky or wooly; there is little hair on the face or body; the skin is black and the eyes dark; the face protrudes markedly (prognathism), the lips are thick and out-turned, and the nose is short and broad; the skull is long; and the stature medium to tall.

Much variation exists among the negroids of the vast continent of Africa, as may be inferred from the subgroups in the classification. Authorities estimate that there are about six hundred different peoples in tropical Africa, and some hesitate to generalize in describing them as I have done in the foregoing sentences. They differ from one another by their general way of life. Each has its own traditions, history, and customs.

It should be explained that the terms "longhead" and "broadhead" are derived from the ratio of breadth to length of the braincase. Those skulls which have a conspicuously greater length than breadth are called longheads, and those in which the breadth approaches the length are called broadheads. The longheads are probably the earliest shape to evolve, but they have continued strong and of superior type, along with the broadheads, which are a rather late human development.

Australoids

The "blackfellows" of Australia were in complete possession of the continent until the white settlers arrived. Today only about 60,000 remain, mainly concentrated along the northern coasts. They are hunters and food gatherers without permanent shelters. They do not plant crops, nor do they have domesticated animals. Metals are not known. Their primitive condition is complemented by physical characteristics that are of low type. The brow ridges are more prominent than any other living race, the jaws prognathic, the nose very broad and flat, and the lips large but lacking the swollen appearance of some of the African Negroes. The skin is brown rather than black, and the hair is somewhat curly but not kinky.

It is generally believed that the Australoids are of an early branch of the Negroid stem and migrated from southern Asia into Australia. They encountered a still more primitive race there, the Tasmanians, and drove them southward out of the continent to the large island of Tasmania. With the white occupation of Tasmania the natives were disseminated until now no purebreds are left. There is some variation among the Australoids, and this apparently is due to mixing with the Tasmanians.

Mongoloids

Most of the millions of inhabitants of eastern Asia are Mongoloids. The Mongoloid physical type is readily recognizable, with the skull of the broadhead variety, the face also broad with prominent cheek bones, the nose small, and the body stocky. The skin is tinted yellow to brown, the eyes are dark, and the hair is long, coarse, straight, and abundant on the head, but scarce elsewhere on the face or body. The upper eyelid has the characteristic double fold and gives the eye an almond shape (Fig. 22-1):[1]

The almond eyes of the Mongoloid are deeply set in protective fat-lined lids, the nose and forehead are flattish and the cheeks are broad and fat-padded. In every way, it has been pointed out, this is an ideal mask to protect eyes, nose, and sinuses against bitterly

[1] William W. Howells, "The Distribution of Man," *Scientific American*, September, 1960.

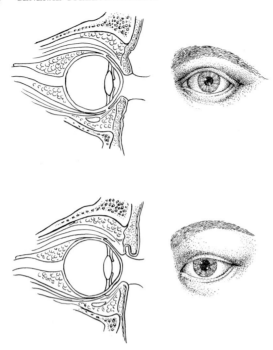

FIG. 22-1 Comparison of Caucasoid and Mongoloid eye. *(After Howells, 1960.)*

cold weather. Such a face . . . reaches its most marked and uniform expression in the cold northeastern part of the continent, from Korea north.

It is reasoned that the ability to live and survive in the extreme cold of northeastern Siberia was only attained in the Late Stone Age (Paleolithic), which, we shall see, occurred during the last glacial stage, or from about 35,000 to 11,000 years ago. The Mongoloid face was presumably developed by natural selection in which the fierce cold would have weeded out the poorly adapted through pneumonia and sinus infections.

The more characteristic features of the Mongoloids become less prominent as one goes southward through China. Many peoples in southeastern Asia, in fact, seem to manifest both Mongolian and Mediterranean features. Referring back to the classification of the races, you will see that the Mediterraneans are longheaded whites. Groups of these people made their way eastward to India and neighboring regions and have left a profound influence in the

bloodstream there. However, the theory of mixing is not the only possible accounting of the characteristics. Consider the Malayans, who differ from their northern relatives in having a still shorter stature and a browner skin. Rather than a mixture, by which the real brown skin would be hard to explain, it is possible that they could have come from ancestors in which the full complement of Mongoloid features had never developed. Even some mixing of this ancestral type may have occurred with other not easily identified peoples. Variants of the Malayan type extend along the islands fringing the eastern coast of Asia to the Philippines and Formosa. The Japanese appear to have a large amount of Malayan blood, and the same may be true of the Koreans. These peoples, hence, are believed to be fairly recent comers to their islands.

According to Fig. 22-2 you can see the postulated distribution on the earth of ancestral, less well-defined Mongoloids (early Mongoloids) and the well-defined Mongoloids (late Mongoloids). The late Mongoloids spread southeastward and northwestward in Asia to stamp their influence far and wide. Those which we call the Eskimos drifted across the arctic from Alaska to Greenland. But the occupants of North and South America, south of the arctic fringe, who were the red men or misnamed Indians of Columbus, are descendants of the early Mongoloids. Anthropologists recognize the possibility that small sea-faring groups may have arrived on the western shores of the Americas from time to time and may have fused with the local inhabitants, but such arrivals are difficult, if not impossible, to document. Several waves of migrants from Siberia by way of Alaska are a distinct possibility, the last of which may have been rather late. This is deduced because of linguistic similarities. Almost all American Indians have the Mongolian broadhead, the prominent cheek bones, and the straight black hair. The skin has more of a brownish or reddish tint, and the nose is in sharp contrast to the typical Mongoloid, being frequently high-bridged and convex. The almond eye is seldom very evident.

The Mongoloids of eastern Asia reached a fairly high degree of culture. Their written sign language was actually the barrier to the high scientific achievements reached by the peoples of the Western world. It was far too difficult for mass education and did not lend itself to mathematics. Little culture was evidently brought by the Ameri-

from the Australoids, visualize a type with persistently long heads, wavy brown to black hair, face and body moderately hairy, brown eyes, brown to light brown skin, and higher and narrower noses. Peoples with such characteristics are easy to find because they populate the countries around the Mediterranean Sea from Spain and Morocco to the Arabic countries and even to India. All these peoples are now generally classified as Mediterraneans. If the above deduc-

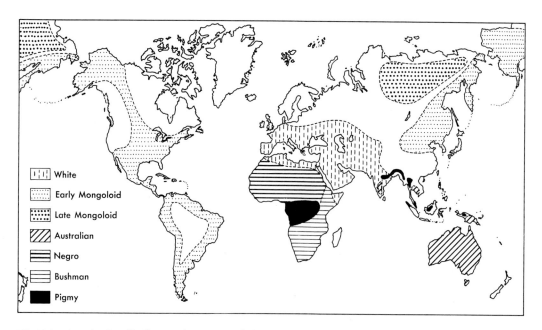

FIG. 22-2 Map showing distribution of races in early historical times. *(After Howells, 1960.)*

White
Early Mongoloid
Late Mongoloid
Australian
Negro
Bushman
Pigmy

can Indians into the Western Hemisphere. This may be accounted for by the fact that peoples of any degree of socialized culture would probably not have chosen to make the long journey into the far north through the subarctic region of the Bering Straits and Alaska; only the Stone Age types of inhabitants of the less desirable fringe areas would possibly have made it across.

Caucasoids (Whites)

Mediterraneans. Anthropologists, in trying to anticipate an evolutionary advance

tion is correct, then the Mediterraneans developed close to the ancestral home and are not migrants.

The Mediterraneans had already spread widely over Europe by Neolithic times (Late Stone Age). Skeletons characterizing this type are found in Palestine, in Egypt even southward to the headwaters of the Nile, and in the Eurasian steppes.

It may be said of the present distribution that the Irano-Afghans are rather tall with hooked noses. The basic Jewish stock is shorter in stature. Ethiopia to the south is occupied by peoples generally called Hamites, which are essentially Mediterraneans but with a certain amount of Negroid blood. The stature is tall in northern Africa west of Egypt, but in Spain a shorter type is present, with features closely akin to those in Arabia. The Mediterraneans north of the sea were overrun by the later fair-skinned broadheads, but in Greece there is still a pronounced ancestral influence, as also found in the Balkans and the Russian coasts of the Black Sea. The Mediterranean blood is strongly represented today in Sicily and southern Italy.

The Late Stone Age peoples of Great Britain were mainly Mediterraneans, but there, as in central Europe, the stock has almost completely disappeared by now. However, it does survive in modified form in the so-called Nordics. In purest form the Nordics are the peoples of Scandinavia and the east Baltic shores. In them we note the following divergences from the typical Mediterranean stock: they are tall, with very light skin, mostly blond hair, and blue to grey eyes. Otherwise they are longheaded Mediterraneans and are regarded as "bleached out" migrants from a Mediterranean source; the fading in pigmentation occurring after arrival in the north. They were already established there in the Iron Age, about 1000 B.C. It is a long story, which cannot be recounted here, that the Nordics originated somewhere between eastern Germany and southern Russia and that from their original language the various Indo-European tongues were disseminated, from Gaelic and English on the west to Sanskrit and derivatives in India on the east.

The Mediterranean peoples spread amazing distances eastward along the mountainous belts through Asia Minor to India and to the Pacific and left their blood influence along the way. Books of information about this subject have been written, but it must all be said in a sentence or two here. The Hindus of peninsular India have strong Mediterranean features, and the Gypsies are an offshoot of this strain. The brunette Mediterraneans have left their mark in the Burmese and in other groups in Indo-China, where the Mongoloid influence is subdued. The Murut people of Borneo are strongly Mediterranean, with some Negroid and Mongoloid admixture. The Hairy Ainus of Hokkaido, the northern island of Japan, are a primitive, longheaded, brunette white stock, and before the modern Japanese came, they occupied all of Japan. They are much contaminated today with Japanese blood and survive in only a few villages.

Indeed, the early Mediterraneans spread into the Americas by a continuation of their drive to the northeast and east across the Bering Strait. The American Indians are classed as Mongoloid, but as indicated before, there are many tribes with many different physical characteristics. The basket makers of the southwest were longheads, the present Indians of the Amazon are longheads, and the natives of faraway Tierra del Fuego bear the same features. The Indians of eastern North America lack a full complement of Mongolian features. These are the reasons for believing that an early "Mongoloid" form, modified by brunette Mediterranean blood, populated the Americas first. These peoples may have come in waves, with the later ones introducing in places more typical Mongolian blood. The most ancient comers of all to America may have been the Australoids or Negroids.

Alpines. The Alpines are the fair-complexioned broadheads of Europe. They are characterized by wavy hair, narrow noses, and brown to light complexions. The final major human evolutionary turn would seem to have been the appearance of these broadheads. This is deduced because of the near-ubiquitous distribution of prehistoric longhead skeletons and the present distribution of the broadheads. The longheads appear to have been driven to the periphery of Eurasia by the broadheads, who occupy all the central region today. It is deduced that the early European broadheads clustered in a zone running from France east along the mountainous zone of the Alps to the Balkans, and on east into the mountains of

Asia Minor. To the north were the Nordics and to the south were the Mediterraneans. It is thus unlikely that the Alpines would have evolved as a pure race; more likely they would have picked up irregularly characteristics of their neighbors. One is impressed with this conclusion as he travels about in Europe.

The origin of the broadheads is poorly understood. Did they evolve in place or are they migrants from the east? Broadheadedness may be a dominant strain in racial crosses, and the Alpines are known to be more prolific than their neighbors. It would seem that migrations of small groups from the east may have introduced the Alpine characteristics, which then flourished and became emergent.

OUR ANCESTORS OF THE LATE PLEISTOCENE

The Fossil Record

Now that we have had a look at *Homo sapiens* as he was in early historical times, we must step down from the secure plateau of abundant record to a fog-shrouded plain of fragmental fossil evidence for an insight into his ancestry. Associated with the last glacial stage in Europe, which spanned an interval of time from about 35,000 to 10,000 years ago, lived a human society known as that of the Late Paleolithic or New Stone Age. It is documented by over 100 skeletal and cultural fossil finds widely distributed over Europe. Such evidence permits the culture to be broken down into a number of substages for which the ways of life and distribution are reasonably well known. This is the age of the Cro-Magnon man, in every physical regard the equal of modern man, if not even slightly larger than the European white of today. His history is within the dating span of carbon-14, so that we can speak with some confidence now about the times of advance from one cultural stage to another.

In the interval between the last glacial stage and the preceding one, in the so-called third interglacial, lived a people in Europe and the Mediterranean region somewhat down the scale from the Cro-Magnon man, both physically and culturally. He is called the Neanderthal man. Partial to complete skeletons have been found in fifteen localities in France, three in Belgium, one in Hungary, one in Romania, two in Gibralter, three in Italy, one in Malta, two in the Channel Islands, and one in Iran. Numerous artifacts and animal remains generally accompany the human bones and permit a fair understanding of his culture.

Now, predating the Neanderthal man is a haze of scattered, fragmental fossil evidence. Just a few twigs of the branches below the crown of the tree of human ascent are known, and the places where these twigs belong are argumentative. These ancient fossil evidences will be discussed on succeeding pages.

Cro-Magnon Man

Figure 22-3 shows the position of Cro-Magnon man in relation to the glacial stages of the Pleistocene epoch. It also shows the cultural periods of his existence as depicted in the *Epic of Man* by Life Magazine, to which the student is referred for a most graphic impression of the race and its activities. Characteristic skeletons were first discovered in a French rock shelter in 1868, known as Cro-Magnon, and from this locality the race gets its name.

The males of Cro-Magnon man were tall, generally 6 ft or slightly more in height. In body, skull, and stature they are modern, without a trace of Neanderthal characteristics. (Fig. 22-4). The skulls are of the longhead type, with large brains averaging in the males possibly slightly larger than the modern Europeans. The forehead and skull vault are high, the face of modern proportions with narrow nose and the chin highly developed. The eye sockets were wide apart and low-set. These characteristics are

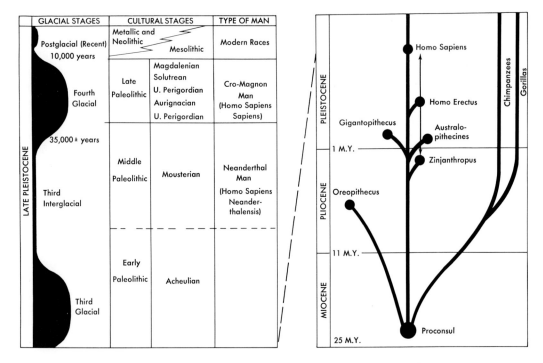

FIG. 22-3 Cultural stages of *Homo sapiens* and family tree of man. M.Y. means millions of years. *Zinjanthropus* has the characteristics of the *Homo erectus* group, and thus the arrowed line is used to indicate that the span of *Homo erectus* was from *Zinjanthropus* to *Homo sapiens*. It should be noted that nearly every writer on man's family tree arranges it differently. On some all fossil species are branches, and on others most of them are on the main stem. We really are only guessing. *(Left, modified from Stokes, 1960; right modified from* Epic of Man, Life Magazine, 1961*).*

FIG. 22-4 Bust of Cro-Magnon man, by Mascré under supervision of Rutot. *(Courtesy of Smithsonian Institution.)*

in contrast to those of the more primitive types. Some variations exist, however, as would be expected when the skeletons of one place of an earlier time are compared with those of another place at a later time perhaps, but according to Romer[2] these are no more than occur in a relatively pure racial group today.

He was a mighty and intrepid hunter. His exploits are depicted by his paintings on the walls of the caves in which he lived and supported by the bones of his prey. The Ice Age bison and wooly mammoth did not daunt him. He passed through at least five cultural stages and climaxed his development about 10,000 years ago by fashioning bone and antler into awls, saws, and

[2] A. S. Romer, *Man and the Vertebrates*, vol. II, Pelican Book Co., Baltimore, Md., 1954.

needles. He was an expert in making stone tools and produced long sharp knives. By making warm clothing and supported by the heat from fireplaces, he could withstand the glacial climates and thus established fairly permanent shelters and settlements. He never seemed to domesticate animals, nor did he come upon the practice of agriculture. He depended on the hunt and in places on fishing for his food supply.

Neanderthal Man

The numerous skeletal parts reveal a squat body about 5 ft 4 in. tall for the Neanderthal race, a barrel chest, bowed legs, and flat feet that suggest a slouch and shuffling gait. A skull with cranial capacity of 1,200 to 1,600 cu cm indicates that he approached modern man in brain size, but not in shape. It was long and low with big, jutting brow ridges, a flat nose, and retreating chin (Fig. 22-5). His jaws were large and protruding, giving a muzzle appearance to his mouth. Although his jaw is larger and he may have had an apelike appearance, his teeth are distinctly human. In restorations he is given a hairy, rough, and brutish appearance, and in paintings he is depicted as an inhabitor of caves.

From stratigraphic evidence he is known to have lived in Europe during the latter part of the last interglacial and into the early part of the last glacial stage. Recent finds suggest that he did not precede Cro-Magnon man entirely but that there was a contemporaneity of the two for a while. The origins of each race are obscure, but at least, it does not now seem that the Neanderthaloids were the direct ancestors of the Cro-Magnon man but perhaps that the Cro-Magnon people had evolved elsewhere and migrated to the European hunting grounds, where they eventually did away with the native Neanderthalers.

Even so, the Neanderthal men were fearless hunters, for they killed the great Pleistocene cave bear and the wooly mammoth with well-formed, stone-tipped spears. They

FIG. 22-5 Bust of Neanderthal man, by Mascré under supervision of Rutot. (Courtesy of Smithsonian Institution.)

used fire and buried their dead. Because of their fairly large brain they are generally classed as *Homo sapiens* by anthropologists.

EARLY PLEISTOCENE AND LATE PLIOCENE FOSSILS

Number and Distribution of Fossil Finds

Fossil records of man before the Neanderthaloids are not many; yet they are fairly instructive. Reference to Fig. 22-3 will show at a glance the chief groups and to Fig. 22-6 the localities of the discoveries. Africa, China, Java, and to a lesser extent Europe are the regions where the fossils of primitive man and the so-called ape-man have been found. There is a tendancy to group the types of pre-Neanderthal man at the risk of error but for simplicity's sake into two general groups, namely, *Homo erectus* and the Australopithecines. These two will be discussed below.

Homo Erectus

Java Man. The most famous of all fossils is *Pithecanthropus erectus*, the Java ape-

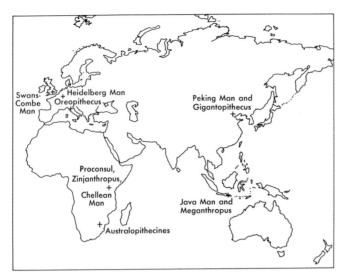

FIG. 22-6 Sites of Pre-Neanderthal men mentioned in the text.

man. With a cranial capacity of 700 to 800 cu cm, flat forehead, heavy protruding eyebrow ridges, large jaw and teeth, and receding chin, he was hailed as half ape and half man and the missing link. Fierce debate, intolerance, and even persecution caused the mild-mannered and sincere discoverer, the Dutch physician Eugene Dubois, to lock the few remains in his vault, where he kept them away from all observers, including scientific friends and authorities, for many years. He made the discovery near Trinal in Java between 1890 and 1893, and the fragments consisted of a skull cap, a thigh bone, and a few teeth. These parts occurred mixed with bones of extinct elephants, rhinos, tapirs, pigs, hippos, antelope, deer, and probably other animals. As the years passed and the fragments remained locked up, doubt grew that he actually had found what he described. However, in 1923, he reopened the safe and allowed certain authorities to examine the material. They confirmed his discovery. Then, in the period 1936 to 1939, a German paleontologist, Dr. R. von Koenigswald, digging in the Sangiran district of Java, found sufficiently more material of *Pithecanthropus* to construct a representative skull and to state something about the rest of the skeleton. In

fact, von Koenigswald believes that all the material together may represent three species of *Pithecanthropus*.

Modern students analyze the skeletal parts of *Pithecanthropus* as more man than ape and place him in the general category of *Homo erectus*. See Fig. 22-9.

Peking Man. The collecting of human remains began in a cave 30 miles west of Peking (now Peiping) in 1918, and with the recognition that very early man was represented, major excavations started in 1927 as a joint effort by Chinese, Americans, and Swedes. As digging proceeded it became evident that the site was an ancient camping ground where the refuse of the occupants had accumulated tens of feet deep. Along with bones of the many animals that this early man hunted, including elephants, saber-tooth cats, and giant rodents, were charcoal layers and crude stone implements. By 1939 remains of at least 45 human individuals had been uncovered pertaining to both sexes and children of various ages, so that the osteology of the species is fairly well known. He was a head-hunter and cannibal, because the basal part of several skulls is broken open, gaining access to the brain.

Peking man has been given the name

Sinanthropus pekinensis, but by comparison with *Pithecanthropus*, he is most similar, and hence has also been called *Pithecanthropus pekinensis* by some and also classed as *Homo erectus*. He was a user of fire and primitive stone tools.

The ages of the Java man and the Peking man are problems. The glacial moraines and other deposits are wanting in these areas, and hence it is impossible to relate the caves and their occupancy to the glacial stages. From stratigraphic relations it is generally concluded, however, that they are early Pleistocene, but we are certainly not sure of this or of the precise glacial stage to which they belong. We are also not able to compare the ages precisely of the two races. We badly need an isotope method that will span the gap from the oldest limit of C^{14} dates to the youngest reliable potassium-argon dates.

Solo Man. Dr. von Koenigswald not only found considerable fossil material of the Java man to supplement Dr. Dubois's finds but also found a skull cap and various parts of a slightly more advanced individual. These were in a terrace deposit clearly higher stratigraphically than the deposits in which *Pithecanthropus* was found, and hence distinctly younger. Considering the geological relations, von Koenigswald conjectured that his younger man, whom he called *Pithecanthropus soloensis*, might be 100,000 or more years younger than *Pithecanthropus erectus*. This is certainly a guess; all we can safely say is that *soloensis* (Solo man for short) is younger than the Java man. Von Koenigswald also postulated that Solo man might be a direct descendant of Java man. See Fig. 22-7.

Pre-Neanderthal Men of Europe. A few odds and ends of skulls of early man have been found in Europe that undoubtedly predate the Neanderthaloids. There is the large lower jaw with 16 teeth intact, found in an earth deposit near Heidelberg, Germany, in 1907. Heidelberg man appears to be more primitive than Neanderthal man, and being obligingly older, at least before

FIG. 22-7   Bust of *Pithecanthropus*, by Mascré under supervision of Rutot. (*Courtesy of Smithsonian Institution.*)

the second glacial stage, Heidelberg man may be the ancestor of Neanderthal man (Fig. 22-8).

There are the Eringsdorf and Steinheim finds, both in Germany, and the Saccopastore remains, near Rome. These fossils occurred in deposits deduced to be second interglacial and are thus probably somewhat younger than Heidelberg man but

FIG. 22-8   Bust of Heidelberg man, by Mascré under supervision of Rutot. (*Courtesy of Smithsonian Institution.*)

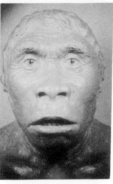

FIG. 22-9 Comparison of Neanderthal man (top), Java man (middle), and Zinjanthropus (bottom). (Courtesy of Smithsonian Institution and Department of Anthropology, University of Utah.)

still older than Neanderthal man. There is some suggestion in these fragments, curiously, of a mixture of Neanderthal and modern characters.

An occipital bone of a human skull, found near Swanscombe, England, is associated with a lower Paleolithic hand axe and is definitely of the second interglacial.

Australopithecines

Significant skeletal parts and fragments of early man have been coming from South Africa since 1925. Five localities have yielded parts of at least 15 individuals. They certainly are primitive and have been termed ape-man, half-man, and man-ape. The localities are in the Transvaal principally, and the bones come from limy fillings of caves and hot-spring tufas. These isolated deposits are next to impossible to date by means of geological relationships, and hence their time relation to each other and their place in absolute time can only be guessed. All are grouped together as the *Australopithecines*.

They had upright bodies but a brain capacity of only 450 to 700 cu cm. This is about that of the modern gorilla. They probably used clubs and the simplest of stone tools. The evolutionary position of the Australopithecines is not yet established (Fig. 22-3).

The Giants

A jaw with enormous teeth was found in Kwangsi Province, China, which in addition to the size seems more apelike than human. This is called *Gigantopithecus*. Von Koe-

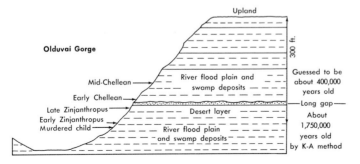

FIG. 22-10 Cross section of one wall of Olduvai Gorge showing various fossil horizons. (After Leakey, 1961.)

nigswald found a jawbone with three enormous teeth in Java, which he called *Meganthropus.* Still another similar jaw, found later, demonstrates the existence of a distinct type. If the rest of the body was proportionally as large as the teeth, compared with modern man, then *Meganthropus* would have been 8 to 11 ft tall and weighed 1,000 lb. There is a suspicion, however, that the huge teeth may have gone with a relatively small skull and body, because another odd find, the African half-man, *Paranthropus,* has huge teeth and a small skull. Not enough is known yet about these questionable giants to justify further speculation on them.

Zinjanthropus and Chellean Man

Probably all fossil material of early man so far discussed is Pleistocene in age, but recently (1958), Dr. L. S. B. Leakey discovered remains of a primitive human that may have lived in the late Pliocene. The find was in Olduvai Gorge, Tanganyika, East Africa. An almost perfect skull and certain limb bones represent an individual he has called *Zinjanthropus.* The skull has no forehead at all, a wide nasal region, a long face, large molars, and small canines and incisors (Fig. 22-9). The specimens were found among cracked bones and crude stone tools on an old camp-site floor that was later buried by river flood-plain deposits. See Fig. 22-10. With his crude stone tools he could cut and skin carcasses and could crack bones to get at the marrow. Among the animals he killed for food were the young colts of zebras, so that probably he could not cope with the large adult zebras. In beds a few feet higher in the section, and hence a little later, more bone fragments were found, with evidence that now this immediate successor of Zinj used a sharpened stick as a spear and hunted successfully the large swamp-dwelling antelope.

In beds somewhat below the *Zinjanthropus* horizon, and thus older, have come in

1960 through the dedicated efforts of Dr. and Mrs. Leakey and their son Jonathan a complete set of foot bones, parts of a skull and collar bone and a beautifully preserved large section of a lower jaw with 13 teeth. The teeth and jaw speak plainly. The first molars are worn down somewhat, the second molars are emerged but are not worn, and the third molars are not yet emerged. This, then is a young person who died when about eleven or twelve years old. There is a massive point of impact in the skull that reaches to the inner wall and fractures that radiate from the point of impact. You thus have the oldest murder mystery. The child can be said to have died from the blow of a blunt instrument.

Not enough is known of this pre-*Zinjanthropus* child to say whether it represents man or ape. In the sense that *Zinjanthropus* made tools after a pattern he must be considered a man, or at least a near-man, in Dr. Leakey's term. He is closely related to the Australopithecines. The child's father was a tool-making creature, probably with a slightly larger brain than Zinj and with somewhat different teeth. He hunted catfish and tortoises in the river marshes and also a few aquatic birds. Possibly we are dealing with two early types of hominids that developed and lived side by side in the Transvaal region.

Now, what is the age of Zinj and the murdered child? Age determinations have been made by the potassium-argon isotope method in the laboratories of the University of California on biotite from volcanic ash beds interlayered with the fossil-bearing river flood-plain muds. The absolute age of about 1,750,000 years was obtained. This date would place the finds in the very late Pliocene, but now we are confronted with later information that potassium-argon dates on volcanic ash may not be reliable. However, the total fauna found associated with the near-human bones is similar to that of the latest Pliocene of Europe, according to Dr. Leakey, and this confirms the isotope date that *Zinjanthropus* and his

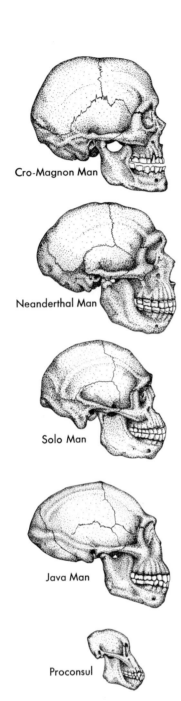

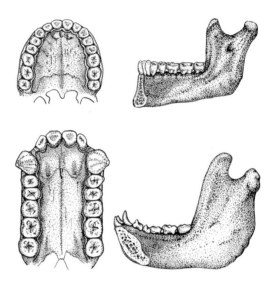

FIG. 22-12 Comparison of lower human jaw and teeth with same gorilla. Gorilla at bottom.

Cro-Magnon Man

Neanderthal Man

Solo Man

Java Man

Proconsul

FIG. 22-11 Comparison of several skulls of early man, including Proconsul.

distant relative, the murdered child, are the oldest men or oldest near-men yet discovered.

A desert climate finally eliminated the lush flood-plain home of *Zinjanthropus,* and after a long time, perhaps several hundred thousand years, but still in mid- or early Pleistocene, the grass lands and river flood plains returned to the Transvaal region, and a new race made its appearance, which Dr. Leakey thinks is the Chellean man. It so happens that since 1846 a primitive Stone Age culture has been known from artifacts but not from the skeletal parts of the man himself. The original site of the finding of these artifacts was at Chelles, France, but the mysterious race that made them had never been identified from actual parts. The easily recognized stone tools have been found over much of Africa, Asia, and southwestern Europe. From the beds above the desert layer Dr. Leakey had unearthed the characteristic Chellean tools and had hoped to find some skeletal parts. Finally, in 1960, he did have the good fortune to come upon a skull of Chellean man. Not much has yet been published about this man except that he had the most massive brow of any early man yet found and was large and powerful enough to throw a bola with extra large stones in it. He lived among giant mammals, such as a proboscidian called *Dinotherium*, a ram as big as a large horse, saber-toothed cats, a giant swamp antelope, a giant porcupine, and an extinct hippopotamus. Dr. Leakey does not speculate on the relation of his Chellean man to *Homo erectus* or to the Neanderthal man.

A MIOCENE ANCESTOR?

Remains of a fossil ape of early Miocene or late Oligocene time may represent a form that could qualify as a candidate for the post of ancestor of both the apes and man. He is called Proconsul, the fossils were found in Tanganyika and represent an individual who had heel and leg bones that would have permitted it to assume an erect or semierect posture. Its arms are the same length as its legs, suggesting that the creature was more at home in the open grasslands country than in the trees. It is conjectured that some tree-dwelling primates came down to the ground to forage for food, and those which made out best were those best suited for walking. These founded the line of hominids that led to man. Proconsul could have been in this early stem. Such is depicted in Figs. 22-3 and 22-11.

Oreopithecus is a mid-Miocene to early Pliocene pre-ape from Tuscany, Italy. Almost complete skeletons display a tendency to an upright bipedal mode of life, with humanlike teeth and chin. He is considered by some students to be in the line of ascent of man, but by others, a side branch.

And thus the record of the lineage of man fades out, as far as fossil evidence is concerned. We can speculate further on more distant monkeylike arboreal ancestors from anatomical considerations, but the highlights of the fossil record have been given. As sketchy and few as they are, they are still impressive.

THE GREAT APES

You hear the statement commonly made that anthropologists claim that man has evolved from the apes and monkeys. This is not the case. The anatomical characteristics are similar (Fig. 22-12), and it is true that we see in tracing man's ancestors back to more primitive types an approach to features like those of the chimpanzees and gorillas. However, we must remember that modern man and the apes are living contemporaneously, and thus the closest relationship that can be claimed is some common ancestral stock. This, possibly, might be Proconsul as represented in Fig. 22-3, but then it is just a guess.

EVOLUTION OF THE BRAIN

The preceding pages on the rise of man have emphasized the approach to the subject that anthropologists characterize as "metrics." Skeletal parts have been measured, shapes noted, and ratios tabulated. On this basis comparisons have been made, and the musculature and mode of life or activity have been interpreted. Of more recent interest and concern has been the study of the brain's evolution and its implications on the events and causes of the evolution of man.

As the brain has increased in size, certain parts have grown much more than others. The human cortex is not just an enlargement of that of the ape, but we note that the areas for the hand, especially the thumb, are tremendously enlarged, and this makes the skillful use of the hand possible. There is also a large cortical area to receive sensations from the thumb and to control its motor activity. Much of the cortex of a monkey is still engaged in the motor and sensory functions. In man it is the areas adjacent to the primary centers that are most expanded. These areas are concerned with skills, memory, foresight, and language. These are the mental faculties that make human social life possible. Man is a kind of animal that can learn to adjust to the complex technical society and is a vastly different creature from the tree-living ape.

Many apes and monkeys can make a wide variety of sounds; yet much effort has been expended to teach them to talk without success. The reason is that there is little in the brain to teach.[3] One is tempted to think that language appeared with the fine tools,

fire, and complex hunting techniques of the large-brained men of the early and middle Pleistocene.

The evolution of speech, of reproduction and care of the young, along with the skillful use of the hands all means that man was conditioned at the beginning with a brain capable of unusual growth. It is suggested that the present and future fossils of early man will be more trenchantly examined in light of the concepts of brain evolution, and the ideas thus related to his evolution will be tested.

[3] Sherwood L. Washburn, "Tools and Human Evolution," *Scientific American,* September, 1960.

Suggested Aids

Readings

The Epic of Man, Life Magazine, 1961.

Garn, Stanley M.: *Human Races,* 2d ed., Charles C. Thomas, Publisher, Springfield, Ill., 1962.

Howells, William W.: "The Distribution of Man," *Scientific American,* September, 1960.

Leakey, L. S. B.: "Exploring 1,750,000 Years into Man's Past," *National Geographic,* vol. 120, no. 4, 1961.

Romer, A. S.: *Man and the Vertebrates,* vol II, Pelican Book Co., Baltimore, Md., 1954.

Stokes, Wm. Lee: *Essentials of Earth History,* Prentice-Hall, Inc., Englewood Cliffs, N.J., 1960.

Washburn, Sherwood L.: "Tools and Human Evolution," *Scientific American,* September, 1960.

Weckler, J. E.: "Neanderthal Man," *Scientific American,* December, 1957.

Chapter 23

DEFINITION

The space age has given birth to a number of new words, and one of them is *astrogeology*. Astrogeology has been defined as the study of the solid bodies of the solar system, but in consideration of the theories of origin of the solar system we must also study its gases. It concerns for one thing the chemistry, mineralogy, and history of meteorites. Our chief attention so far has been the moon, because its surface can be so clearly photographed and because it is the first objective of space travel. Our study has been earth-bound, but soon, perhaps, there will be direct observation and sampling. Breaking these earthly ties are the Russian lunar satellite that photographed part of the back side of the moon, the U.S. Mariner Space Probe, passing near the planet Venus, which measured some of the physical characters of and beneath the heavy cloud cover, and the U.S. Ranger 7 Spacecraft which televised close-up photographs of the moon.

Astrogeology

THE SOLAR SYSTEM

Planets and Asteroids

The solar system is made up of a central star (the sun), 9 planets, 31 moons, 30,000 asteroids, and about 100 billion comets, plus innumerable dust particles, gas molecules, and dissociated atoms. The sun contains 99.86 per cent of the total mass, and of the remaining 0.14 per cent only 1 per cent is contained in the earth and its moon. The sun is the nucleus of the system and by its gravitational field controls the movements of the other bodies. The relative size of the sun and the planets and their order away from the sun are shown in Fig. 23-1. Their relative distances from the sun and their orbits are illustrated in Fig. 23-2.

The nine planets can be divided into two groups according to their size and density (see Table 23-1). The four small innermost ones, the terrestrial planets—Mercury, Venus, Earth, and Mars—are heavy and solid, whereas the next four outer ones are the giants and composed mainly of lighter elements. The outermost one is tiny Pluto, which hardly fits either category and does not follow closely the pattern of the orbits of the other planets.

All planets circle the sun in the same direction and in about the same plane. The earth dips and rises through slightly more than 14° of solar latitude as it circles around the sun, and the other planets, except for Pluto, also revolve about the sun within this limit of variation from the sun's equatorial plane. The orbits are elliptical, with a nearest approach to the sun and a most distant position. The innermost planet, Mercury, comes within 28 million miles of the sun at one end of its elliptical orbit and swings out to 43 million miles at the other.

It will be noted in Fig. 23-2 that the farther each planet is from the sun, the slower it travels and the longer it takes to make the orbit. Mercury speeds

Table 23-1   MEMBERS OF THE SOLAR SYSTEM

Name	Mean distance from the sun, astronomical units	Sidereal period*	Equatorial diameter, miles	Mass (earth=1)	Average specific gravity	Rotation	Number of satellites
Sun	—	—	864,000	332,000	1.42	25–35 days	
Mercury	0.38	88 days	3,100	0.054	4.8	88 days	0
Venus	0.72	225 days	7,700	0.81	4.9	(1 ?)	0
Earth	1.00	1 year	7,927	1.00	5.51	23 hr 56 min	1
Mars	1.52	1.88	4,215	0.11	3.95	24 hr 37 min	2
Jupiter	5.20	11.86	88,700	317.00	1.34	9 hr 50 min	12
Saturn	9.54	29.46	74,000	95.00	0.69	10 hr 2 min	9
Uranus	19.19	84.01	32,000	15.00	1.36	10.7 hr	5
Neptune	30.07	164.8	27,700	17.00	1.30	15.8 hr	2
Pluto†	39.46	247.70	3,600 (?)	0.1 (?)	—	—	0

* The sidereal period is the period of the planet's revolution around the sun measured with respect to the stars.
† Pluto may not be a planet in the usual sense but rather an escaped satellite of Neptune.

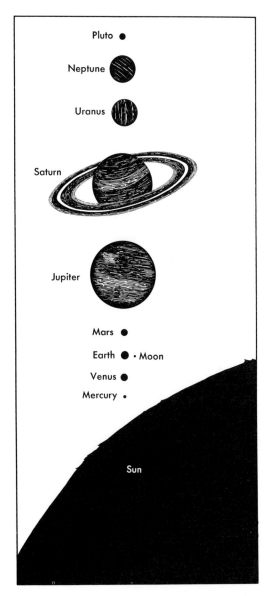

FIG. 23-1 Relative sizes of the nine planets of the solar system. Note that Uranus spins with an axis inclined nearly vertical to the plane of the orbits of the nine planets. Note also the rings of Saturn, which on occasion, when we see the planet directly at its equator, appear as a thin line. Note further the color bands of Jupiter. These are now regarded as Van Allen type of belts. None of the moons is shown except that of the Earth. *(After the Universe, Life Nature Library, 1962.)*

through space at 110,000 miles per hr and takes only 88 days to circle the sun. The earth moves at 67,000 miles per hr and takes a year. The outermost Pluto, down to a walk of 10,000 miles per hr, needs nearly 248 years. They are locked in these definite orbits, which are fixed because the velocity of fall toward the sun equals the velocity of departure from the straight line. Without the sun's strong gravitational pull the planets would fly off in a straight line.

A great gap exists between the inner small planets and the outer giant planets, and here are found in a broad belt the asteroids. They circle the sun the same as the planets. They are small rough masses of rock and metal and altogether total less mass than 5 per cent of that of the moon. Ceres is the largest asteroid, with a diameter of 480 miles. Pallas is 300 miles in diameter, Vesta 240 miles, and Juno 120 miles. Today about 30,000 sizable asteroids are thought to exist, from large ones like Ceres to small ones like Icarus, just 1 mile in diameter. Then there are billions of still smaller ones the size of boulders, pebbles, and sand grains.

Jupiter exercises great power over these asteroids and a number have been brought into the same orbit as the giant planet. These are called the Trojans. Nine orbit a respectful and constant distance in front and five the same distance in back, all in a west to east direction. This distance is just one-sixth of the orbital distance and has been shown mathematically to mark a point of gravitational equilibrium.

Jupiter's tyrannical pull on the asteroids sometimes swings them on voyages toward the sun or away toward the outer planets. Icarus's orbit is one of these, it appears, and it passes twice as close to the sun as Mercury. Hildalgo whirls out as far as Saturn. Once in an errant way they may get yanked still farther astray or drawn back into Jupiter's fold. Eros, a cigar shaped rock 15 miles long and 5 miles wide tumbles end over end and last came within 14 million miles of the earth. Five others

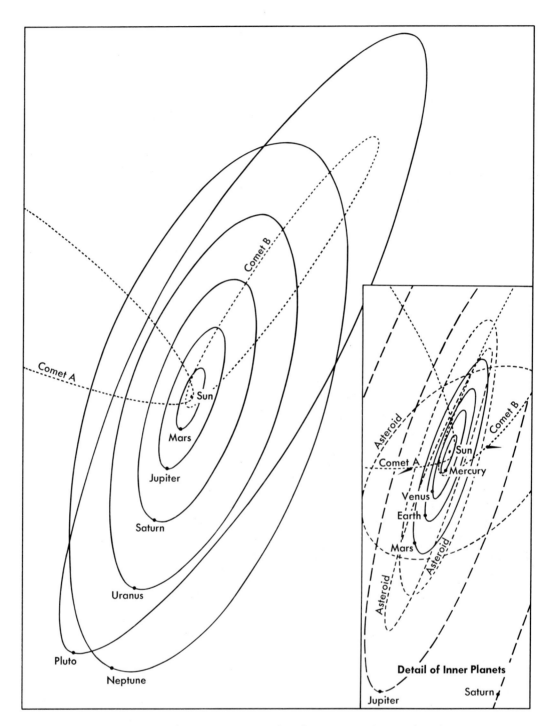

FIG. 23-2 Orbits of the planets and representative asteroids and comets. Note the irregular orbit of Pluto. Note also that the axis of the ellipse of comet A stands nearly vertical to the planar ecliptic and that the axis of the ellipse of comet B is approximately in the ecliptic, but that the ellipse itself is about vertical. The asteroids are mostly in a zone between Mars and Jupiter, but some have unusual orbits, as shown. Of the inner planets, only Mars is shown on large diagram. (*After The Universe, Life Nature Library, 1962.*)

have come even closer, with Hermos, in 1937, passing like a jet, only 500,000 miles away.

Asteroids of boulder size collide with the earth an estimated fifteen hundred times each year. These are called meteorites. Geological investigations have pointed out a considerable number of wounds or craters on the earth due to explosive impact of these stray space bodies. The moon is pitted with many craters, as if it were struck much more often than the earth, but this is probably not so, as will be shown later. When asteroids strike the earth or moon, the impact is like a rock thrown into a pool of soft mud—the asteroid is swallowed explosively in the surface, and considerable fragmental material is thrown upward and outward.

Jupiter, Saturn, Uranus, and Neptune are a different species than the terrestrial planets, both in scale and kind of materials. Jupiter fills a volume thirteen hundred times the earth, its mass is more than twice as great as all the other planets put together, and it has highly turbulent atmosphere hundreds of miles deep. The atmosphere is present because of Jupiter's high gravity, which is 2½ times that of the earth's. The atmosphere is believed to be composed of hydrogen, ammonia, and methane and to be very cold. Possibly the innermost core is of rock or metal, but it may be hydrogen compressed into a heavy metallic state. For all Jupiter's monstrous size its density is only a quarter of the earth's. It has a retinue of 12 satellites, 2 of them larger than the earth's moon.

Saturn is an immense half-formed world, ninety-five times as massive as the earth but only seven-tenths as dense as water. It has a turbulent atmosphere such as Jupiter. It also has three flat rings around the equator about 10 miles thick and extending 6,000 to 48,000 miles beyond its surface. The rings are believed to be composed of ice-coated grit particles. Saturn has nine conventional moons. The largest, Titan, is as big as Mercury, as orange as Mars, and

the only moon with an atmosphere, which is cold and mostly of methane. The outermost satellite, Phoebe, revolves in a direction opposite to that of rotation of its mother planet. Two of the satellites appear to be smooth spheres of pure ice.

Uranus and Neptune are not visible to the naked eye. Uranus is composed of methane with a temperature 270° F below zero. Its · axis of rotation is tilted nearly perpendicular to the plane of its orbit, and so also its five moons revolve about Uranus nearly perpendicular to the ecliptic (plane of the earth's orbit). If you were on Uranus you would see all five moons racing along the horizon with startling rapidity, because the planet rotates once in 10 hr and 49 min.

After the discovery of Uranus, astronomers found intolerable irregularities in its orbit and concluded that a planet beyond must be causing the disturbance. Pointing the telescope where the mathematicians predicted, Neptune was discovered in 1846. Similarly Pluto was discovered in 1930.

At the beginning of this space age we are particularly interested in the compositions, atmospheres, temperatures, and escape velocities of the nearby planets, Mercury, Venus, and Mars, and of the Earth's moon. As for Mercury the planet rotates on its axis once while it orbits once around the sun. This means that one face of Mercury is always toward the sun and being baked at 60° F, while the other side is always in darkness and in subzero temperatures. Its gravitational pull is only three-eighths of that of the earth, and this has not been enough to prevent the heat on the hot side to accelerate any gaseous molecules to escape velocities. There is thus no atmosphere on Mercury. If an astronaut should ever land on the planet he would only need a speed of 2.6 miles per sec to escape, in contrast to 7 miles per sec for the earth.

Venus has an atmosphere that is unbroken and impenetrable by light rays. The planet therefore has a mysterious character. The dazzling veil of yellowish white clouds conceals the rotation of the planet and its poles, so that the period and inclination of the axis to the plane of its orbit are not known. It is much like the earth in mass, volume, density, and escape velocity. The cloudy atmosphere is believed to be mostly carbon dioxide with a little water but no free oxygen. Spectral analysis of the planet's light shows that the cloud layer may range as low as −100° F. The insulating of the carbon dioxide atmosphere is so effective, however, that astronomers have long suspected that the surface temperatures may be very high, and just now a newspaper note relates that the American Mariner Space Probe that flew past Venus on December 14, 1962, at a distance away of 21,594 miles recorded a surface temperature of 800° F. No magnetic field was recorded, which is interpreted to means that Venus's field must be less than 5 to 10 per cent of the earth's field.

Although Mars is only one-tenth as massive as the earth it is more inviting to life than Venus. Its average temperature is about 60° F below zero. Its atmosphere is extremely thin but it does contain some water, because an ice cap, or a film of frost that looks like an ice cap, advances and retreats with the round of Martian seasons. The existing thin atmosphere is probably mostly CO_2. The escape velocity is 3 miles per sec, less than half that of earth.

There are shifting areas of grayish green which no one denies and which may be regions of lowly vegetation or due to dust being moved about by weak seasonal winds.

It may be concluded that the earth is the only hospitable place in the solar system for life, such as we know it. It is hard to conceive that the basic life materials could be other than those composed of hydrogen, oxygen, carbon, and nitrogen, and unless the temperature range is suitable for the existence of water at times and places (32 to 212° F), then the necessary chemical reactions could probably not take place. At the high temperatures that exist on some of the planet surfaces the bonds between carbon and hydrogen would be ruptured. Mars is the only planet with a remote chance of conditions that would be favorable to life, and this only in the lower plant forms.

The earth's moon is devoid of an atmosphere, and its surface is believed to reach a temperature of 214° F in full sunlight at its equator, − 58° F at sunrise, and − 243° F on the dark side. The rocks a few feet below the surface are probably perpetually below 32° F.

Comets

The comets are members of the solar system but odd ones. They are composed of grit and frozen gas particles somewhat like the rings of Saturn and, when seen out in space, are no more than a few miles in diameter, with a density less than water. Some comets orbit in the flat disk of the planets, but others ignore it entirely and travel in ellipses at all angles to it. We know those particularly which swing in close around the sun on their elliptical paths, because the solar energy vaporizes the outer layers of the comets to form great swollen heads. These are generally plainly visible to the unaided eye. Also some of the vaporized material points outward from the sun in an incandescent tail. At this time the comet may appear as large as the sun but is so attenuated that it is made up of "bucketfulls of nothing." At still closer range the sun's energy creates explosive pockets of gas within the comet, and the tail stretches out even more. The great comet of 1843 had a tail that stretched 500 million miles.

The 100 billion-odd comets presumed to exist roam the icy edges of the solar system as a halo some 12 billion miles out from the sun. This is far beyond the reaches of Neptune or Pluto. Occasionally one is believed to be "kicked" out of its track by the gravitational attraction of a passing star. If the direction is toward the solar nucleus, it has three possible destinies (Fig. 23-3). It can make one big loop around the sun and return to its regular path in the halo. It can

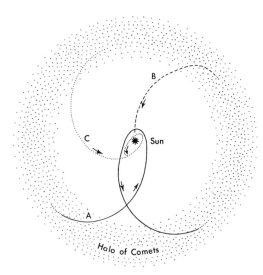

FIG. 23-3 Errant ways of the comets. Comet A sweeps in toward and around the sun, then out to resume former course, approximately. Comet B's course is too close to the sun and is obliterated. Comet C, upon circling the sun, is wrenched into a new small orbit, like Halley's comet. *(After The Universe, Life, Nature Library, 1962.)*

be dragged so deep in the solar system and so close to the sun that it disintegrates. As a third fate, it can be locked into a new smaller orbit around the sun. Halley's comet whizzes through the disk of revolution of the planets every 75 or 76 years and has been noted at every passage by the Chinese and Japanese since 240 B.C. except once.

An example of a comet that skirted the sun and earth too closely is instructive. The story is known as the "short and wild career of Biela." Biela's comet was first observed approaching the sun in 1772. After its first flirtation with the sun it began reappearing at regular 6½-year intervals. As it approached in 1846 it became two comets moving side by side, and then on its next appearance in 1852, still in its split form, it vanished or, better said, was lost by the astronomers. Twenty years later the whole of Europe was treated to a meteorite shower such as has never before or since been described. As the storm reached England people could see 100 blazing shooting

stars a minute. Mathematical calculations have since shown that this was the last of Biela's comet. It had probably crossed close to the earth in past journeys but this time, in playing tag, got drawn into the earth's gravitational net and thus really vanished in a most surprising pyrotechnic extravaganza.

Another remarkable collision of a comet with the earth is now clear after many years of mystery. A tremendous explosion shook an area of northern Siberia in 1900 along the Tunguslea River. Trees were felled like dominoes out to more than 30 miles from the blast center. Window glass was broken at a distance of over 100 miles. Earthquakes were felt for 400 miles. Barometers were affected as far away as England. Much fine material that had been shot up into the upper atmosphere produced week-long unusual and beautiful sunsets. The strange thing was that no impact crater was formed; only small fused pellets, apparently of terrestrial origin, were found in the eye of the explosion, driven into the ground like buckshot. The Soviet Academy of Science, after considerable study, concluded in 1960 that a mighty explosion had definitely occurred and that it was in the head of a comet just before or as it collided with the earth's surface. It was only a small comet in relation to other marauders of the solar system and is estimated to have had a diameter of several miles and weighed about 1 million tons. The apparent internal explosion as it reached the earth's surface may be accounted for by the fact that the comet met the earth head-on at a relative speed of 25 miles per sec, instead of overtaking the planet from behind.

THE MOON'S SURFACE

Photogeologic Mapping

The moon will be the destination of man's first space journey, other than orbital trips around mother earth. It is therefore the subject of much geologic study. Fortunately the absence of an atmosphere and its close proximity to earth have permitted the taking of crisp and clear photographs of half of its surface. Objects can be discerned on them as small as ½ mile in diameter. Unfortunately, however, the lack of an atmosphere means high temperatures on the surface when illuminated by sunlight and low temperatures when in the shade or dark. Besides insulation man will also need to take with him his oxygen, water, and food supply.

A small team of geologists of the U.S. Geological Survey has been assigned the task of preparing a geological atlas of the moon's surface, and already the first colored quadrangle geology map has appeared off the press. A number of others are in progress.

The moon orbits the earth in approximately 27½ days at a distance averaging 239,000 miles. As it orbits it keeps one face constantly toward the earth, thus completing exactly one rotation on its axis with each revolution around its orbit. We have, therefore, a photographic and telescopic knowledge of only half of the moon's surface. Actually, it is a little more than half, because the moon has apparent slight oscillations that enable us to see a little more around the edge at one time than another.

The moon's axis is tilted 1½° to the plane of its orbit, which in turn is inclined 5° to the plane of the earth's orbit. Thus at times, it is possible to see 6½° beyond the "north" pole and at other times 6½° beyond the "south" pole. The oscillation is called latitudinal libration.

As the moon travels in its elliptical orbit it appears to accelerate relative to the rotation on its axis, and thus at times we see about 8° more on one side and then later 8° more on the other side than at any one time of full moon. This is called longitudinal libration, and because of it we can view photographs of the moon stereoscopically. A stereoscopic pair of photographs is one in which the same object is photographed but from a slightly different posi-

tion but equal distance. This apparent small rotation of the moon gives the same effect that the earth is farther along at the time of one photograph than at the time of the other. In Fig. 23-4 the moon is shown to oscillate through 12°, and if photographs are taken at the limits of oscillation, it will give the effect of a stereopair taken 50,000 miles apart at a distance of 239,000 miles. With photographs having 12° or more difference of libration the minimum relief that can be discerned is 1,000 ft. For relief features less than 1,000 ft in elevation one must rely on shadow effects, and those as small as 200 ft high are clearly visible on photographs of the lunar landscape when the angle of the sun is low.

The half of the moon that has been photographed has been laid off in latitudes and longitudes, and these constitute the bound-

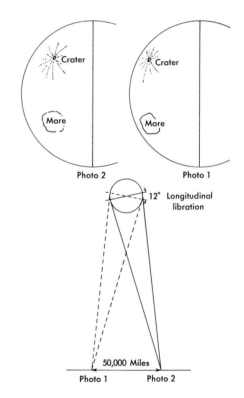

FIG. 23-4 Stereopair of photographs taken from the earth through 12° of moon libration. (After Hackman, 1961.)

aries of the geologic quadrangle maps. The first published map, the Kepler Region, covers an area that lies between 30° and 50° west longitude and 0° to 16° north latitude.

Geologists have had an experience of thirty years now in the geological interpretation of vertical aerial photographs, but at the same time they have had the advantage of being able to go into the field and to make rock identifications and see the structural relations at close hand. Thus they can interpret the strata and rock bodies shown on photographs by going from the known to the unknown, and it has been amazing how much geology can be discerned from photographs with fair reliability. Photographs have speeded up geologic mapping immensely. But now coming to the moon, everything is inference. Not until the first astronaut returns with rock samples and direct, close-up observations will we know whether our inferences are correct. It must also be remembered in interpreting lunar photographs that objects less than ½ mile across are not discernible, whereas on earth photographs we can see roadside mailboxes. Even so, it is surprising to note that on this first atlas sheet of the moon four major rock divisions are recognized and each division has two to four subdivisions. No doubt the geologists who have been skillfully discerning their way through photographs are hoping that one of them may be selected to be the scientist on the first astronaut journey to the moon. This one will then see the minutia, the reality, the relations that he has anticipated and some that he has not expected. He will have in mind a hundred things to look for, and he will perceive a great deal in one short visit.

Major Physiographic Divisions

The visible lunar surface has been divided into two major divisions, the highlands and the lowlands. See Figs. 23-5 and 23-6. The highlands constitute two-thirds of the visible surface of the moon, and their most conspicuous forms are craters. About 30,000 craters are readily distinguishable, and perhaps a million other poorly defined depressions may be craters. The largest crater has a diameter of 146 miles (Clavius), and the others range on down to those so small as to be indistinguishable on photographs. Extensive but less conspicuous are rugged relief forms that look more like the peaks and ridges of mountain systems as we think of them. These generally ring the lowlands and they present steep and imposing fronts toward the lowlands.

About one-third of the moon's visible face is lowlands. These are the dark regions and make the imaginary eyes and nose of the "man in the moon" (Fig. 23-7). The lowlands came to be called maria (seas) and in early times were thought to be oceans, but photographs plainly show that they are plains, and apparently smooth, at least from our distance. They are pock-marked by numerous craters, and wrinkled and faulted in places.

Photointerpretation

Weathering. Without an atmosphere, rock weathering by chemical decay and solution would be absent. Also erosion by running water and wind would not exist. It is believed that there is much talus due to the mechanical effects of heating and cooling and also much debris due to explosion impact of meteoroids and asteroids. Even so the topographic forms must be long-lived and a high crater rim will last in fair shape perhaps a billion years, whereas it would be subdued to almost unrecognizable form on the earth in a million years.

Craters. The many craters that you see on the photographs of the moon reproduced in this chapter are now generally believed to be impact craters. The shape of the craters is that of explosive impact as testified by ballistic experts, and the distribution is mostly a random scattering, unlike the pattern of volcanic cones on earth.

In Figs. 23-6 and 23-7 it will be noted that from a few major craters long rays extend

rial derived primarily from the craters from which they radiate.[1] The good reflection comes from a high sun position, but very poor reflection from a low sun. The ray craters are recognized as very young compared with the nonray craters, with the ray-forming material having been thrown out by the mighty impact explosion fairly recently, geologically speaking. After a while either the weathering effect of the sun's insolation dulls the reflective capacity, or the reflecting particles are covered by dust. The thin skin of fragments is probably still there but no longer visible. It has been suggested that we may be dealing with a beaded-screen effect and that drops of glass, created by fusion at impact, were thrown out, and these reflect the sun's rays

[1] Robert J. Hackman, "Photointerpretation of the Lunar Surface," *Photogrammetric Engineering*, June, 1961.

FIG. 23-5 View of half of moon with sun's rays from left. *(From Photographic Lunar Atlas, 1960.)*

FIG. 23-6 View of half of moon with sun's rays from right. *(From Photographic Lunar Atlas, 1960.)*

out and appear to mask the other features. These rays are particularly strong when photographed in direct sunlight (central part of full moon), but when the same region is photographed in inclined light (quarter moon), the rays are inconspicuous or even not visible. Compare the crater Tycho in Fig. 23-6 with that of 23-7 and 23-8. If a stereopair of photographs is studied, one showing the rays and one not, then a maximum understanding can be gained of the geology, and it has been concluded that the rays are thin layers of highly reflective mate-

FIG. 23-7 Full moon. Note emphasis of rays from craters in contrast to Figs. 23-5 and 23-6. (From Photographic Lunar Atlas, 1960.)

most profusely directly back at the sun.

It should also be pointed out that the brightness of the full moon is twelve times that of the half moon, and therefore, we must conclude that the entire surface has the property of "retrodirecting" light. The most likely condition is an open mesh or skeletal structure such that it will be in good part shadow in obliquely reflected light, but with no shadow in directly reflected light. Studies of radar echos and

heat radiation suggest that the skeletal structure is probably no more than a few inches thick.

Laboratory experiments have been carried out on the size and packing of dust particles responsible for the reflective properties of the moon. It is concluded that the upper limit of the lunar dust particles is about 60 microns and that the average diameter is about 10 microns (a micron is 1/1,000 of a millimeter). They must be

FIG. 23-8 Comparatively young Tycho Crater in central part of photograph. This is the great ray crater of Fig. 23-7 that appears like the north pole of the moon. Note the very old and large crater in upper left quadrant that has been so badly battered by subsequent impacts. It and similar old craters have flat floors, as if partially filled, whereas the fresh and young craters have cup-shaped floors. This fill is called the maria material. Tycho Crater is about 50 miles across. *(From Photographic Lunar Atlas, 1960.)*

arranged into a loose porous material with a density only 10 per cent that of rock.[2]

Craters of different ages are easy to recognize. For instance, in Fig. 23-9 a sequence of formation of five craters may be perceived, simply because one crater rim cuts or interrupts another. They are numbered from 1 (oldest) to 5 (youngest). In geological mapping of the moon three broad classes of craters have been designated:

✦ *Class I.* These are craters with conspicuous rays and are regarded as the youngest. The rims are sharp and crisp, and the pits deep.

✦ *Class II.* The crater rims are sharp and fresh, like those of Class I, but there are no radiating streaks. In fact the rays of craters

---

[2] Bruce Hapke and Hugh Van Horn, "Photometric Studies of Complex Surfaces, with Applications to the Moon," *Journal of Geophysical Research,* vol. 68, p. 4545, 1963.

of Class I overlap or lie across those of Class II.

✦ *Class III.* Crater rims and walls are battered by numerous large and small impacts, and crater bottoms are commonly filled by a new material to a dark plain similar to that of the maria. Mechanical weathering has also contributed to their dissection and reduction. See old craters of Figs. 23-8 and 23-9.

Maria. The conspicuous large dark areas of the moon, such as seen in Fig. 23-7, are the maria. They appear as vast plains, with scattered ridges rising a few hundred feet above the general surface, and are commonly interpreted as lava fields. Since we cannot discern objects much below 1 mile across, the surfaces should not necessarily be construed as like one of our desert surfaces. They could be large block fields.

It is evident that the maria material has filled depressions to produce the plains. A number of the old craters are flat-bottomed because of the maria fill. (See Plato crater, Fig. 23-10). Many young craters are superposed on the maria material and are sharp, fresh-rimmed, and deep. These craters are about equally distributed over all the maria, and hence it is concluded that the maria material is everywhere about the same age. The fill, then, becomes a moonwide datum or reference, and lunar events are logically and rather obviously dated as premaria material or postmaria material.

U.S. Ranger 7 Spacecraft. The guided spacecraft U.S. Ranger 7 impacted on the mare, Sea of Clouds, on July 31, 1964, and was remarkably successful in relaying over 4,000 television photographs to the Blackstone Receiving Station in southern California. The photographs were taken from an altitude of 1,300 miles above the moon's surface on down to impact. The first and highest photographs were about equivalent in resolution to those of a 100-inch telescope, but photographs relayed just before impact revealed craterlets as small as 3 feet in diameter. This is a resolution about 1,000 times better than that of our telescopic photographs.

It can now be said that the maria are not block fields, but are rather smooth surfaces, except for the craters, which are probably blanketed with finely or fairly finely cominuted material. Also revealed is a profusion of small craters in the mare, Sea of Clouds, not recognized on telescopic photographs. Most of the small craters are judged by experts who have studied the telephotographs to be impact craters of explosive debris (large rocks) from the major crater Copernicus which lies about 200 miles north.

According to Drs. M. A. Cook and A. G. Funk, authorities on explosives, if the impact velocity is sufficiently high, such as that of an infalling meteorite (15 km per sec), then all material whether loose dust, sand grains, or basalt will deform plastically, and a smooth crater will form. It follows that if all small craters are smooth and regular, then the nature of the maria surface material cannot be discerned if of meteorite origin. If the impact velocity is slower than that required for plastic deformation, and the material is hard rock such as basalt, then angular blocks of rock should strew the rim and surrounding area of the small craters. It is calculated that if blocks of rock are ejected from Copernicus at an angle of 45 degrees and have a projectory to travel 200 miles, that the impact velocity will be about 0.7 km per sec, which will result in shattered rock and block fragments around the crater. Such information has not yet been noted, or at least published to date, and hence it would be concluded that a layer of fine fragments exists. Mr. Shoemaker of the U.S. Geological Survey has been quoted in the newspapers as saying that he thinks there exists in the maria a layer of loose fine-grained material about 1 foot thick resting on hard rock. Dr. Cook, however, thinks that the smooth, small, cup-shaped craters indicate loose fine-grained material hundreds of feet deep.

Old Mountain Chains. The oldest relief features are rugged ridges and peaks of

FIG. 23-9 Succession of craters. Number 1 is oldest; 5 is youngest. Note maria material forming plane on large crater bottoms. Crater 1 is about 60 to 70 miles across. (From Photographic Lunar Atlas, 1960.)

apparent mountain chains. These are partly buried by the maria material and therefore older. They are older than a succession of craters that are also partly filled with maria material. Two large mountain systems nearly encircle the Mare Imbrium and the Mare Serenitatis. In places the mountain system has a linear pattern as if cut by many faults. The nature of the rocks and the origin of these old chains is certainly obscure. Figs. 23-10, 23-11, and 23-12.

Folds and Faults. The surface of the moon exhibits an intricate system of scarps and linear features interpreted as faults and flexures. Two great grabenlike depressions in Fig. 23-12 are postmountain-system and postmaria material, and the grain to the northeast in the old mountain system may be due to faulting of a very old age.

The "Alpine Valley" in the southwest corner of Fig. 23-10 is approximately 83 miles long, 3 to 6 miles wide, and in places

Autolycus · Archimedes

Aristillus

Cassini

Mare Imbrium

Plato

FIG. 23-10 Mare Imbrium and associated craters. Archimedes and Plato are filled with the maria material, but Aristillus and other craters are not. *(From Photographic Lunar Atlas, 1960.)*

small depressions in them that may be the vents. The low slopes and low reflectivity of the sun's rays from these domes suggest that they are of basaltic composition.

Example of Lunar History. Dr. Hackman[3] has selected the area of Fig. 23-10 to illustrate a typical sequence of events and possibly the highlights of lunar history:

✦ Formation of the mountain system, here called the Alps. Their origin is discussed under the heading Old Mountain Chains.

✦ Formation of the craters Plato, Cassini, and Archimedes. These are examples of premaria impact craters.

✦ Deposition of maria material, producing flat surfaces in the crater bottoms and plains across the maria.

✦ Formation of postmaria craters without rays. An example is Autolycus, which is clearly superposed on the Mare Imbrium.

✦ Formation of ray craters, such as Aristillus.

See cross section of Fig. 23-14.

10,000 ft deep. It is interpreted by U.S. Geological Survey geologists as a graben.

The maria plains are interrupted by fault scarps or monoclines that have only a few hundred feet relief. See Figs. 23-10 and 23-13. Almost all of these are not sharp fault scarps but appear to be formed by the maria deposits bending or draping over fault blocks below. There are also long sinuous anticlines in the maria material. They look like pressure ridges on lake ice and then again not much different from the monoclines or fault scarps in the maria. Some occur in belts, and this sets them apart from the fault scarps. Those in Fig. 23-13 look like compaction or drape structures over old buried crater rims.

Lava Domes. Some blisterlike hills, which have been mapped as volcanic flows and domes, are circled in Fig. 23-11. Some have

METEORITE IMPACT CRATERS ON EARTH

Paucity of Craters and Meaning

The most surprising realization is that the earth's surface has only a few scattered craters that can reliably be called meteorite impact craters. After we have studied lunar photographs and seen the great profusion of impact craters, we would expect that the earth should have had as many collisions per square unit of area as the moon, if not more. The earth and the moon are constantly sweeping meteoroids and asteroids out of space in the path of the earth's orbit with a screen the size of the moon's orbit. Each has a gravitational focusing effect on the meteoroids dependent upon each

[3] Hackman, *op. cit.*

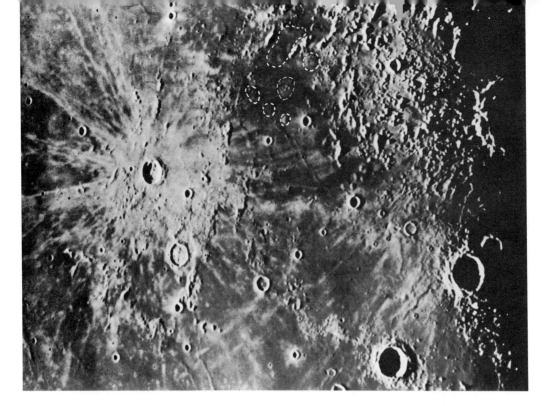

FIG. 23-11 Kepler Crater and surrounding area. The rays attest to its youthfulness. The dashed lines surround small mounds that are believed to be lava domes. *(From Photographic Lunar Atlas, 1960.)*

one's gravitational attraction. The earth might therefore get more than its share. Yet, where are the impact craters?

Of course the oceans covering three-fourths of the earth's surface swallow up a proportionately large amount of meteorites, and the atmosphere burns up and disseminates them in a rigorous manner, preventing them from striking the earth in original size and speed of approach. For instance, the largest well-studied and observed meteorite fall occurred in 1947 in Sikhote-Aline on the eastern coast of Siberia. A large meteorite entered the atmosphere at a calculated velocity of 14 to 15 km per sec, broke up, and left a field strewn with fragments and a small group of impact craters, the largest of which was 28 m in diameter. More than 30 tons of meteoritic matter was recovered, and the total mass that fell immediately to the ground is estimated to be about 100 tons. Also it is calculated that nearly 200 tons was left in a dark turbulent wake that remained in the atmosphere for several hours.

FIG. 23-12 Photograph showing old mountain system, old and young impact craters, two trenches called graben, and probably a high fault scarp.

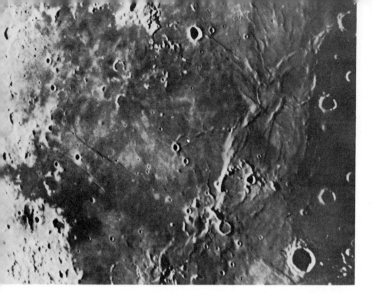

FIG. 23-13 Folds and scarps in the Mare Tranquil-litatus. *(From Photographic Lunar Atlas, 1960.)*

The initial mass is thus presumed to have weighed about 300 tons.

The atmosphere not only serves as a buffer and protector of the earth's surface to meteorite bombardment, but through the rapid weathering and erosional activities incident to the atmosphere impact craters are quickly destroyed. More important still, in obliterating impact craters, is the earth's hydrosphere. The uplands are being eroded, and the lowlands covered with outwash deposits or invaded by shallow seas where fresh sediments cover the bottom. Reference to the paleotectonic maps of Chap. 14 will show the spread of seas and sediments over the continent and thus indicate the probable succession of burials of older craters. The Cretaceous and Cenozoic deposits, for instance, must cover half of the continent of North America. Consider also that the mountainous areas have had thousands of feet of rock eroded away to supply the sediments. Certainly in these areas only meteorite impact

craters of the last 10,000 to 100,000 years (the latter part of the Quaternary) could have survived.

We should search those parts of the continent for impact craters which have not been buried lately by sediments and which have not suffered much erosion for a long time, but such regions are hard to find. The Canadian Shield has supposedly been gently emergent for the longest time and has not been, in general, deeply dissected. However, it has been heavily glaciated just yesterday, so to speak, and thus the erosional effects of the ice, on the one hand, and the comparatively recent blankets of drift on the other, diminish prospects of finding craters (Fig. 23-15). The central stable region south of the shield and south of the glacial drift, and not covered by Cretaceous and Cenozoic deposits, might be the best place to hunt. Even so, erosion here has been considerable since the Paleozoic era (200 million years) or the Mesozoic era (70 million years), and only craters where the rock was broken and disturbed down to depths of several hundred feet would show in any respect today. It turns out that this is the only region that does contain a number of circular structures that have been interpreted to be of meteorite impact origin. See Fig. 23-16.

It will be noted that most of the postulated meteorite impact craters occur in a limited region that has not been covered by Cretaceous and Cenozoic deposits, has remained low and not affected by mountain building, and hence rapid erosion, and has not been blanketed by glacial drift. Three have been found north of the drift front, but there the drift is practically absent and the bedrock crops out, or water wells have

Kepler crater   Ejecta   Maria material
Rock of old mountain system

FIG. 23-14 Generalized cross section of Kepler Crater and adjacent region. *(After Hackman, 1961.)*

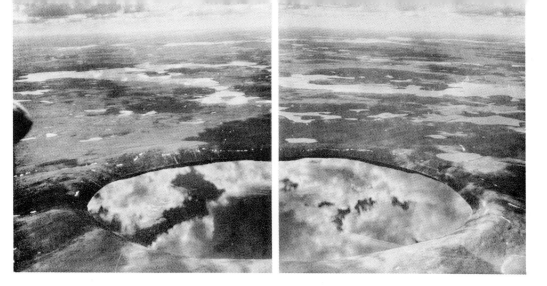

FIG. 23-15 Aerial oblique view of New Quebec Crater. It is a little over 2 miles in diameter from rim to rim (11,500 ft). *(Reproduced from Dominion Observatory, vol. 18, 1956.)*

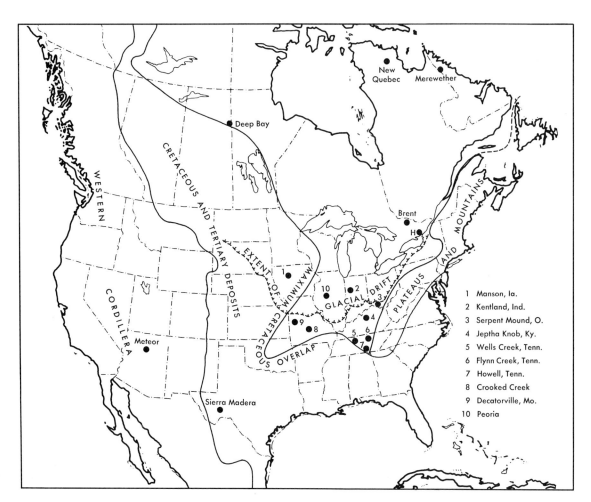

1 Manson, Ia.
2 Kentland, Ind.
3 Serpent Mound, O.
4 Jeptha Knob, Ky.
5 Wells Creek, Tenn.
6 Flynn Creek, Tenn.
7 Howell, Tenn.
8 Crooked Creek
9 Decatorville, Mo.
10 Peoria

FIG. 23-16 Probable and possible meteorite impact structures of North America.

FIG. 23-17   Geologic Map of Wells Creek Basin, Tennessee. 1, Wells limestone (Lower Ordovician); 2, Mid-Ordovician limestone; 3, Hermitage limestone (Mid-Ordovician); 4, Silurian and Devonian formations; 5, Lower Mississippian formations; 6, Warsaw limestone (Mid-Mississippian); 7, St. Louis limestone (Mid-Mississippian); 8, Alluvium. (Reproduced from Bucher, 1933.)

penetrated the irregular structure. The one in Iowa involves the Lower Cretaceous shales and hence is post-Early Cretaceous in age. A typical structure in this region is illustrated in Fig. 23-17.

A type of terrestrial impact crater that may be preserved for a long time is one that is buried immediately after formation. Suppose that the Ordovician seas were encroaching upon the Canadian Shield as they did and that, just before the seas reached a certain area, a meteorite fell in it and formed a crater. The sea advanced over the crater, and it was buried by the sediments of the sea. This is the situation, apparently, of the Brent and Holleford structures of southern Ontario. Three diamond drill holes across the side of the

Holleford structure showed a profile below the sediment fill like an impact crater and shattered Precambrian rock below.

The Deep Bay structure of northeastern Saskatchewan is 8½ miles wide, by far the widest of any yet discovered possible meteorite impact crater on earth. Drills have reportedly penetrated Cretaceous rock in this depression.

A possible filled impact crater has just recently been reported near Peoria, Illinois. It was discovered by drilling and lies buried 1,200 ft below the surface. Below this for another 1,500 ft the rock is badly broken and shattered. The shattered area is about 2½ miles in diameter. The strata, both those which bury and those which are shattered, are of Ordovician age, so that the age of the structure is definitely Ordovician, regardless of origin.

All the structures shown in Fig. 23-15 range in diameter of the badly broken central area, which may have marked the diameter of the rim of the crater, of ½ to 3 miles except the Deep Bay, which measures 8½ miles and is questionably an impact crater. Now craters of this size on the moon would be barely visible. We are not aware of any bona fide impact craters on earth of 10 to 150 miles across, but there are many on the moon. We cannot say that the earth and moon have long since swept clean from their orbital path all large asteroids, because there are some huge ray craters on the moon of comparatively young age, and there are a number of known asteroids flirting with the earth at present. Here is a real enigma. Why no large craters of meteorite origin on the earth? Do you have any good ideas? Some students of the moon believe that the material that fills the lunar maria is very old and dates back to times when the earth's crust first took form. On this basis the rate of impact of asteroids on the moon may not be different than that on the earth.

FIG. 23-18 Aerial view of Meteor Crater, Arizona. *(Courtesy of Dorsey Hager.)*

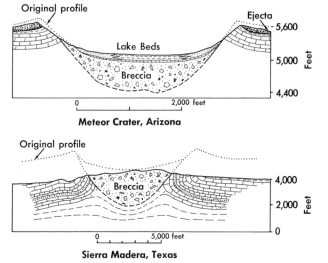

FIG. 23-19 Sections of Meteor Crater and Sierra Madera, showing greater erosion and age of the Sierra Madera. (After Shoemaker, 1961.)

Any effect of an impact on earth as old as Precambrian time is not likely to survive to the present.

Meteor Crater of Arizona (Fig. 23-18) is interpreted as an impact crater by most students and occurs in the nearly flat-lying Permian limestone and sandstone. It is about ¾ mile in diameter and is interpreted as shown in Fig. 23-19. A circular structure known as the Sierra Madera in west Texas is supposedly a structure like Meteor Crater, but much older, in which erosion has reduced the surrounding area considerably, leaving the central broken rock (breccia) in relief. These are two regions of erosion and comparatively flat-lying sedimentary rocks, but of sufficiently fast erosion so that impact craters of the size found would not endure very long, perhaps not over 2 or 3 million years. Certainly the craters could not date back far into the Tertiary. It has been estimated that Meteor Crater is postglacial and only a few thousand years old.

Mechanics of Impact

The mechanics of impact and crater formation as visualized at Meteor Crater are shown in Fig. 23-20. The quick sequence of events recognized from the study of nuclear explosion craters and from compressibility theory, is as follows: first, penetration with compression of target rocks and meteorite by shock; second, hydrodynamic flow of the compressed material; third, dispersal of the meteoric material in the flowing mass; fourth, the shock wave is followed by a rarefaction wave, and broken and fused rock is exploded outward. Beds are turned up to form a rim.

The depth of penetration and the size of the crater are primarily functions of the velocity and size of the meteorite at impact and the densities and equations of the state of the meteorite and target material. As illustrated, the crater is much larger than the meteorite.

Shatter Cones and Coesite

In support of the contention that a number of the small circular structures in North America are of meteorite impact origin, now eroded to various degrees, is the discovery of shatter cones in the limestones and sandstones of the rim rock. These are generally thumb-sized shear cones due to shock energy. Also found scattered in the vicinity of some of the

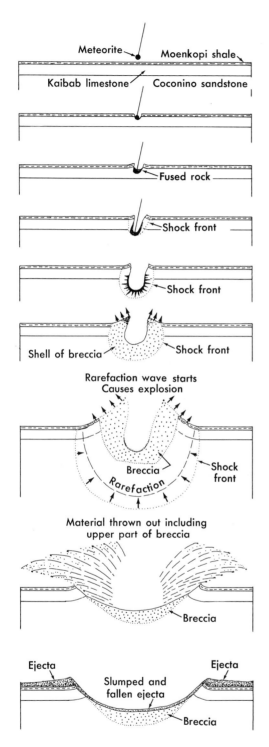

FIG. 23-20 Postulated sequence of events in formation of Meteor Crater, Arizona. *(After Shoemaker, 1960.)*

structures is the high-density silica mineral called coesite, which is believed due to high pressure on quartz incident to impact.

CORRELATION OF TERRESTRIAL AND LUNAR HISTORIES

It would appear that the fill material of the lunar maria is the most striking datum there for correlation purposes, because the profuse craters are in two great divisions, older than the maria and younger. If the age of the fill were known, then the density of different-sized craters and the frequency of fall of different-sized meteoroids and asteroids could be determined.

If the distribution pattern and density, and also frequency of fall, of the meteoroids and asteroids on earth could also be determined, then conceivably, the two histories could be compared. Needless to say, any calculations are made with bold assumptions, and especially for the earth, on very inadequate data. For information on attempts, see Shoemaker et al.,[4] but for purposes of this book it will simply be said that the subject is technical and that little progress of value has been made to date.

IN RESPECT TO THE DISSIDENTS

A dissident is one who disagrees, and there are many geologists who disagree with the whole theory of impact craters, both on the moon and the earth. They contend that the craters are volcanic and that the broken circular structures here are due to concealed volcanic activity and, for a few, perhaps, to salt plug intrusion and collapse. Their arguments are substantial, but in the wake of the space age their shouts are largely overheard. Let's wait until the first lunar astronaut returns.

[4] Eugene M. Shoemaker, "Interplanetary Correlation of Geologic Time," Open File Report, U.S. Geological Survey, 1961.

FIG. 23-21 Drawings of tektites. Upper row represents front, side, and back views of a button type of tektite from Australia. Lower two are types found on the Island of Billiton between Sumatra and Borneo. All show ablation markings. *(After O'Keefe, Scientific American, 1964.)*

METEORITES—MATTER FROM SPACE

Significance

Meteorites are the sole representatives so far available of extramundane material. They are our most important source of information of interplanetary and interstellar masses. Most probably many meteorites that have been swept up by the earth were orbiting within the solar system and may be regarded as part of it. Others may have come from without and by chance passed through the solar system. So the possibility is evident that meteorites represent the materials of the solar system and also those from the much more remote spaces of the universe.

Kinds of Meteorites

Three classes of meteorites are recognized: the iron ones or *siderites*, the stony ones or *aerolites*, and the mixtures of stony minerals and iron called *siderolites*. The meteorites that we commonly see in museums are of metallic iron, with the iron containing considerable nickel. There are two subdivisions of iron meteorites, namely,

those carrying 5 to 6 per cent nickel and those carrying 10 to 20 per cent. On polished surfaces a coarsely crystalline texture will generally be seen with lamellar bands arranged according to the planes of an octahedron. Different iron-nickel minerals separate out in the solid state as the temperature drops, to produce the laminae.

The stony meteorites are in two subgroups, namely, the *chondrites* and the *achondrites. Chondrules,* which make up the mass of the chondrites, are aggregates of rounded grains containing olivine and pyroxene. These minerals are magnesium and iron silicates. The achondrites are made up of plagioclase and pyroxene and have more or less calcium besides iron, magnesium, and silica.

The stony-iron meteorites are transitional from pure irons to pure stones.

The minerals of the stony meteorites are many and most are common in the rocks of the earth's crust,[5] but those of the irons are not found here on the earth's surface. It is believed that the irons represent the material of the core of the earth, that the

[5] Paul Ramdohr, "Opaque Minerals in Stony Meteorites," *Journal of Geophysical Research,* vol. 68, p. 2011, 1963.

stony-irons represent the transitional layer from the core to the mantle, and that the stony represent possibly the mantle, but in a low pressure form.

Unusual Minerals

In addition to three singular iron-nickel minerals there is a new carbide mineral, a new nitride, a new phosphide, three new sulfides, and a new chloride. Almost all of these are rare in the meteorites. The metal germanium is more abundant in the irons than would be expected from crustal minerals and may indicate that the core has considerable of this element.

Of recent interest have been reports of minute amounts of carbon and hydrogen compounds in the meteorites in such form that they are presumed to have come from life somewhere in the distant past and distant space. It is all very conjectural, but we seem to want to know or learn that there is life elsewhere, and so scientists sometime stretch a bit to recognize the evidence. Small diamond crystals have also been identified.

Rate of Fall

A recent study of meteorite recovery in the eastern United States, Europe, Japan, and northern India by Millard[6] resulted in the conclusion that about fifteen falls occur per year in each million square kilometers of earth surface.

TEKTITES—DEBRIS FROM THE MOON?

What They Are

Tektites are small black glassy stones, until recently objects of curiosity to a few, but now of considerable interest to many because they may have come from the moon and bear direct information of moon material. Drawings of three specimens are collected in Fig. 23-21. The glass is chemically similar to somewhat silicic volcanic glasses and, if crystalline, would have a

[6] Hugh T. Millard, Jr., "Rate of Arrival of Meteorites at the Surface of the Earth," *Journal of Geophysical Research,* vol. 68, p. 4297, 1963.

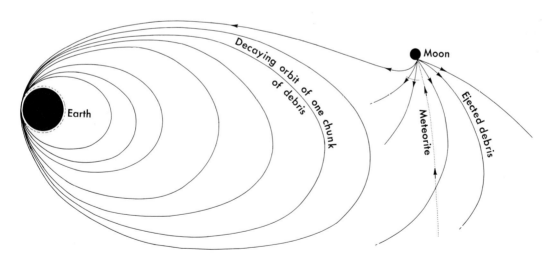

FIG. 23-22 Lunar origin of tektites. Meteorite strikes the moon, debris is ejected in all directions greater than 45°; some goes into orbit about the sun, some around the earth. Here, one chunk goes into a decaying orbit about the earth because it passes through the upper atmosphere on each revolution.

density of about 2.8. This composition renders them similar to the earth's continental granitic crustal layer, and thus, by an early theory, they have been assumed to be solidified droplets of glass thrown out from meteorite impact craters on the earth. But there are a number of reasons for believing they came from the moon, to be regarded as debris exploded from impact craters there and hurled upward with velocities sufficient to escape the lunar gravitational field.

They appear to occur in considerable numbers in a few places. Many have been found in Australia and Tasmania, in Java, Borneo, the Philippines, and in Indochina. This large region may all be one tektite province in the sense that they fell as a shower at one time. Another province is in southern Ontario and the Great Lakes region in general. A few other localities around the world have yielded the small objects.

Theories of Origin

Evidence that tektites are related to meteorites, those which strike either the earth or the moon, and are some sort of impact debris comes from a unique mineral content. Tiny spherules found in some of the tektites are made up of kamacite, schreibersite, and toilite, nickel-bearing minerals known only in meteorites. Complementary to this meteorite relationship is the finding that the tektites do not contain the radioactive isotope aluminum-26, which meteorites do contain. Since Al^{26} results from bombardment by cosmic rays, it is reasoned that the tektites either are terrestrial in origin or have come only a short distance in a short time through space, such as a journey from the moon.

Ablation Experiments

Evidence pointing to a trip through space comes from *ablation* features of certain tektites. These features are circular or spiral groves and marginal folds, as if the forward surface of the tektites had been slightly melted and the melted material moved to the edges to form a lip. The resultant shape is like a button (Fig. 23-21). The interesting button tektites of Australia have been duplicated by passing hot gasses at high velocities over small glass objects in wind tunnels. The idea is thus proposed that the tektites have passed into the earth's atmosphere at velocities above 7 km per sec, according to the experiments, and have thus been ablated as noted.

These experiments were made by Dean R. Chapman and are recounted by John A. O'Keefe, who then proceeds to analyze the results of meteoroid impacts on the moon and the projectories and paths of the exploded debris (Fig. 23-22). Debris is ejected in all directions. Most of it goes into orbit around the sun, but a small amount may be captured by the earth and goes into elliptical orbit around the earth. The elliptical orbit decays almost to a circle as a result of slowing during repeated passages through the earth's atmosphere. The larger fragments break up into small tektite sizes, become ablated, and fall to the earth as showers, sweeping across considerable territory.

Moon Materials

If the tektites originate in the moon they indicate a fairly silicic crust to the moon and suggest, according to O'Keefe, that the moon is differentiated into a crust and mantle and that it is either a chunk of the primordial earth or a small brother formed at the same time and of the same materials.[7] This postulate is, of course, contrary to another idea that the moon is a captured errant celestial body, as recounted on following pages.

---

[7] John A. O'Keefe, "Tektites and Impact Fragments from the Moon," *Scientific American*, February, 1964, pp. 52-57.

FIG. 23-23 Lagoon Nebula in Sagittarius, a nebula of gas and dust something like one from which the solar system is presumed to have evolved. (*Courtesy of Mount Wilson and Palomar Observatories.*)

ORIGIN OF THE SOLAR SYSTEM

Introduction

A number of remarkable conditions hold in the solar or planetary system that have piqued the curiosity of astronomers and mathematicians for the past 200 years. Consequently several hypotheses for the origin have been proposed, each of which has risen to popularity and then fallen, owing to patent impossibilities that later students have exposed. These hypotheses will be of

Clues to Origin

Any theory of origin should account for the following observed astronomic conditions:

✦ The spacing of the orbits of the planets is nearly regular and follows a geometric progression known as Bode's rule.

✦ The orbits of the planets lie nearly in one plane.

✦ The orbits are nearly circular and all planets travel in the same direction.

Table 23–2

CHARACTERISTIC PARAMETERS OF THE MOON AND SOME PLANETS

Planet	Radius (Earth = 1)	Mean density	Mean density at zero pressure	Percentage iron-nickel phase
Moon	0.2728	3.34	3.31	0
Mercury	0.38	5.46	5.4	72
Mercury	0.403	4.58	4.5	50
Venus	0.961	5.06	4.4(?)	45
Earth	1	5.515	4.4	45
Mars	0.520	4.24	4.02	30
Mars	0.523	4.17	3.95	27

SOURCE: Harold C. Urey, "The Origin of the Earth," *Scientific American*, October, 1952. The two values of Mercury and Mars are the results of computation of different authorities.

interest to anyone with more than a cultural interest, but for the present purposes only the current, most acceptable thoughts will be reviewed. Observed relations considered in the light of known physical laws point to an origin of the sun and planets from a cloud of gas and dust, such as represented by the Lagoon Nebula of Sagittarius in Fig. 23-23.

What are the physical relations and laws that hold and should be noted and explained in any theory of origin? They are listed below.

✦ Over 99 per cent of the mass of the solar system is in the sun, yet it has only 2 per cent of the angular momentum. The angular momentum cannot be created or destroyed, and hence this momentum must have been present from an early beginning. Its distribution must have resulted from some circumstances during the origin of the system.

✦ The farther each planet is from the sun, the slower it travels.

✦ The outer planets are light; the inner ones are heavy.

✦ The satellites of the inner planets orbit in the same direction as the planets.

✦ Most of the moons of the outer planets, especially those of Jupiter and Saturn, also orbit in "regular" directions, but some outer ones travel in the reverse direction and have orbits appreciably inclined to the ecliptic. These are certainly exceptional.

✦ The sun rotates in the same direction as the orbital motions of the planets and its axis is only slightly inclined to the average plane of the orbits. Thus we see a system in regular motion—rotations and orbits are generally in the same direction.

✦ Orbits of comets are highly eccentric and inclined at all angles to the ecliptic.

Additional evidence must also be considered. Table 23-2 shows the calculated densities of the inner planets and the earth's moon, the mean densities if no pressure existed, as it does at great depth, and then the percentage of the iron-nickel phase, the other phase being the silicates. The earth has an iron-nickel core, and it is believed that Venus has such a structure. Mercury, Mars, and the moon have lower densities and lower internal pressures. Although an appreciable amount of the iron-nickel phase exists in Mercury and Mars, it is not believed that these planets have a core of iron and nickel. The moon consists almost entirely of the silicate phase.

Now, we have seen that the infalling meteorites consist of two phases, iron-nickel and silicate, and if this is the basic material from which the planets were formed, then the fractions have been partially separated, and one has been lost in variable amounts. An acceptable model of the solar system must take this into account. The high amount of nickel and iron in Mars without having separated into a core suggests that the planet was never molten. Also it appears that the earth was not molten during its late stages of formation because certain elements that are volatile at the melting temperatures of the silicates are not concentrated on the earth's surface.

These are reasons proposed by Urey[8] in favoring low average temperatures during the formation of the inner planets.

Beginning Stages of the Solar System

The formulation of modern concepts of the origin of the solar system began with von Weizsäcke of Germany. These were modified by others, particularly G. P. Kuiper of the United States, and the postulate is commonly referred to as the Weizsäcker-Kuiper hypothesis. It would start with a "globule" or dense region in our galaxy, the Milky Way, such as the Lagoon Nebula in Sagittarius (Fig. 23-23). It was composed presumably of gas and dust, the so-called cosmic material. The nebula was about 1 light-year in diameter and is assumed to have had a very slow rotation.

The cosmic globule began to shrink under its own gravitation, and as it shrank, its rotational speed increased. About 90 per cent of the material condensed eventually to become the early sun, and the other 10 per cent remained outside, where rotation caused it to flatten and spread out into a disk. In simple orbital motion the inner part of this disk of gas and dust particles would move faster than that of the outer, and hence, it is conceived that great turbulent eddies resulted. The moving of one part past another was a source of friction that slowed down the inner rotating mass somewhat. The eddies were the sites of large condensations of smaller clouds. Within them substantial bodies of asteroidal and perhaps even of lunar dimensions together with their gaseous envelopes existed. These drew together through mutual gravitational attraction to form the "protoplanets." The protoplanets were many times larger and more massive than the present planets. The central sun had not yet begun to shine.

The large protoplanets were subject to the tidal action of the sun and like the

[8] Harold C. Urey, "The Origin of the Earth," *Scientific American*, October, 1952.

moon-earth relation kept a constant face toward the sun. Gradually the heavier materials of each protoplanet settled to a central denser nucleus, leaving a disk of dust and gas around it. In this disk the satellites evolved. As the shrinkage occurred, rotation speeded up, and thus the planets acquired variable rotational velocities faster than the original. The earth and its moon are conceived to have evolved from two nuclei in the original protoplanet and developed so to speak as a double planet.

The tidal action of the sun determined the spacing of the protoplanets, according to Bode's law, and the temperatures at this stage are believed to have been low.[9]

Later Stages

Eventually the compression of the sun under its own gravitation resulted in a heat build-up until it began to shine. Radiation pressure and streams of particles ejected from the sun swept away much of the light gases surrounding the inner protoplanets. The massive outer protoplanets were able to hold large amounts of hydrogen, helium, methane, and ammonia, while the inner planets lost practically all but the heavy elements. Hence the inner planets are rocky and metallic, whereas the outer planets are largely gaseous. The earth is judged to contain only one-thousandth of its original protoplanet material and Jupiter about one-tenth. Urey concludes that several factors at this stage contributed to bring about high temperatures for a while. These were adiabatic compression of the gases, a temporary high temperature of the sun, and collisons of the solid objects. Consequently much material was volatilized and selectively lost.

As the material of the earth became more compact under its own gravitation, its interior heated up, owing to compression and supposedly a greater abundance of potassium-40 and uranium-235 than now

[9] *Ibid.*

exist. These radioactive elements were great sources of heat, and the interior of the earth melted to such an extent that the separation of the metallic core and the silicate mantle occurred.

After the separation of core and mantle the earth cooled, with the mantle solidifying from bottom upward, according to Urey. This stage is believed to have occurred about 4.5 billion years ago. The radioactive elements were concentrated in the uppermost layer as this process took place and perhaps caused the outer layer to be remelted. The condition may have resulted in an early differentiation of lighter granitic material from the heavier silicates and the formations of the original continents. Since the oldest rocks yet found in the crust are about 3 billion years old, we might assume that this was the time of the last molten crust and the beginning of evolution of the continents and ocean basins.

Evolution of the Earth-Moon System

It is well established that the rate of rotation of the earth on its axis is gradually slowing and that this is due to lunar tidal friction. The amount of lengthening of the day is calculated to be 1.8 msec per century. To give you an idea of what this means, we can calculate back 2,000 years and find that the day started about 2 hr earlier then than now. But another effect is significant also. The earth rotates and the moon orbits in the same direction. See Fig. 23-24. The earth's rotation drags the high tides east of the position directly opposite the moon, the sublunar point A, to the position B. The force due to the nearer high tide is greater than the force of the more distant low tide, so that the net torque is such as to accelerate the moon. Thus the energy lost by the earth in loosing rate of rotation is imparted to the moon. An increase in angular momentum of the moon means that its orbit will increase in size (the moon will get further away from the

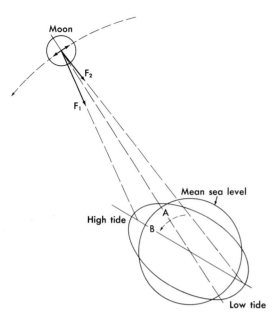

FIG. 23-24 Acceleration of the moon. The earth rotates and the moon orbits in the same direction, west to east. The earth's rotation drags the high tide east of the sun's lunar point A to B. The force F_1, due to the high tide is larger than the force F_2 due to the low tide, so the net torque is such as to accelerate the moon.

earth), and also it will take the moon longer to orbit around the earth. The increased circumference of the orbit more than compensates for the higher angular momentum. Now, as is thought, the slowing of the earth's rotation and the slowing of the moon's orbiting will continue, and the two rates will approach each other until they are equal, and at this time they will both have a period of 55 present days. This will be about 50 billion years hence. At this time the tides will be stationary and no tidal friction will exist. The moon-earth relation will thus have reached a stable condition.

But now, if we calculate backward to see what the lunar orbit and terrestrial day looked like several billion years ago, some rather exciting conclusions are reached. Both the earth's rotation and the moon's orbital velocity increase, with the moon

ultimately catching up with the earth to produce a condition again of stationary tides. But at this time the moon was only at a distance of a few earth radii from the earth and the resultant tide was very great. In fact the great lunar tide would have resonated with the solar tide, and according to George Darwin, the British astronomer and son of Charles Darwin, the effect was to pluck out a chunk of the earth's outer layer and pull it into orbit with the moon. The scar, supposedly, is the Pacific Ocean. This so-called *resonance theory* is not widely held today, for several mathematical reasons, but there seems little doubt that the moon was once precariously close to the earth.

Recently a teacher in a girls' school in Hanover, Germany, Dr. Horst Gerstenkorn, published a paper in which he computed the history of the moon-earth relationship backward to the near-earth position, but instead of a pulling of a mass of the earth away in a tidal bulge, he postulated that, when the moon reached the closest to the earth, which was 2.89 earth radii, momentum was transferred from the moon to the earth, and the moon began to fall away from the earth in larger orbits. This occurred about 1.4 billion years ago.

Continuing the calculations backward, Gerstenkorn concluded that under the reversed torque the moon not only moved farther away, but the inclination increased until a polar orbit was achieved. In other words the moon moved around the earth in a polar orbit instead of the near-equatorial orbit. This happened at a distance of 4.7 earth radii. Further calculations involving this eccentricity carried the moon into a near-parabolic orbit, and thus he concluded that the moon was *captured* by the earth.

The prominent Swedish astronomer H. Alfrén, took up Gerstenkorn's calculations and concluded that at the moon's closest approach it was the moon that was disrupted, not the earth, and that much of it rained down upon the earth to form the outer mantle and crust. If the moon were twice as big before it was torn assunder, then an outer shell of the earth would have been built up 50 km thick.

Another point of the Gerstenkorn theory is that the orbit of the moon was retrograde before the polar orbit was achieved, and this corresponds to the outer moons of Jupiter and Saturn and thus suggests that they also are captured moons but have not yet been drawn in as far as the earth's moon.

Suggested Aids

Readings

Barnes, Virgil E.: "Tektites," *Scientific American,* November, 1961.

Beals, C. S., et al.: "Search for Fossil-Meteorite Craters," *Contributions of the Dominion Observatory,* vol. 4, no. 4, 1960.

Beiser, A.: *Our Earth,* E. P. Dutton & Co., Inc., New York, 1959.

Brown, Harrison: "The Age of the Solar System," *Scientific American,* April, 1957.

Field, George B.: "The Origin of the Moon," *American Scientist,* vol. 51, p. 349, 1963.

Hackman, Robert J.: "Photointerpretation of the Lunar Surface," *Photogrammetric Engineering,* June, 1961.

Hapke, Bruce, and Hugh Van Horn: "Photometric Studies of Complex Surfaces, with Applications to the Moon," *Journal of Geophysical Research,* vol. 68, p. 4545, 1963.

Heller, R. L. (ed.): *Geology and Earth Sciences Sourcebook,* Holt, Rinehart and Winston, Inc., New York, 1962.

Juiper, G. P. (ed.): *Orthographic Atlas of the Moon,* University of Chicago Press, Chicago, 1960.

————: *Photographic Lunar Atlas,* University of Chicago Press, Chicago, 1960.

Millard, Hugh T., Jr.: "Rate of Arrival of Meteorites at the Surface of the Earth," *Journal of Geophysical Research,* vol. 68, p. 4297, 1963.

Millman, Peter M.: "Profile Study of the New Quebec Crater," *Publications of the Dominion Observatory,* vol. 18, no. 4, 1956.

Ramdohr, Paul: "Opaque Minerals in Stony Meteorites," *Journal of Geophysical Research,* vol. 68, p. 2011, 1963.

Shoemaker, Eugene M.: *"Interplanetary Correlation of Geologic Time,"* Open file Report, U. S. Geologist Survey, 1961.

————: *Penetration Mechanics of High Velocity Meteorites,* International Geologic Congress, Session XXI, Norden, 1961. Part 18, pp. 418-434.

Urey, Harold C.: "The Origin of the Earth," *Scientific American,* October, 1952.

White, J. F. (ed.): *Study of the Earth,* Prentice-Hall, Inc., Englewood Cliffs, N.J., 1962.

Movie

The Solar Family, Encyclopaedia Britannica.

NEED FOR OCEANOGRAPHIC STUDY

The oceans cover 71 per cent of the earth's crust. If viewed in terms of the Northern Hemisphere the water area is 51 per cent of the total, and in terms of the Southern Hemisphere it is 90.5 per cent. The oceans serve as a tremendous heat exchanger and air conditioner. Without them the temperature changes would be intolerable to almost all forms of life. They equalize and regulate the temperatures on the continents. All weather stems from the oceans. Their surface waters teem with life that has been a major food supply to mankind, and it is believed that, as population rises, this food supply will become of even greater importance. Also, plant life may be cultured and harvested as a source of energy.

The extensive oceans set the earth apart from all other planets of the solar system, because it is doubtful that the others have any permanent water bodies at all on their surfaces.

Geology of the
Ocean Floor

DIVISIONS OF OCEANOGRAPHIC STUDY

Oceanography is an immense study, for it includes in the broadest sense the chemistry of the ocean waters, the variations in temperature, the circulation of the waters both at the surface and in depth, the tides, the waves, the plant and animal populations and their relation to the physical and chemical environments, the hydrologic cycle and all weather generated at sea, and the geology of the shore lines, continental shelves, and ocean basins. It is only this latter aspect that can be reviewed here.

KINDS OF GEOLOGIC RESEARCH

Oceanographic research from the geologic point of view was sporadic and of little consequence until 1923. A few soundings by wire line had been made in the several oceans, and a few samples had been dredged from the deep bottom sediments.

The perfection of the bathometer or continuous depth sounder in the years 1923 to 1930 started a surge in oceanographic research that is at its peak today. Amazing detail of the topography is recorded in all depths of water, and the profiles are accurately positioned great distances from land by means of radio devices. Topographic features undreamed of have been discovered by the thousands, and researchers seeking to explore them soon perfected a number of new and remarkable instruments for the purpose. Core barrels were built that procure an undisturbed core of the deep-sea sediments, 75 ft long under favorable circumstances, and this in places is a record of the entire Pleistocene epoch. Artificially excited compression waves in the water by dynamite explosions penetrate into the bottom sediments and even into deeper crustal layers. They are reflected and refracted and return to the surface to be recorded for study. The difference between ocean crust and continental crust, recited in previous chapters, has been largely determined by this method and the layering of the sediments on the oceanic crust recorded. Gravity-recording meters for use at sea were perfected, and some unexpected large anomalies in the earth's gravity field over the oceans were un-

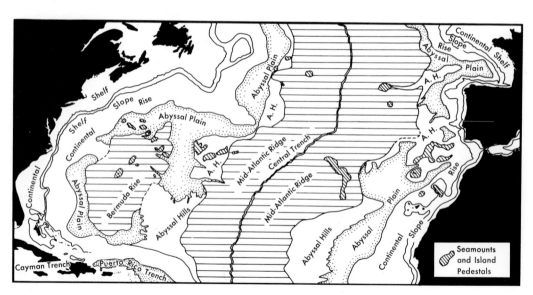

FIG. 24-1 Physiographic provinces of the North Atlantic Ocean. *(After Heezen et al., 1959.)*

covered. They are now fairly well understood, but only after seismic data were related to them.

Magnetometers have been trailed behind ships over hundreds of thousands of miles, and the results contoured to produce some surprising patterns in the earth's magnetic field. What do they mean? In places, most surely, they indicate great fault zones, with hundreds of miles of horizontal displacement.

The rate of heat flow or loss from the interior may now be measured by lowering and sinking temperature-measuring instruments into the bottom muds. We have thus learned that there are zones on the ocean floors where more heat is escaping from

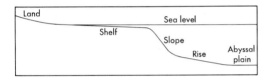

FIG. 24-2 Common divisions of the continental shelf. Slopes exaggerated.

the interior than others, and these zones are now being related to seismic, gravimetric, magnetic, and volcanic data for an explanation. The major inquiries pry into such problems as, Why do ocean basins and continents exist? Have the continents really shifted about? What causes the great belt of earthquakes, volcanoes, and crustal deformation around the Pacific Ocean? In what ways and why is the Atlantic basin different from the Pacific?

MAJOR GEOMORPHIC DIVISIONS

Three extensive geomorphic divisions of the ocean floors are becoming recognized, namely, the continental shelves, the ocean-basin floors or abyssal plains, and the mid-oceanic ridges. These divisions are particularly clear in the Atlantic, where each

accounts for about one-third of the area. See Fig. 24-1. Projecting upward from each are the conspicuous seamounts, some of which rise even to the surface and appear as islands. The seamounts are numerous and widespread throughout all the oceans. The floors of mediterranean seas and those around island arcs are partly exceptional and will need special attention.

CONTINENTAL SHELVES

Divisions

The typical form of a continental shelf is shown in Fig. 24-2. It has a gently sloping upper "tread", known as the *shelf* proper, the steep slope down into deep water, the *continental slope*, and the gentle slope at the foot, the *continental rise*, that leads to the *abyssal plain*. There are many variations in relative width, slope, and depth of these divisions, but it is common for the shelves to grade out to a depth of about 100 fathoms (600 ft) and then break into the steep slope, even though some shelves are several hundred miles broad and others are only a few miles. Almost all atlas maps of the oceans and continents show the varying width of the shelves plainly.

The shelf and slope divisions are fairly uniform and relatively smooth-surfaced, but the rise is likely to be irregular and studded with seamounts.

Constitution

The continental shelves are continuous with, and part of, the emerged coastal plain, and the present position of the shore line is simply a transient or ephemeral one. During the past ice age, the sea level fluctuated up and down about 400 ft, and the shore line moved in and out in places hundreds of miles (Fig. 24-2).

Wells drilled for water and oil along the Atlantic Coastal Plain permit tracing the base of the coastal plain sediments out to the shore line, and then seismic traverses reveal the continuation of the deposits under the shelf, slope, and rise to the deep sea floor. A typical cross section would appear as in Fig. 24-3. Now this is a deposit of sediment that has been built both outward (seaward) and upward and is essentially a great delta deposit like that

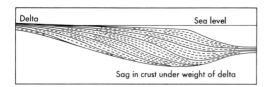

FIG. 24-3 Delta type of continental shelf.

of the Mississippi River. You will see that, as far as the old buried floor is concerned, it appears that a downwarp or trench has been filled. This trench, however, is probably due to sagging of the crust under the weight of the sediment load and was not there at the beginning. The phenomenon is the same as we dealt with in the ice caps; their weight depressed the crust, and since melting, the crust has adjusted upward, seeking its former position. If such a response to loading had not occurred and the great mass of delta sediments were simply supported by a very strong crust, then the pull of gravity over the delta deposit would have been increased. Since the gravitational field is normal there, we conclude that the crust has adjusted downward in response to the sediment load.

Along the Atlantic shelf slope from Cape Hatteras to Cape May, minor benches and slopes have been followed lengthwise and interpreted to mean that formations composing the shelf extend out to the shelf front. See Fig. 24-4. Cores and dredgings substantiate the conclusion that the beds continue nearly horizontal to the shelf slope. This then is another type of continental shelf and by some oceanographers is believed to be a common occurrence

around the world. Offhand, it might be concluded that it is one that has been built only upward and not outward. If so, however, the front or shelf slope is hard to account for. It may have been swept clean of sediments or even eroded while sedimentation continued on top, or it may be a great fault scarp. If a fault scarp, then faulting must have occurred during or after the Tertiary, because Tertiary sediments build the upper part of the shelf. Other evidence does not support the idea of such late geologic faulting in most places, so that such a continental shelf is not obviously explainable. Detailed contouring of the shelf south of New York reveals many valleylike features running down the slope, as if submarine erosion were very active here. See Fig. 24-7.

Still other types of shelves may be erosional platforms or complex deformational, erosional, and depositional features. See the remarkable electrosonic profiles of Fig. 24-5.

Certain shelves have unusually steep slopes, which are known to be due to reef building (Fig. 24-6). The periphery of a modern coral reef is composed of a buttress of limestone built by alga that resists the onslaught of the waves. It protects the loose or less resistant material landward. The reef may build an almost vertical cliff facing the ocean. Such is the Great Barrier Reef of Australia. The platform of the Bahama Islands is a continuation of the

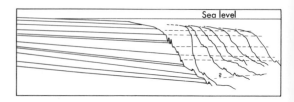

FIG. 24-4 Continental shelf built by deposition on shelf top, or by erosion on slope. Typical of the Atlantic shelf between Cape Hatteras and Cape May. Benches along slope reflect similar beds.

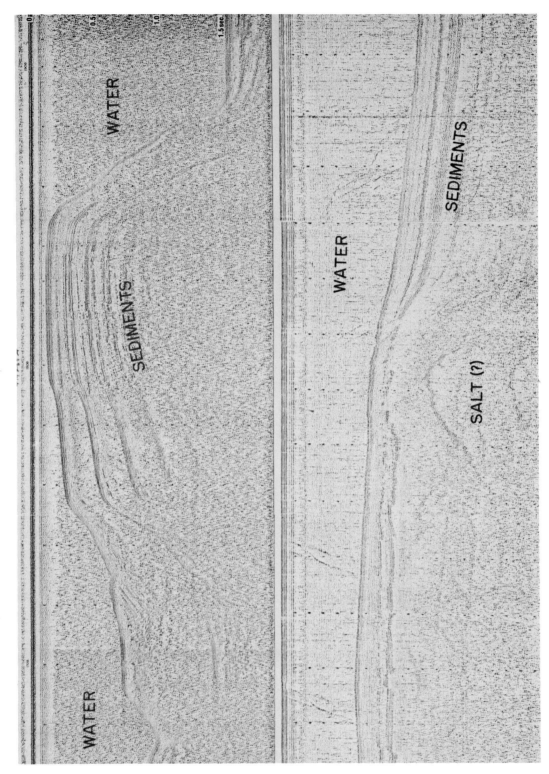

FIG. 24-5 Upper, electro-sonic record off the southeast end of Santa Catalina Island, California, showing eroded edges of beds at bottom of water on left, general folding of beds, and later sediments in basin on right (1 sec indicates a depth of about 2,400 ft). Lower, portion of continental shelf off Corpus Christi, showing probably a salt intrusion and small-scale attendant faulting of the sedimentary layers. *(Courtesy of Raflex Exploration Company.)*

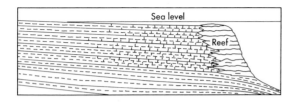

FIG. 24-6 Continental shelf due to reef build-up.

Atlantic Coastal Plain but is now a region of almost pure carbonate deposition. On the Atlantic side it slopes steeply into great depths, and the steep slopes appear to be held up by reef limestone. A well drilled on Andros Island penetrated carbonate sediments to a depth of over 12,000 ft, which suggests that the region has been subsiding slowly since the Early Cretaceous (oldest sediments penetrated) and that carbonate sediments have been deposited at the rate of subsidence, keeping the region at sea level. Thus a steep continental slope over 12,000 ft in height could have been built.

Observations about Origin

The several pulses or stages of the Pleistocene have been accompanied by an equal number of rises and falls of sea level each on the order of 400 ft, and this has produced a seesaw battle between erosion and deposition, but along the Atlantic margin deposition and permanent accumulation has generally won out as an upbuilding process, but erosion appears to be active on the slope. The Pacific Coast of California, Oregon, and Washington, however, is a belt of active crustal deformation and is largely one of surf-cut benches. The postglacial rise of sea level has resulted in a recent drowning of these wave-eroded and narrow shelves.

The average relief of continental slopes above the sea floor is 12,000 ft. Along almost half of the continental shelf slopes of the world are deep trenches, and in such places the slope descends to as much as

30,000 ft below sea level. The trenches will be described in later paragraphs. The grade of the shelf slope to a depth of 1 mile averages 4°17', and somewhat less at greater depths. The mountain fronts of the Sierra Nevada, Wasatch Range, and Teton Range of late Cenozoic age in our western Cordillera average greater than this.

Continental slopes are remarkably straight, measured in hundreds and, in places, even in thousands of miles. Protruding bulges are rare. If one presumes that the shelves are due to a series of coalescing deltas, then the almost lack of bulges argues against this premise. The Mississippi delta is a form unlike the normal continental shelf and slope, because it has an average slope of only 1°21' for the first 6,000 ft. The shelf edge of the delta along the Gulf of Mexico could be a drowned delta related to a 300-ft rise in sea level in Recent time.

Submarine Canyons and Fans

The shelves are dissected by many trenches or valleys that are called submarine canyons. They are of two classes, namely, those which furrow the shelf slope and those which cut the shelf and extend in places almost to the present shore. These latter are the typical, deep, submarine canyons, and their origin has been a subject of much controversy. See Fig. 24-7. In this figure the Hudson submarine canyon is clearly related to the Hudson River and, at least down to a depth of 300 ft, may have been partially eroded while the shelf was emergent during the last glacial stage. A submarine canyon like the Monterey, which extends seaward from Monterey Bay on the California coast, does not have a large complementary river adjacent on land (Fig. 24-8).

The large submarine canyons have continuous downhill longitudinal profiles, V-shaped transverse profiles, and tributaries much like subaerial stream valleys. It is,

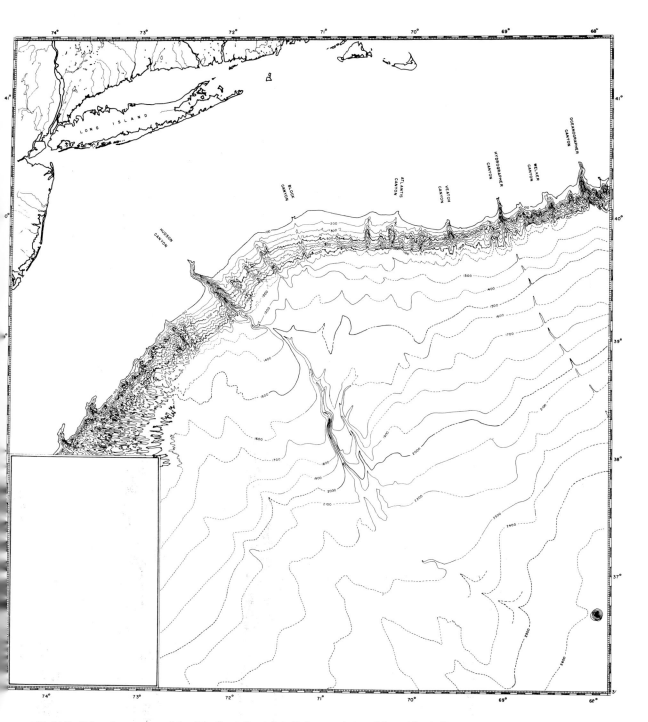

FIG. 24-7 Submarine canyons of the Atlantic continental shelf slope, and rise off Long Island. *(From Heezen et al., 1959.)*

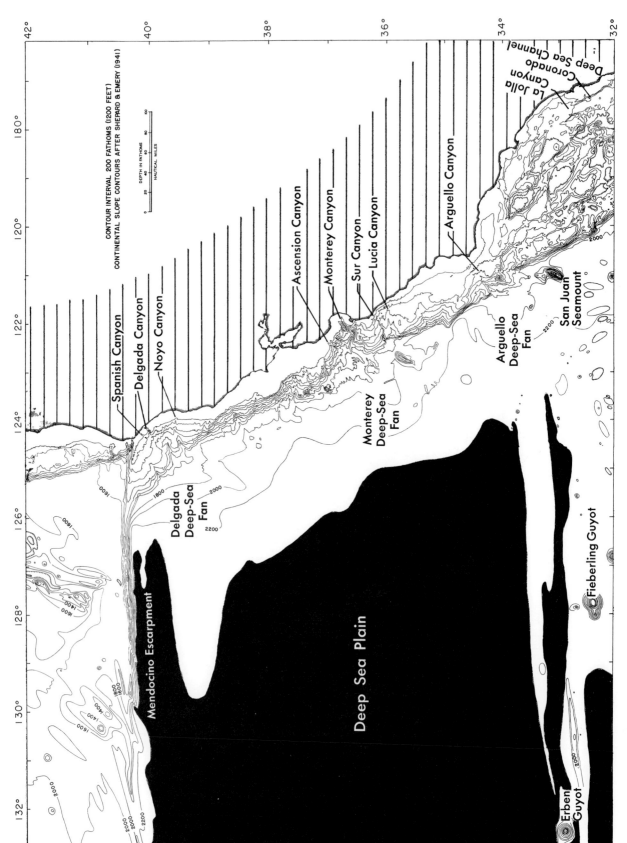

FIG. 24-8 Bathymetric chart of sea floor off California, showing submarine canyons and fans. (After Menard, 1955.)

therefore, little wonder that a few pioneer researchers proposed that the sea level was once thousands of feet lower than now and that the canyons were cut by subaerial rivers. With echo sounders tracing some of them to 10,000 ft and more in depth, this proposal became untenable. No one could conceive of the oceans shrinking to such an extent or that so much water could be piled on continental ice caps during a glacial stage. Some suggested that certain coasts were locally elevated thousands of feet and dissected. They then subsided, and deep canyons became drowned, but investigation of the geologic history of the adjacent land did not bear out this idea. It must also be born in mind that sampling from the walls of the submarine canyons showed that they had been cut through partially and well-lithified sediments, and in places even in metamorphic and granitic rocks, so that some energetic abrasive process is active.

The present most widely accepted theory for the origin of submarine canyons is still not entirely satisfying, but probably because we do not know enough about the process proposed. It is this: sediment-laiden and hence heavy currents pour down the bottoms of the canyons at appreciable velocities and affect the erosion. These are called turbidity currents and may be dramatically produced in laboratory tanks or outside canals. They are heavier than the clear water because of the rock and mineral particles that they carry and flow along the bottom even at low gradients attended by little mixing with the clear water. They most probably can move fair-sized particles, such as pebbles, cobbles, and boulders, and thus by the abrasive activity of these large particles affect considerable erosion. The turbidity currents may be generated by muddy rivers flowing into the ocean but possibly more likely by submarine landslides, which cave from the canyon walls occasionally from place to place and discharge suddenly large volumes of heavy currents into the canyon bottoms. Submarine landslides also account for the widening of the valleys.

The turbidity currents so far have only been observed in shallow depths, and the observation of a strong turbidity current in a canyon bottom and its activity have largely avoided oceanographers.

There can be no doubt that the canyons are the lines of transit of great volumes of clastic sediment, because the detailed topography at the lower end of the canyons is commonly one of fanlike deposits (Fig. 24-8). These have been described as *deep-sea fans, leveed deep-sea channels,* and *abyssal cones.* They build the continental rise. The rise is undoubtedly due largely to the deposits of turbidity currents.

SHELF DEPOSITS AS GEOSYNCLINES

In Fig. 24-9 it will be seen that the old floor upon which the shelf deposits rest has a medial ridge that divides the deposits in two groups. Those continental-ward of the ridge are of the coastal-plain type, such as sands, silts, clays, and some limestones that have been deposited largely in lagoonal and estuarine environments. Those oceanward of the ridge are mostly turbidity current sediments with graded bedding. They commonly contain much graywacke. Volcanoes are likely to exist in this sedimentary province, namely, the continental rise, and add considerable volcanic rock to the sediments.

It has been proposed that the sediments toward the continent and mostly under the shelf are typical of the ancient miogeosynclines of the continental margins and that those under the slope and rise are typical of the eugeosynclines. This is an engaging thought, but in our Cordilleran eugeosyncline there are voluminous sediments of fairly shallow water origin, and the

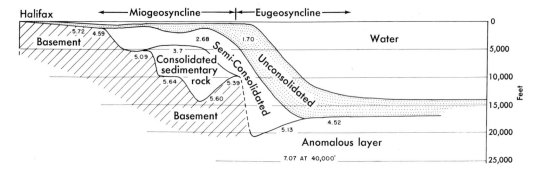

FIG. 24-9 Constitution of continental shelf off Nova Scotia, showing the two divisions that might be analogous to ancient geosynclines. Numbers represent seismic velocities in kilometers per second. *(After Drake et al., 1954.)*

basins and uplifts within the miogeosyncline show a much greater irregularity than develops commonly along continental shelves.

ABYSSAL FLOORS

The abyssal floors are the deepest part of the ocean basins, aside from the trenches, and in part are remarkably flat. They have two divisions, namely, the plains and the hills. The hills are small relief features that rise slightly above the plain. The smooth abyssal plain is regarded as a turbidy current deposit that has flooded and buried an irregular terrane. The abyssal hills at first glance appear to be unburied parts of the old floor, but the texture of the abyssal hills is sharp and rugged to such an extent that a fabric pattern of faulting seems to have emphasized them in times later than most of the turbidity current deposition of the plain. The abyssal hills have a cover of clay, probably thin, and of very slow rate of deposition.

The abyssal plain of the western Atlantic has a low gradient from Baffin Bay, Iceland, and the Grand Banks of Newfoundland all the way southward to the deep Puerto Rican Trench off the West Indies. A great landslide on the shelf slope of the Grand Banks, which broke trans-Atlantic cables in 1929, is believed to have fed a turbidity

current that flowed down the abyssal plain some 2,000 miles to the Puerto Rican Trench.

SEAMOUNTS

A *seamount* is defined as any isolated elevation that rises more than 3,000 ft above the sea floor. Some rise as high as 12,000 ft above the abyssal floor and reach almost to the surface. Such high ones may be 35 miles in diameter at the base. Seamounts occur on the continental rise, on the abyssal floor, and even in the trenches. Most rise abruptly from the general bottom, and it is thus reasoned that their bases have been covered by bottom sediments. This supposition is based further on the theory that they are volcanic piles or cones

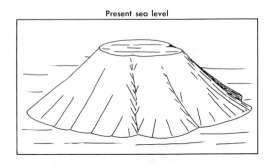

FIG. 24-10 Truncated volcanic cone with top below sea level, called a guyot.

built on the ocean floor. Their shape, the many samples dredged from their sides, large magnetic anomalies, and actual submarine eruptions all support the volcanic theory of origin of the seamounts.

Some seamounts have flat tops and appear as if the volcanic cones had been decapitated. Such are called *guyots* (Fig. 24-10). The flat tops generally range in depth in both the Pacific and Atlantic oceans from 3,000 to 5,000 ft. Dredgings from the flat tops contain sand and gravel, like beach deposits, and shallow water Cretaceous and Tertiary microfossils.

Photographs show ripple marks and, on one at least, solitary corals. These characteristics have led to the belief that the guyots are in reality wave-truncated volcanic cones, that the cones were built above sea level and then planed off slightly below sea level by the waves, and that the ocean floor or crust on which the cones were built then subsided. The amount of subsidence is measured by the present depth below sea level. No fossils older than Late Cretaceous have yet been recovered from the sediments of the flat tops, and hence, we are left with the rather

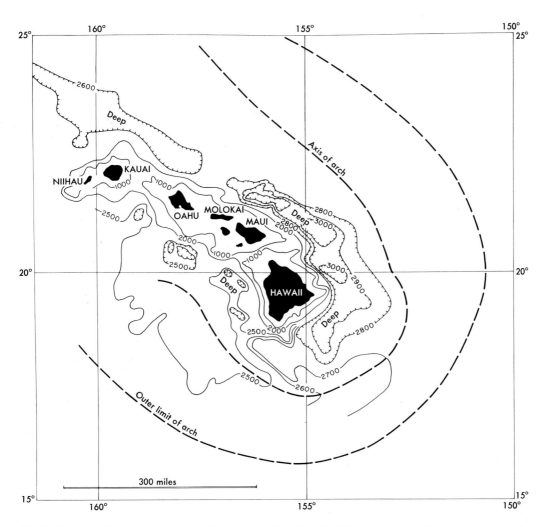

FIG. 24-11 Generalized topography around southern end of Hawaiian Ridge, showing peripheral deep and arch. Contours in fathoms. *(After Hamilton, 1957.)*

strange conclusion that in both the Atlantic and Pacific where the guyots occur the subsidence has occurred since the Cretaceous period. Why none older?

RISES

Apart from the continental shelf rises are broad relief features on the abyssal floors that stand surrounded by deep water. For instance, the Bermuda Rise is an oval-shaped uplift over 300 miles across and about 3,000 ft high above the abyssal plain. From it rises a cluster of volcanic cones that peek above the ocean surface to form the Bermuda Islands. It has a fine-textured relief, as characterized by the

volcanic mass depressing the crust.

The rises generally are blanketed with globigerina ooze that has been cored and dredged in many places. Globigerina are microscopic, single-celled organisms that live in the surface waters and have silica shells. Upon death the shells sink to the ocean floor and constitute in places the bulk of the sediment. They provide, indeed, a slow rate of sedimentation.

MID-OCEANIC RIDGES

Probably the most significant discovery in oceanographic research has been the mid-oceanic ridges. These are typified by the Mid-Atlantic Ridge, which is a broad

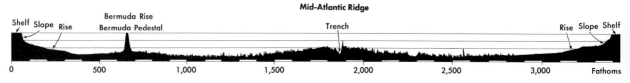

FIG. 24-12 Profile across the North Atlantic from Cape Henry to Rio de Oro. Horizontal scale is in nautical miles and vertical scale in thousands of fathoms. *(After Heezen et al., 1959.)*

oceanographers, that contrasts with the smooth slopes of the continental margin and abyssal plain. From the topography the rise itself, but not the volcanoes, is regarded as an old ocean-bottom feature. It is bounded on the east by a bold escarpment over 3,600 ft high in places and 600 miles long that is probably a fault scarp of younger age.

An example of a rise in the Pacific Ocean is that of the Hawaiian. It is a mound-shaped feature 450 miles long and 175 miles wide and supports many volcanic piles that reach to the ocean's surface and above to form the Hawaiian Islands (Fig. 24-11). The entire rise may be of volcanic origin and probably more recent than the Bermuda Rise. The Hawaiian Rise is surrounded by a sag in the ocean floor that is considered to be the result of the weight of the great

swell or rise running lengthwise of the Atlantic basin and about midway between the continents of the Eastern Hemisphere and those of the Western. The maps of Life Magazine's publication *The Sea* are very vivid. As shown in the profiles of Fig. 24-12, the ridge is rough topographically, with numerous small ridges and seamounts on either flank and a spectacular trench or rift in the center. The broad arch occupies the central third of the ocean floor, and in its central "backbone" ranges are less than 9,500 ft below sea level, whereas the abyssal hills are approximately under 16,500 of water. The Mid-Atlantic Ridge, thus, has a relief of 7,000 to 8,000 ft.

On an average profile of the rift valley the floor lies at about 12,000 ft, and the adjacent bounding peaks at about 6,000 ft below sea level, but the depth of the valley ranges from 2,000 to 12,500 ft. The width of the valley between crests of adjacent peaks ranges from 15 to 30 miles.

The walls flanking the rift valley are steep and appear to be fault scarps of uplifted and tilted blocks, like those of the Great Basin of the western United States. The immediate outer slopes of the mountains adjacent to the rift seem to be minor tilted fault blocks as much as 3,000 ft high and 10 miles wide. Many other sharp relief features appear to be volcanic accumulations superposed on the tilted fault blocks. Dredged rocks from the rift valley and adjacent mountains are of the basic igneous varieties, namely, basalt and gabbro, with some samples of the metamorphic serpentine, and one of sedimentary limestone, presumably of Tertiary age.

Seismic operations at sea reveal a layering of the crust under the Atlantic which is strikingly thinner than that of adjacent continents and which is interpreted as shown in Fig. 24-13. It should be noted that the crystalline basement or "granitic" layer is absent under the ocean and that the gabbroic layer is much thinner.

A world-wide mid-oceanic rift system has been recognized and partially explored. It is shown in Fig. 24-14. Of particular interest is the rift of the Indian Ocean, which projects to the Rift Valleys of Africa and the Red Sea. The same crustal forces operative in forming these continental rifts where we can study them easily are believed responsible in forming the mid-oceanic rifts, and these forces in effect are *tensional*. As a result of this world-wide tensional pattern of rupture of the crust, an expanding earth has been postulated. Not much expansion, however, is conceded possible by the physical chemists unless gravity was once much less than now. Perhaps, regardless of earth expansion, the Mid-Atlantic Ridge and Rift represent a progressive widening of the Atlantic Ocean by means of many cycles of rifting, block tilting, and volcanism. Could North and South America be pulling away from

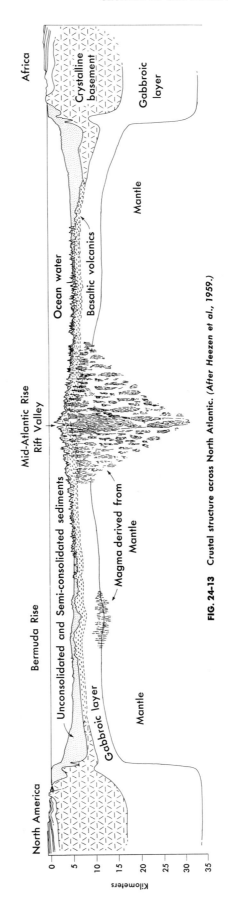

FIG. 24-13 Crustal structure across North Atlantic. (After Heezen et al., 1959.)

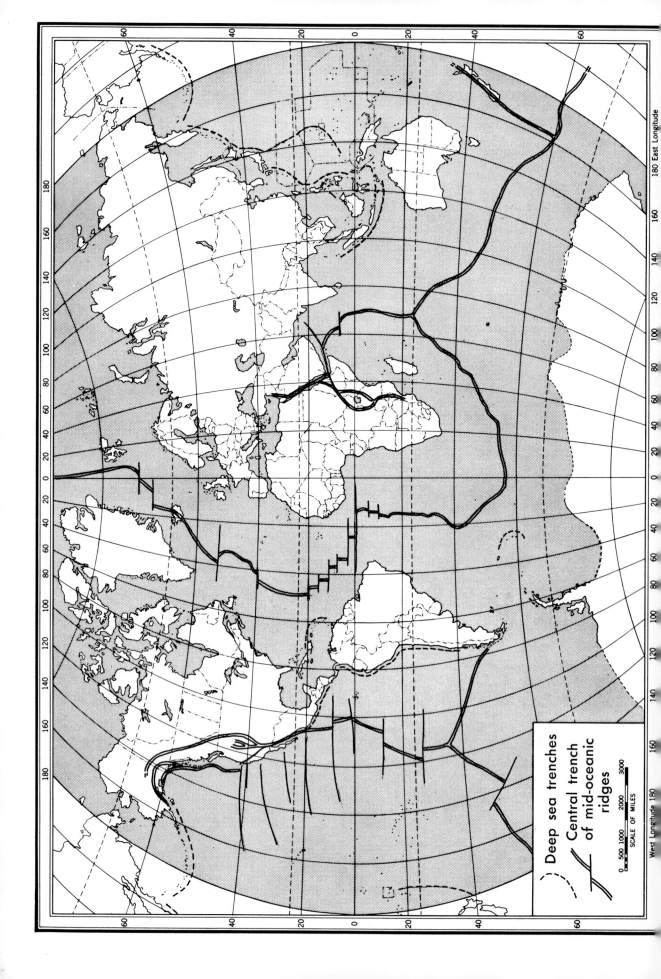

West Longitude 180

Deep sea trenches

Central trench
of mid-oceanic
ridges

0 500 1000 2000 3000
SCALE OF MILES

180 East Longitude

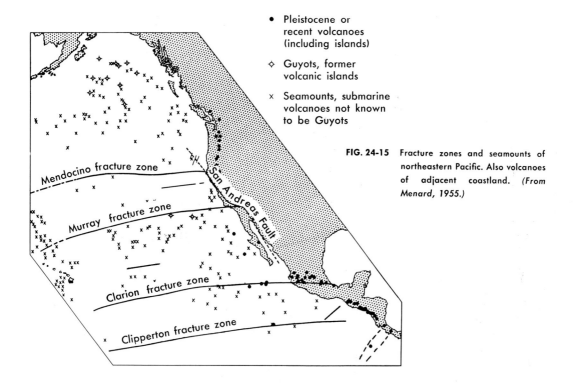

• Pleistocene or
recent volcanoes
(including islands)

◇ Guyots, former
volcanic islands

× Seamounts, submarine
volcanoes not known
to be Guyots

FIG. 24-15 Fracture zones and seamounts of northeastern Pacific. Also volcanoes of adjacent coastland. *(From Menard, 1955.)*

Europe and Africa by means of crustal drifting? This theory has been postulated on the basis of paleoclimatic and fossil evidence in Chap. 17.

FRACTURE ZONES

A number of linear relief features mark the bottom of the northeastern Pacific Ocean. Four of these extend westward from the coast of North and Central America and range up to 3,300 miles long and 60 miles wide (Fig. 24-15). The northern two, the Mendocino and Murray, stretch across the Pacific floor to the Hawaiian Rise. All follow great-circle courses and are approximately parallel. A number of others, now known, are shown in Fig. 24-14. These linear zones are characterized by parallel

narrow troughs, asymmetrical ridges, escarpments, and scattered seamounts. The block of crust between the Mendocino and Murray fracture zones is ¼ to ½ mile lower than the adjacent blocks on north and south. Because of the several characteristics listed above the linear features are postulated to be zones of faults and hence are called fracture zones.

Movements along the fracture zones opposite North America are not now taking place because few earthquake foci occur along them. The magnetic field reflects the fracture zones strongly, as shown in Fig. 24-16, and comparison of the unusual anomalies along the north and south sides demonstrates rather conclusively that many miles of horizontal displacement along them has occurred.

Since no movement is occurring today, it is concluded that the observed displacement took place sometime in the geologic past. The fracture zones seem to be unrelated to the San Andreas fault system of California, which reflects movement chiefly

---

FIG. 24-14 Mid-Oceanic ridges with central trench, and the deep sea trenches associated with volcanic archipelagoes.

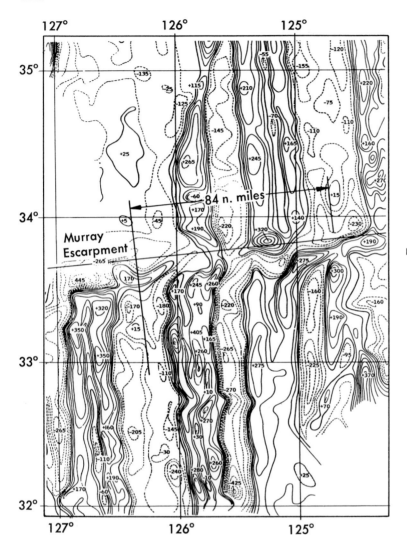

FIG. 24-16 Total magnetic intensity of an area off the California coast. Contour interval is 50 gammas. *(From Menard and Vacquier, 1959.)*

during the Cenozoic, so that it is concluded that the movement on the fracture zones was pre-Cenozoic (Fig. 24-17).

PACIFIC CRUSTAL LAYERING

The layering of the Pacific crust is essentially the same as that of the Atlantic. See Fig. 24-18. The crystalline basement of the continents is absent, and the basaltic or gabbroic layer (lower crustal layer of Fig. 24-18) is much thinner than under the continents. Here in places the depth to the mantle is less than 10 km, and a possible

site for the projected deep drill hole through the discontinuity known as the Moho. Refer back to Chap. 13.

ISLAND ARCS AND TRENCHES

The margins of the vast Pacific Ocean are marked in places by arcuate rows of volcanic islands, such as the Aleutians. Each island arc is bordered on the convex side, usually the side toward the ocean, by a deep trench. Whereas the deep ocean floor may be 12,000 ft deep, the trenches have been sounded to depths of 35,000 ft.

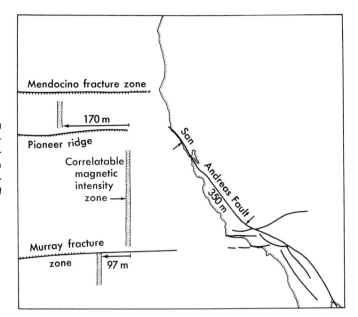

FIG. 24-17 Horizontal displacements along fracture zones indicated by the offset magnetic intensity field. Horizontal displacement along San Andreas fault also shown. Distances are in miles. *(After Menard —private map.)*

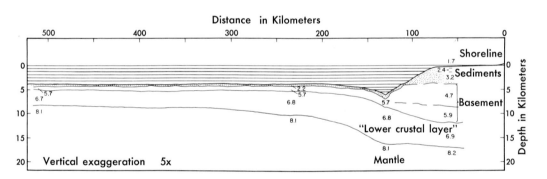

FIG. 24-18 Crustal layers across Middle America Trench. Numbers represent wave velocities in kilometers per second. *(After Fisher and Shor, ms., 1959.)*

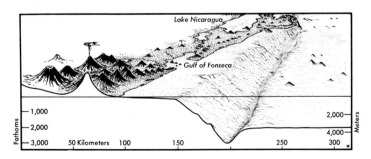

FIG. 24-19 View of the southeastern end of Middle America Trench. *(After Fisher and Shor, ms., 1959.)*

Although much restricted in area, these are truly the profound depths of the ocean floors. The western margin of South America is marked almost continuously by a trench, and so is Central America. Rows of active volcanoes lie adjacent to the trenches on the border of the mainland throughout part of the length of the trenches (Fig. 24-19). The best graphic maps showing these features are probably those of Life Magazine's publication *The Sea.*

The trenches are everywhere the sites of the greatest seismic activity, and hence, it is believed, the crust is actively being deformed in these belts and is buckling downward under compressive stress. A current theory proposes that a great convective cell in the mantle is dragging the oceanic crust against the continent and plunging it downward and under the continental margin. The volcanoes and trenches are presumably surficial manifestations of this activity.

The volcanic arcs and trenches have received much study by geologists and geophysicists because they are undoubtedly the regions of active mountain building today, and an extensive bibliography exists on them. If further information is desired refer first to some of the references listed below.

Suggested Aids

Readings

Eardley, A. J.: *Structural Geology of North America,* 2d ed., Harper & Row, Publishers, Incorporated, New York, 1962.

Fisher R. L., and Roger Revelle: "The Trenches of the Pacific," *Scientific American,* November, 1955, pp. 36–41.

Heezen, Bruce C., et al.: *The Floors of the Oceans,* Geological Society of America, Special Paper 65, 1959.

Hill, M. N. (ed.); *The Sea,* John Wiley & Sons, Inc., New York, 1963, 3 vols.

King, C. A. M.: *An Introduction to Oceanography,* McGraw-Hill Book Company, Inc., New York, 1963.

Munk, Walter H.: "The Circulation of the Oceans," *Scientific American,* September, 1955, pp. 96–104.

The Sea, Life Nature Library, 1961.

Shepard, Francis P.: *Submarine Geology,* 2d ed., Harper & Row, Publishers, Incorporated, New York, 1963.

Sverdrup, H. U., et. al.: *The Oceans,* Prentice-Hall, Inc., Englewood Cliffs, N.J., 1946.

Movie

Challenge of the Oceans, Planet Earth Series, CSC-214.

Index

Set in Linotype Caledonia

Format by Frances Torbert Tilley

Composition by The Haddon Craftsmen

Printed by The Murray Printing Company

Manufactured by The Haddon Craftsmen

QE 26
E2

20722

Eardley, Armand John
    General college geology

Date Due			
MR 2 '72			
MAR 4			
F 82			
OCT 10 1987